Éric Chevreau

Globe Report'air

Les Contrebandiers
de la Méditerranée

Illustrations de
Oriol Vidal

Collection dirigée par
Michel Piquemal

(●) SEDRAP *Jeunesse*

Éric Chevreau a enseigné à des enfants de tous âges, de la grande section au CM2, pendant une quinzaine d'années. En parallèle à cette activité, il a écrit pour ce même public plusieurs histoires publiées dans la presse et l'édition.

Il aime par-dessus tout lire et écrire des romans d'aventure historique et de science-fiction. Il est également lecteur et traducteur pour l'édition d'ouvrages parus en langue anglaise.

Passionné de voyages, il partage aujourd'hui son temps entre Londres et Bruxelles, deux villes qu'il aime beaucoup.

Oriol Vidal est un illustrateur qui vit à Barcelone, en Espagne. Diplômé des beaux-arts, c'est un artiste complet : en plus d'illustrer des livres et des magazines, il a aussi travaillé dans l'animation, puisqu'il a développé des personnages et proposé des *story-boards* pour des projets américains, français, britanniques ou encore coréens et, bien sûr, espagnols !

Aujourd'hui, il continue de dessiner, entouré de sa petite fille et de sa femme, sans oublier ses deux complices : son chat et sa pipelette de perruche !

LE PROJET « SOS PLANÈTE »

Nous sommes cinq, venus des cinq continents, embarqués dans une aventure extraordinaire : un tour du monde qui doit durer toute une année ! Nous voyageons à bord du *Wakaroa*, un dirigeable géant qui se déplace dans les airs grâce à l'énergie solaire. Ce moyen de transport insolite nous permet de franchir les océans, survoler les mers et les fleuves, jouer à « saute-montagne » ou surfer sur la cime des forêts, à la rencontre des habitants et des animaux de ces régions.

Notre mission : répondre aux appels au secours que nous adressent les enfants des pays visités. Chacun notre tour, nous écrirons pour toi le récit de nos aventures, accompagné de notes sur le pays, ses habitants, sa faune et sa flore. N'hésite surtout pas à ajouter des commentaires sur notre forum !

Tu es passionné de nature et d'aventure? Alors rejoins-nous vite à bord du *Wakaroa*.

QUI SOMMES-NOUS ?

KWANITA (SURNOM : « MAMITA »)
ÂGE : à 12 ans, c'est l'ainée de la bande.
ORIGINES : Sault Ste. Marie (lac Supérieur), Canada.
LANGUES : français, anglais et ojibwé, sa langue maternelle (elle est d'origine amérindienne).
QUALITÉS : douce, attentionnée et ouverte aux autres, toujours prête à consoler ou à conseiller.
DÉFAUT : tendance à prendre un peu trop au sérieux son rôle de grande sœur.
SIGNES PARTICULIERS : parle dans son sommeil, fait parfois des rêves étranges.
AMBITION : passionnée d'histoire, voudrait devenir journaliste.

VAIANA (VAI. SURNOM : « LA SIRÈNE »)
ÂGE : 11 ans.
ORIGINES : ile de Raiatea, Polynésie française.
LANGUES : français, tahitien.
QUALITÉS : dynamique, sportive et débordante d'énergie.
DÉFAUT : très coquette, elle passe des heures dans la cabine de bain !

SIGNES PARTICULIERS : nage comme un poisson…
et chante comme une casserole.
AMBITION : devenir biologiste marine.

FATOUMATA (FATOU. SURNOM : « LA LIONNE »)

ÂGE : 10 ans.
ORIGINES : village de Kango, Gabon.
LANGUES : français, fang.
QUALITÉS : sensible, généreuse et franche,
elle a le cœur sur la main.
DÉFAUTS : assez susceptible, râleuse, tendance
à « bouder ».
SIGNE PARTICULIER : amoureuse des animaux,
elle n'a pas son pareil pour prendre soin d'eux.
AMBITION : devenir vétérinaire.

FABRIZIO (FAB. SURNOM : « LE VOLCAN »)

ÂGE : 10 ans.
ORIGINES : Taormina, Sicile.
LANGUES : français, italien.
QUALITÉS : malicieux, inventif et débordant
d'enthousiasme, toujours le premier à vouloir
donner un coup de main.
DÉFAUTS : désordonné, maladroit, gaffeur
et extrêmement bavard, il a aussi tendance
à se vanter et se moquer des autres.
SIGNES PARTICULIERS : aime faire des blagues
et la cuisine (les deux pas toujours au gout
de tout le monde…).
AMBITION : devenir géologue ou guide de haute
montagne.

CHEN (SURNOM : « L'ENCYCLOPÉDIE »)

ÂGE : 9 ans (le « petit frère » de l'équipage).

ORIGINES : Shangai, Chine.

LANGUES : français, chinois.

QUALITÉS : sérieux et très organisé, bon camarade, il ne prend jamais part aux disputes.

DÉFAUTS : facilement distrait, et très maniaque !

SIGNES PARTICULIERS : le cerf-volant est son loisir préféré.

AMBITION : voudrait bien être ornithologue ou météorologue.

SOFIA (SURNOM : « MAITRESSE »)

Institutrice dans la « vraie vie », cette jeune femme de 28 ans est chargée de l'éducation à bord du Wakaroa, en particulier des leçons et de la rédaction des articles pour le blog.

ORIGINES : Bruxelles, Belgique.

LANGUES : français, anglais, néerlandais… et pas mal d'autres langues.

QUALITÉS : débordante d'enthousiasme et d'énergie, elle ne se laisse jamais aller au découragement (« Haut les cœurs ! »).

DÉFAUT : ne supportant pas l'injustice, a tendance à s'emporter.

SIGNE PARTICULIER : douée d'un sixième sens, elle semble lire dans les pensées de ses petits protégés et finit leurs phrases (ce que Fabrizio trouve très flippant…).

⋯TEMATAI (SURNOMS : « SKIP » OU « LA BOUSSOLE »)

Sofia est peut-être la maitresse des enfants mais, quand il s'agit du *Wakaroa*, ce géant de 34 ans est le seul maitre à bord !

ORIGINES : Whakatane, Nouvelle-Zélande.

LANGUES : maori, anglais.

QUALITÉS : sérieux, navigateur accompli et doué d'un sens de l'orientation incroyable, on peut toujours compter sur lui.

DÉFAUT : pas très bavard, voire taciturne.

SIGNES PARTICULIERS : ses tatouages ! Passe de très longues heures à sculpter des figurines en bois.

⋯MACODOU (SURNOM : « DADOU »)

Cet Africain jovial est le cuisinier, mais aussi à l'occasion le médecin du bord : il connait les secrets des plantes qui guérissent les petits bobos.

ORIGINES : Dakar, Sénégal.

LANGUES : wolof, français.

QUALITÉS : toujours de bonne humeur et optimiste (« Il n'y a pas de problèmes, que des solutions. »).

DÉFAUT : très superstitieux…

SIGNE PARTICULIER : a toujours un dicton à citer ou une histoire à raconter.

L'APPEL
AU SECOURS

Chaque mois, un enfant nous écrit pour nous demander de l'aide. Nous nous rendons dans son pays pour essayer de comprendre la situation et de l'améliorer. Et grâce à notre blog, nous attirons l'attention sur le sujet.

Aujourd'hui, c'est Dounia qui nous écrit de Tunisie :

Chers Globe Report'air,
J'ai regardé votre départ à la télévision, et j'ai lu tout ce qui concerne le projet « SOS Planète ». C'est super ce que vous faites ! Alors voilà, puisque vous commencez votre voyage par la Méditerranée, j'ai pensé que vous pourriez faire une escale dans mon pays, la Tunisie, et faire un reportage sur le phoque de Méditerranée. Le phoque moine (c'est comme cela qu'on l'appelle) est l'une des dix espèces mondiales en voie de disparition, et le mammifère marin le plus

menacé d'Europe. Autrefois, on en trouvait dans toute la Méditerranée, mais aujourd'hui il n'en reste plus qu'environ cinq-cents. Il y a une petite colonie sur l'île de la Galite, au nord de Tabarka, la petite ville où j'habite avec mon père, qui est pêcheur. Je devrais dire « il y avait », car depuis quelque temps, les phoques semblent avoir disparu ! Je serais très triste d'apprendre que la colonie s'est éteinte, alors si vous pouviez m'aider à résoudre ce mystère…

Je vous attends avec impatience.

Bisous, Dounia

L'HEURE DES ADIEUX

Rives du lac Supérieur • Sault Ste. Marie • Canada

Assise sur le ponton, les pieds se balançant à quelques centimètres de la surface du lac, Kwanita ferme les yeux pour mieux écouter le clapotis de l'eau. Trois jours. Dans trois jours, elle va quitter son petit coin de paradis et s'envoler, avec quatre autres enfants, pour un tour du monde en ballon. Kwanita n'en revient pas de la chance d'avoir été choisie pour représenter le continent américain dans ce projet un peu fou. Ambassadrice de l'Amérique pour l'association SOS Planète !

Un bourdonnement familier se fait entendre : elle lève les yeux vers le point qui grossit à l'horizon. C'est l'avion-taxi de son père, qui revient de l'île Royale, de l'autre côté du lac, où il vient de déposer des touristes. L'hydravion vire sur son aile, puis se pose en douceur sur l'eau. Kwanita saute sur ses pieds, prête pour aider à la manœuvre d'amarrage. L'engin vient glisser le long du ponton et la portière se rabat. Un barbu souriant met le pied sur le flotteur et lui lance la corde qu'elle attrape au vol.

« Comment va ? » lui demande son père.

Kwanita hausse les épaules. Son père sait bien ce qui préoccupe sa fille : elle a beau être excitée à l'idée de l'aventure qui l'attend, ses parents vont lui manquer. Bien sûr, il y aura les vacances. Tous les trois mois, les enfants regagneront leur maison pour des vacances en famille. Tout de même, trois mois, c'est long…

Mais ce n'est pas cela qui préoccupe le plus Kwanita. Ce que son père ne sait pas, c'est que la jeune fille a encore fait un cauchemar cette nuit. Dans son rêve, elle a la vision d'une petite fille tombée à l'eau. Elle ne sait pas nager, elle est en train de se noyer. Kwanita voudrait l'aider, mais elle est impuissante. Cela fait plusieurs nuits qu'elle fait le même rêve. Chaque fois, elle se réveille avant de pouvoir sauver la fillette.

« Et si on faisait une dernière partie de pêche tous les deux, avant ton départ ? »

Kwanita sourit, et son père l'attrape par les épaules. Puis ils se dirigent vers la maison en rondins qu'ils habitent au bord du lac. Sa « cabane au Canada » comme elle l'appelle, qu'elle va bientôt quitter pour plusieurs semaines.

Baie de Hangzhou • Shanghai • Chine

Le cerf-volant prend de la hauteur, emporté par un courant ascendant. C'est un Rokkaku à une ligne, que Chen a construit de ses propres mains, en bambou et papier de soie. Ses couleurs vives font le bonheur des promeneurs sur la plage, qui interrompent leur balade pour lever le nez vers ce spectacle. D'habitude, Chen équipe son cerf-volant d'une petite caméra, ou bien d'instruments météorologiques. La météo, c'est sa passion. Mais aujourd'hui, il se contente d'enchaîner acrobatie sur acrobatie. Ainsi, il laisse s'évader son esprit vers les hauteurs.

Des hauteurs qu'il est impatient de rejoindre à bord du dirigeable qui va l'emmener tout autour de la Terre. Voler, comme vole son cerf-volant, voir le monde d'en haut, pas grâce à une petite caméra, mais de ses propres yeux.

Lors des entretiens de sélection, il a croisé les quatre autres ambassadeurs. L'Européen, Fabrizio (le seul autre garçon), n'a pas la langue dans sa poche. Chen est fils unique, mais il espère qu'il s'entendra bien avec tous : l'espace est compté dans la nacelle, alors il faudra peut-être faire des efforts pour cohabiter.

Chen décide de ramener le cerf-volant. Déçu de voir se terminer le spectacle, un petit garçon lui demande pourquoi. Il lui explique qu'un orage va bientôt arriver. Interloqué, le garçonnet lève le nez vers le ciel d'un bleu uniforme : aucune trace d'orage à l'horizon.

Une demi-heure plus tard, à peine Chen est-il rentré chez lui qu'un violent orage éclate.

Village de Kango • province de l'Estuaire • Gabon

Fatoumata serre Como très fort dans ses bras. Le bébé hippopotame se met à bailler à gueule déployée, découvrant ainsi ses deux petites dents sur le côté. Qui va lui donner le biberon, à présent ? Depuis qu'elle a recueilli le petit orphelin, elle est la seule à s'en occuper. Pourtant, il va falloir quitter Como, et tous « ses animaux », comme elle les appelle. Elle a grandi parmi eux, sur la petite réserve à l'embouchure du fleuve, cernée par la grande forêt.

Malgré tout, Fatou est impatiente de prendre le départ. Elle sait que ce voyage sera l'occasion de rencontrer des animaux du bout du monde. Et elle sent qu'elle va bien s'entendre avec les deux autres filles du bord : Kwanita l'Américaine, et Vaiana l'Océanienne. Pour les deux garçons, elle est moins sure, on verra.

Fatou est inquiète de laisser Como seul. On dirait que l'hippopotame sent que le moment de la séparation approche. Depuis hier, il fait des difficultés pour manger. Fatou approche sa bouche de l'oreille de l'animal et lui murmure quelques mots de réconfort. Et Como, docile, boit son biberon jusqu'au bout…

« Fatou, viens manger ! »

Sa mère l'appelle. Fatoumata repose à terre Como, qui s'en va fureter du côté de la mare.

Baie de Faaroa • ile de Raiatea • Polynésie française

Le poulpe remonte lentement le long du bras de Vaiana et passe un tentacule autour de ses épaules. On dirait qu'il va lui murmurer une confidence à l'oreille. Délicatement, Vai décroche Paul (c'est comme cela qu'elle a surnommé le poulpe qui vient chaque jour la saluer) et le remet à l'eau. Vai chausse ses palmes et son masque, prend en bouche l'embout de son tuba et s'allonge dans l'eau. Le nez à quelques centimètres des poissons colorés qui se cachent dans les coraux, elle nage vers le tombant du récif. En quelques mouvements de palmes silencieux, elle a rejoint l'endroit où celui-ci tombe à pic vers le fond, soixante mètres plus bas. Vai prend une inspiration, et descend sans effort à une dizaine de mètres. Elle salue une colonie de rougets réfugiés dans leur grotte, croise son ami le mérou et aperçoit du coin du masque un requin de récif croisant à distance prudente.

Le lagon va lui manquer pendant ces quelques semaines passées dans les airs. Comme disent ses parents, Vai « la petite sirène » a su nager avant même de marcher. Le lagon, c'est son terrain de jeu depuis toujours. À présent, elle aura les mers du monde entier pour terrain de jeu. Et le ciel sera son océan.

Vai pourrait rester des heures à nager. Soudain, elle sent sur sa peau un curieux frémissement.

Elle connait bien cette sensation. Avant même de regagner la surface, elle sait que sa mère l'appelle. Elle doit avoir besoin d'elle pour l'aider au restaurant. La caresse qu'elle a sentie sur sa peau, c'est le son de la conque, qu'elle ressent avant même de l'entendre, comme si l'onde sonore, portée par les vagues, l'atteignait avant de parvenir à son oreille. En effet, quand elle sort la tête de l'eau, Vaiana entend mugir la conque dans laquelle souffle sa mère pour l'appeler. Il est déjà midi. Il est temps de rentrer.

Pentes du mont Etna • Sicile • Italie

Six heures trente, record battu ! Fabrizio laisse glisser à terre son sac à dos pour prendre sa gourde. La montée au pas de course, ça donne soif. Son père le félicite d'une tape sur l'épaule. C'était la dernière occasion avant longtemps de faire avec lui l'ascension de l'Etna.

Partis à l'aube du refuge de Sapienza, ils ont atteint le sommet juste à temps pour le déjeuner ! Mais Fabrizio n'a pas très faim, il ne se sent pas très bien, à cause de l'effort intense. Ça ira mieux dans une demi-heure, après un peu de repos.

Il se laisse tomber sur les cailloux et s'allonge, bras le long du corps et paumes tournées vers le bas, en fixant les franges nuageuses qui strient le ciel d'un bleu profond. Tout à coup, une sensation bizarre l'envahit et il se redresse d'un bond, sous l'œil surpris de son père :

« Un problème ? »

Il espère que non, mais pendant un instant, il a cru… ou plutôt, il a senti sous ses mains la terre qui… frissonnait… tremblait ? Non, il doit s'être trompé. Surement son imagination qui lui joue un mauvais tour. Ce doit être le départ prochain qui le perturbe.

Son père l'interroge toujours du regard, un sourcil levé. Fabrizio préfère chasser cette curieuse impression de son esprit :

« Pas de problème ! Je suis juste un peu tourné, à cause de la marche. Je vais manger mon sandwich, ça ira mieux. Pour le retour, on fait la course ? Le dernier arrivé prépare le diner ! »

1

LE DÉPART

JOURNAL DE BORD DE SOFIA

3 septembre, Cité de l'espace, Toulouse.
Et voilà, c'est parti ! Nous sommes en route pour les bords de la Méditerranée. Le départ a été émouvant. Les enfants ont pris possession des lieux et fait connaissance. Ils vont devoir apprendre à vivre ensemble pendant plusieurs mois dans un espace restreint. J'ai demandé à Fabrizio d'écrire le premier chapitre de nos aventures.

RÉCIT DE FABRIZIO

En avant pour la grande aventure ! Le décollage a eu lieu ce matin, devant les caméras du monde entier et, bien sûr, nos parents très émus. C'est la première fois que je les quitte pour une aussi longue période : la prochaine fois que je les verrai, c'est dans trois mois, pour les vacances de Noël !

Au moment des adieux, j'ai senti une grosse boule dans ma gorge, mais je me suis retenu de pleurer. Pas comme Fatoumata, qui sanglotait à gros bouillons dans les bras de sa mère. TROP la honte! Fatoumata, c'est la déléguée de l'Afrique (elle vient du Gabon).

La cérémonie du départ m'a fait penser à un documentaire sur le lancement du *Titanic*. Derrière les barrières, au moins mille journalistes et spectateurs se bousculaient pour suivre des yeux l'ascension du *Wakaroa*. J'espère au moins qu'on ne connaitra pas le même sort que le *Titanic*… Je plaisante. Il parait que le dirigeable a fait l'objet d'essais pendant deux ans! Et puis, un nuage, ça fait moins de dégâts qu'un iceberg!

Les spectateurs s'éloignaient peu à peu, se faisant de plus en plus petits. Bien sûr, techniquement, c'est nous qui étions en train de nous éloigner… Mais, vu d'en haut, on avait vraiment l'impression que le sol se dérobait sous nos pieds. Depuis la coursive extérieure, nous avons agité nos mouchoirs en direction du public (sauf Fatoumata, trop occupée à se moucher dedans).

Il faut que je vous décrive le *Wakaroa*. Il est TROP géant! Son nom signifie « longue pirogue » en maori (la langue de Tematai, le pilote, ou plutôt le *skipper*, comme sur un bateau): il possède une nacelle allongée, en forme de chaloupe. Sauf que

ce vaisseau-là ne surfe pas sur les vagues, mais sur les nuages ! Le ballon, lui, ressemble à un énorme cigare.

La coursive est une passerelle ouverte qui court tout le long de la nacelle. À l'arrière, elle forme une terrasse assez large pour une table et des chaises. J'espère qu'on pourra y manger lorsqu'il fera beau, car la vue est incroyable ! À l'avant, la passerelle se rétrécit en une sorte de bec, d'où l'on a une sensation extraordinaire, comme dans le gaillard d'avant sur un voilier.

C'est là que je me suis réfugié, quand notre port d'attache a disparu, pour échapper aux yeux rougis et aux reniflements des autres passagers. Pour détendre l'atmosphère, j'ai pris la pose de Leonardo DiCaprio, debout, les bras en croix à la proue du *Titanic*, et j'ai crié :

« Je suis le roi du moooonde ! »

Les autres n'ont pas eu l'air très impressionnés par mon imitation. Kwanita a levé les yeux au ciel, Vai a secoué la tête, Chen haussé les épaules et Fatoumata, entre deux reniflements, a hoqueté :

« N'importe quoi… »

Je leur pardonne : ils sont trop tristes pour apprécier mes talents d'acteur…

La seule à rire, c'était Sofia. Sofia, c'est notre prof. Dans la vie, elle est maitresse. Et membre de SOS Planète. Lorsqu'elle a su qu'ils recherchaient une enseignante pour encadrer cinq enfants lors d'un tour du monde en ballon, son sang d'aventurière n'a fait qu'un tour. Sofia est jeune, belge, très sympa, pleine d'énergie, et on voit bien qu'elle est sportive. En plus, elle a bon gout, puisqu'elle rigole à mes blagues! C'est elle qui m'a demandé, après la conférence de presse, de raconter en détail tout ce que nous allons vivre pendant la première partie de notre voyage.

La conférence de presse était TROP impressionnante! On était assis tous les cinq au centre d'une longue table posée sur une estrade. Dans la salle, les flashs des appareils photo clignotaient (eh oui, on est des stars!).

À notre droite, pour répondre aux questions, il y avait les représentants de SOS Planète. Ils ont rassuré les journalistes à propos de la sécurité à bord, mais aussi de l'enseignement que nous allons recevoir (il parait que nous ne sommes pas en vacances…). Sofia, qui est chargée du « suivi éducatif », a expliqué : l'histoire, la géographie, les sciences et même les maths seront abordées en rapport avec nos découvertes.

Je vois d'ici le type de sujets : « Un dirigeable parti de Toulouse à 9 h 30, avec à son bord cinq enfants entre 9 et 12 ans, et naviguant à une vitesse moyenne de 60 km/h, doit effectuer un vol de 800 km. Calculez l'âge du navigateur. »

Il parait que nous aurons même des devoirs! En plus d'écrire à tour de rôle le récit de nos aventures pour le blog, nous devrons rédiger des articles documentaires sur les pays visités.

« Une pratique quotidienne de l'écriture », a dit Sofia.

Une torture quotidienne, plutôt !

À notre gauche, étaient assis les deux autres membres d'équipage : Macodou, le cuisinier africain, et Tematai, le *skipper* (ça veut dire « navigateur »), un Maori de Nouvelle-Zélande. Macodou est plutôt gros, très drôle, et aussi démonstratif que Tematai est silencieux. Le Maori, lui, est une vraie montagne de muscles tatoués ! Les tatouages les plus impressionnants sont ceux qui couvrent la moitié de son visage. Le premier jour, je ne pouvais m'empêcher de le fixer des yeux, complètement hypnotisé par ces dessins.

« Je suis sure que vous n'avez pas le cœur à travailler, a dit Sofia après le décollage. Si on rejoignait Tematai dans le poste de pilotage ? Il pourrait nous parler de son travail… »

Hier matin, pendant la visite privée de notre nouvelle maison volante, un ingénieur de l'Aérospatiale nous a expliqué comment tout fonctionnait. Les moteurs et tous les appareils électriques sont alimentés par l'énergie solaire. Et un système de captation recycle l'eau des nuages, stockée dans une citerne ! Une douche à l'eau de nuages, c'est top, non ?

Tematai nous a présenté le poste de pilotage, qui est aussi le centre de communication. Nous sommes reliés au monde (et à nos familles) par satellite: nous pourrons parler à nos parents en visioconférence tous les jours, envoyer des mails, consulter Internet et alimenter le blog avec le récit de nos aventures. Ce qui est trop TOP, c'est l'écran géant installé au-dessus de la porte: on peut suivre notre itinéraire en temps réel, comme dans un avion, mais aussi voir les images prises par les caméras disposées sous la nacelle.

Je me demande comment fait Tematai pour s'y retrouver avec tous ces cadrans et ces instruments de navigation! Il a essayé de nous montrer comment « faire le point », c'est-à-dire calculer notre route. Chen avait l'air très intéressé. Moi, je me suis contenté de faire semblant de comprendre…

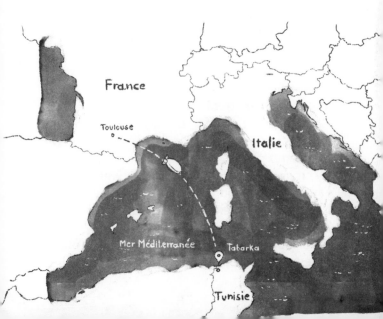

Notre destination pour cette première étape, c'est Tabarka, une petite ville à la frontière algéro-tunisienne. Une fille qui vit là-bas, Dounia, nous a écrit pour nous demander de l'aider à résoudre un mystère : la disparition des phoques sur une ile près de chez elle. Je suis très excité à l'idée de commencer ce voyage par un survol de la Méditerranée !

« Est-ce qu'on va survoler la Sicile ? » ai-je demandé à notre *skipper*.

Je nous imaginais déjà, rasant le sommet de l'Etna, « ma » montagne, puis passant au-dessus de Taormina, ma ville coincée entre volcan et Méditerranée.

« Non, a répondu Tematai dans son français hésitant. Le route passe ouest de Sardaigne. »

Trop dommage !

« Désolé, les gars, vous n'aurez pas la chance de voir la plus belle ile du monde ! ai-je dit.

– Surement pas aussi belle que la mienne, a répliqué Vai. »

Vai (c'est le diminutif de Vaiana) habite sur l'ile de Raiatea, près de Tahiti. Depuis hier, elle n'arrête pas de nous rebattre les oreilles de « son » ile, avec ses plages pleines de cocotiers. Elle a trop l'air de s'y croire, cette fille. Tout ça parce qu'elle habite à l'autre bout du monde.

« Pas besoin d'aller dans le Pacifique pour trouver de jolies iles », ai-je dit.

Vai a haussé les épaules et Sofia est intervenue :

« Il est temps de prendre possession des cabines.

Vous avez une demi-heure avant le déjeuner pour ranger vos affaires ! »

Inutile de nous le dire deux fois. Plantant là Sofia et Tematai, nous nous sommes rués vers les cabines. La nacelle du *Wakaroa* n'est pas très grande. De part et d'autre du poste de pilotage, il y a deux petites cabines : celle de Sofia, et celle que se partagent Tematai et Macodou. À l'arrière, se trouvent le cabinet de toilettes et nos deux cabines, une pour les filles et une pour les garçons. Chacune comporte quatre couchages. Chen et moi avons de la chance : nous pouvons ranger nos affaires sur les deux couchettes inoccupées.

J'ai renversé mon sac sur la couchette du bas et fais deux tas grossiers : l'un de vêtements, l'autre de mes objets personnels, livres, iPod, etc. Puis j'ai décoré le bout de cloison au-dessus de la couchette du haut avec des photos de ma famille et de paysages siciliens, surtout de l'Etna. Puis je me suis couché, les bras derrière la tête, en attendant que mon « colocataire » ait fini.

Chen, lui, a pris la couchette du bas. Sur celle du haut, il a disposé un à un ses vêtements en piles bien séparées : les shorts, les teeshirts, les pulls, les sous-vêtements. Il a même pris le temps d'aligner ses paires de chaussettes, en les classant par couleurs, du plus clair au plus foncé ! Trop bizarre ! L'appel a retenti avant qu'il ait eu le temps de finir : « À table ! »

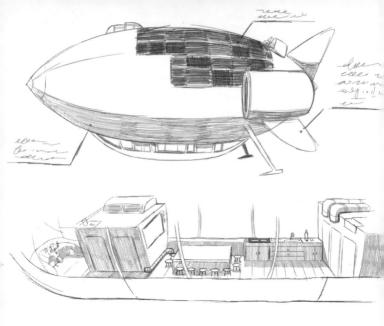

Les cabines ouvrent toutes les quatre sur le « carré », l'espace commun qui est à la fois salon, salle à manger… et salle de classe. C'est aussi le domaine de Macodou, puisqu'une cuisine occupe tout un côté.

Macodou a préparé une assiette de sandwichs et une carafe de citronnade. Normalement, nous devons prendre nos repas dans le carré. Mais il fait tellement beau que, pour notre premier déjeuner à bord, il a déposé le tout sur la terrasse.

« Allez, les gonés (ça veut dire "les enfants" dans sa langue). Régalez-vous ! Comme on dit chez nous en Afrique, "le crocodile affamé n'écoute pas les leçons de la gazelle !" » a-t-il dit avant d'éclater d'un gros rire sonore.

Nous avons échangé des regards interloqués, pas sûrs de comprendre l'humour africain.

Pendant que nous dévorions les sandwichs, nous pouvions voir se dérouler, dans notre sillage, le ruban vert du canal du Midi.

Puis nous avons survolé la cité de Carcassonne. C'était incroyable! Du haut des remparts, des touristes hauts comme des bâtonnets de glace nous ont salués. Nous avons agité les bras en retour. Je me demande quel effet cela fait de voir passer au-dessus de sa tête un ballon de la taille d'un nuage…

Malheureusement, tout s'est gâté quand Sofia est venue nous annoncer que c'était l'heure de rentrer dans le carré pour travailler. Chaque jour, nous aurons trois heures de cours, réparties selon le temps laissé par nos occupations à bord et l'écriture des articles pour alimenter le blog. Notre premier cours est une leçon de géographie et d'histoire de la Méditerranée.

Travailler par ce temps, c'est TROP pas juste!

 ZOOM SUR LA MÉDITERRANÉE. ÉCRIT PAR KWANITA

Son nom vient du latin **mare medi terra,** *qui signifie «mer au milieu des terres». En effet, c'est une mer presque entièrement fermée: elle ne*

s'ouvre sur l'océan Atlantique que par le détroit de Gibraltar, large de 15 km. Située entre l'Europe, l'Afrique et l'Asie, la « grande bleue » fut dès l'Antiquité une importante voie de communication entre les peuples de la région : Mésopotamiens, Égyptiens, Perses, Phéniciens, Carthaginois, Berbères, Grecs, Romains...

Divisée en deux bassins, occidental (ouest) et oriental (est), elle a une profondeur moyenne de 1 500 m. Son point le plus profond est de 5 267 m, en mer Ionienne.

La Méditerranée ne représente que 0,8 % de la surface totale des océans, mais 8 à 10 % de la biodiversité marine : 20 à 30 % des espèces présentes ne se rencontrent que là.

2

DE BELLES RENCONTRES

4 septembre. Nous avons passé notre première nuit à bord, ancrés au large de l'île de Riou, au sud de Marseille. Ce matin, en route vers la Corse et la Sardaigne, nous avons croisé des compagnons de route…

J'ai dormi comme une masse pendant cette première nuit à bord. Il faut dire que la fin de journée avait été bien remplie.

Après la « classe », nous sommes sortis sur la coursive. Le paysage était très différent. Des étangs et des marécages se déroulaient à perte de vue. Et des troupeaux de chevaux sauvages paissaient et trottaient en toute liberté !

« Tematai, on peut se rapprocher ? » a crié Sofia en direction de la cabine de pilotage.

J'ai senti que nous perdions de l'altitude. Skip (j'ai décidé de l'appeler ainsi pour faire plus court) manœuvrait pour nous permettre d'observer de plus près le spectacle. À notre approche, un groupe de chevaux a levé le museau et s'est éloigné en renâclant.

Tout à coup, un cri a retenti à bâbord, de l'autre côté de la coursive. Je me suis précipité.

« Regardez, des flamants roses ! » s'est exclamé Chen. Des oiseaux à la silhouette gracieuse nous coupaient la route en s'enfuyant.

« C'est superbe ! s'est extasiée Fatoumata. Comment s'appelle cette région ?

– C'est le parc naturel de Camargue, a répondu Sofia. Nous sommes en train de survoler le delta du Rhône, une région très marécageuse qui abrite de nombreuses espèces d'oiseaux. »

Chen ne savait plus où donner des yeux. Il faut dire que les oiseaux sont sa passion. Il m'a dit que, plus tard, il voudrait être ornithologue.

 ZOOM SUR LA CAMARGUE. ÉCRIT PAR CHEN

Ce parc naturel est situé dans les Bouches-du-Rhône, une région comprise entre les deux bras principaux du delta du Rhône, le fleuve qui se jette

dans la Méditerranée. Bordé d'étangs salés et de marais, la Camargue est connue pour la récolte du sel, la culture du riz et l'élevage des chevaux et des taureaux. C'est un espace très important pour la faune et la flore, notamment pour les oiseaux migrateurs, comme les flamants roses. Depuis 1975, la Camargue est classée réserve naturelle nationale.

Nous avons continué à survoler quelques minutes la Camargue, orange dans la lumière déclinante. Puis, nous avons amorcé notre descente vers une ville s'étendant à perte de vue : Marseille, point de départ de notre excursion en Méditerranée.

« Vous saviez que Marseille était la plus vieille ville de France ? » a dit Chen.

Nous sommes passés au-dessus du Vieux-Port à hauteur de la basilique Notre-Dame-de-la-Garde, perchée sur sa butte, d'où la statue de la Bonne Mère semblait nous saluer. Puis nous avons survolé les calanques au sud de la ville, des petites criques encaissées au pied de falaises qui m'ont fait penser à chez moi. Skip a amorcé la descente. Tout en douceur, il a posé le dirigeable sur sa nacelle, qui flotte comme une coque de bateau. Il a jeté les ancres (une à l'arrière, l'autre à l'avant) entre deux falaises tombant à pic dans la mer cristalline.

« Des volontaires pour la baignade ? a demandé Sofia.

– Moi ! a répondu aussitôt Vai, la plus impatiente de nous tous. »

Inutile de nous le répéter : vite, nous sommes allés dans nos cabines enfiler nos maillots de bain ! Une minute après, nous étions tous de retour sur la coursive. Sofia n'a pas été la dernière à plonger. Barboter dans l'eau turquoise, après cette première journée de voyage, c'était trop bon !

Notre cuisinier et notre *skipper* étaient restés à bord : Macodou pour préparer une bouillabaisse, la soupe de poissons locale… et Skip pour pêcher les poissons. Chen lui aussi est resté sur le pont, pour aider Skip à pêcher. On a eu beau l'appeler pour qu'il nous rejoigne, il n'a jamais voulu. Trop nul !

« Eh, il parait que tu te débrouilles pas mal dans l'eau ? m'a lancé Vai. Ça te dit un concours d'apnée ? »

Elle a plongé et je l'ai aussitôt imitée. Je l'ai suivie pendant un temps dans l'eau cristalline. Elle nageait avec la grâce d'une sirène. Mais au bout d'une minute, j'ai dû faire surface, les poumons en feu. Vai, elle, est encore restée un temps interminable… À croire qu'elle avait des branchies. Ça me tue de le dire, mais cette fille est vraiment incroyable sous l'eau !

Après le diner, il était temps de regagner nos cabines pour lire un peu. On se couche tôt quand on n'a pas la télé ! Heureusement pour moi, Chen ne ronfle pas…

Ce matin, Chen et moi étions levés avant les filles. En regardant par la baie vitrée, j'ai aperçu Sofia, sur la coursive. Vêtue d'une tunique ample, elle prenait des poses, balayant l'air de mouvements au ralenti ou levant les bras au ciel.

« Ça alors, ai-je dit, Sofia fait son yoga !

– Pff, mais non, c'est du tai-chi, a répliqué Chen. Un art martial chinois basé sur la respiration.

– Ça, un art martial ? On dirait plutôt de la relaxation.

– C'est une technique de combat vieille de plusieurs millénaires. D'ailleurs, son nom veut dire "boxe avec l'ombre", car on a l'impression que la personne se bat contre le vent. Là, par exemple, c'est la posture de la "grue ouvrant ses ailes". »

Les filles nous ont rejoints. Elles ont observé avec curiosité cette drôle de gymnastique. Puis la faim nous a appelés à la table du petit déjeuner. C'était trop bizarre de partager ce repas avec les autres. D'habitude, je ne suis pas obligé de supporter au réveil la vue de quatre têtes chiffonnées, aux cheveux en pétard. Ni le bruit de quatre bouches en train de mastiquer des céréales. En plus, Fatoumata faisait une tête pas possible.

« On dirait que quelqu'un a le réveil difficile, ai-je dit en la regardant.

– Comment je pourrais me réveiller, alors que je n'ai pas fermé l'œil de la nuit ? a grogné Fatou.

– Pourquoi ? Kwanita a ronflé ? Ou bien Vai a battu des records de crawl sur sa couchette ?

– Non, j'ai fait un cauchemar : j'ai rêvé de toi ! Et quand j'ai réalisé que je devais te supporter pendant trois mois, cela m'a empêché de me rendormir…

– Ouah ! Comme on dit chez nous en Afrique, ai-je dit en imitant Macodou, "la lionne qui a mal dormi rugit plus fort". »

À ce moment-là, Sofia est entrée. Elle a voulu connaitre la raison de cette dispute matinale.

« C'est juste Fatou qui fait un air de bœuf, a expliqué Kwanita. Elle est tannée, car elle a passé la nuit sur la corde à linge. Et Fab lui a parlé bête. »

Je ne vous ai pas encore parlé de Kwanita ! C'est la plus vieille du groupe. Elle vient du Canada. Je trouve son accent TROP drôle ! Cette fille a vraiment une façon bizarre de s'exprimer… La preuve, pour dire bonjour, elle dit « allo » !

« Euh… traduction en français ? ai-je demandé

– C'est du français, t'sais ! s'est fâchée Kwanita. Ça veut dire : "Fatou est de mauvaise humeur, car elle a mal dormi"…

– Peut-être qu'elle aurait mieux dormi si elle ne s'était pas levée toutes les cinq minutes pour relever le store du hublot, a lancé Vai.

– Je n'y peux rien, s'est défendue Fatou. Chez moi, je n'ai pas de volets, je n'ai pas l'habitude de dormir dans le noir complet. »

Macodou, qui passait par là, en a profité pour placer l'un de ses proverbes africains :
« Quelle que soit l'obscurité de la nuit, le jour finit toujours par se lever…
– Je viens de parler à Tematai, intervient Sofia. Nous devons partir maintenant. Chen, tu vas l'aider aux manœuvres ? »
Sofia nous explique que, chaque matin, il y a un programme de tâches à respecter : nous devons à tour de rôle aider aux manœuvres, se partager le rangement et le ménage des cabines et du carré, la cuisine et l'entretien du pont.
Je m'acquitte de ma tâche en deux temps, trois mouvements : deux temps pour débarrasser la table du petit déjeuner et trois mouvements pour ramasser les vêtements qui trainent chez les garçons (enfin, surtout les miens, car Chen a déjà plié soigneusement ses affaires sur son lit).
Nous avons laissé la terre derrière nous, direction le détroit des bouches de Bonifacio, au sud de la Corse.
Notre premier cours est un cours d'anglais (nous aurons aussi de l'espagnol).
« Les langues sont très importantes, a précisé Sofia, car nous survolerons de nombreux pays où l'on ne parle pas français. »
Ça tombe bien, les langues sont ma matière préférée ! Mon père est français, ma mère italienne, et moi je parle les deux langues.

« Les langues, j'adore ! C'est trop facile pour moi, je suis déjà bilingue !

– Ah ouais, d'enfer ! s'est extasiée Kwanita. Dommage pour toi : tout le monde ici parle deux langues…

– Ça m'étonnerait ! dis-je.

– Tu serais moins baveux, poursuit Kwanita, tu saurais que Fatou parle le fang, sa langue maternelle, et le français. Vai parle français et tahitien, Chen français et chinois. Et moi, je parle français et anglais couramment, comme beaucoup de Canadiens, mais aussi l'ojibwé, la langue de ma mère. Alors, pas de quoi faire ton frais ! »

Apparemment, Vai n'est pas la seule des filles à se la jouer…

« Désolé d'interrompre votre dispute, mais il est temps de se mettre au travail », a rappelé Sofia.

Nous avons commencé à travailler sur le texte que Sofia nous avait donné. Mais une surprise nous attendait ! Une surprise… de taille.

Une heure après notre départ, la cloche a retenti. C'est ainsi que Skip nous prévient qu'il y a quelque chose à voir au dehors. Tous les regards ont convergé vers le grand écran, mais on ne voyait rien d'autre que le bleu de la mer. Une seule façon de savoir ce qui se passe…

Aussitôt, c'est la débandade ! L'occasion est trop belle pour laisser nos devoirs en plan. C'est à qui sera le premier à gagner le pont extérieur. Courbés en deux au-dessus du garde-corps, nous examinons l'étendue d'eau sous le ventre du *Waka-roa*. Mais j'ai beau m'abimer les yeux à scruter les reflets étincelants, je ne distingue rien.

« Là ! Regardez ! »

Je tourne mon regard dans la direction indiquée par Kwanita. Et tout à coup, je vois comme un panache de fumée. Sauf que ce n'est pas de la fumée, mais un puissant jet d'eau. Puis je distingue la forme de trois dos courbés, surmontés d'une nageoire en forme de crête effilée. Aussitôt, je sais de quoi il s'agit :

« Des baleines ! J'en ai déjà aperçu au large de l'ile de Stromboli, au nord de la Sicile. Skip a dû les repérer grâce à leur souffle. »

Jouant à rase-mottes au-dessus de l'eau, le *Waka-roa* suit les évolutions des trois cétacés. On pourrait presque caresser leur dos !

« Ce sont des rorquals communs, commente Sofia, la baleine la plus fréquente dans ces eaux. Nous sommes en train de survoler Pelagos, une réserve pour mammifères marins. »

Les baleines continuent à faire le dos rond dans les vagues, avec de temps à autre un jaillissement de gouttelettes d'eau. Soudain, comme pour nous saluer, la plus grosse des trois hisse la moitié de son corps monumental à la verticale. Puis elle retombe dans une immense explosion d'eau qui monte jusque par-dessus la passerelle, nous éclaboussant copieusement ! Comme obéissant à un ordre silencieux, les trois cétacés disparaissent sous la surface. Ils ont plongé.

« Quel dommage ! s'exclame Fatou.

– Vous saviez, dit Chen, qu'après la baleine bleue, le rorqual est le deuxième plus gros animal de la planète ? C'est aussi le mammifère marin le plus bruyant. Et l'un des plus rapides ! Il peut parcourir… »

Je l'interromps avant qu'il ait une chance de réciter tout l'article de Wikipédia :

« Euh, merci, Chen, c'est assez. Cétacé. Vous pigez ? »

Après un temps de réflexion, ils comprennent enfin le jeu de mots.

« Elle est platte, ta *joke*, commente Kwanita.

– Quoi, on n'a pas d'humour au Canada ?

– Elle a raison, renchérit Vai, elle est nulle ta blague ! »

Décidément, j'ai un public très exigeant…

Difficile, après ce spectacle incroyable, de nous remettre à travailler. Vai s'est lancée dans la rédaction d'un article sur les parcs marins de Méditerranée, tandis que Fatoumata s'intéresse aux cétacés qu'on peut y rencontrer. J'aimerais bien finir d'écrire sur le sujet des volcans d'Italie, mais mon regard est sans cesse attiré vers le ciel bleu de l'autre côté des hublots.

Cette première rencontre était un beau cadeau. Pourtant, aujourd'hui, nous ne sommes pas au bout de nos surprises…

 ZOOM SUR LES BALEINES DE PELAGOS. ÉCRIT PAR FATOUMATA

Le rorqual commun, appelé aussi « à dos en rasoir » à cause de sa nageoire crochue, se rencontre dans le sanctuaire marin de Pelagos, au nord du bassin occidental de la Méditerranée. Il y trouve sa nourriture, constituée principalement de krill, des petites crevettes. On le repère facilement à sa grande taille et à son souffle puissant, une colonne d'eau qui s'élève à 5 ou 6 m au-dessus de l'eau. C'est le deuxième plus gros animal sur la planète, juste derrière sa cousine la baleine bleue : il mesure jusqu'à 22 m, et pèse de 30 à 40 t. Chaque année, on peut observer des naissances et des nourrissons à proximité des côtes de Provence et de Corse.

3

MAUVAISE SURPRISE

📝 JOURNAL DE BORD DE SOFIA

5 septembre. Après deux belles rencontres, nous en avons fait une bien mauvaise…

📝 RÉCIT DE FABRIZIO

Un peu plus tard, alors que nous approchons du détroit de Bonifacio, entre Corse et Sardaigne, la cloche retentit à nouveau. C'est donc une nouvelle ruée vers la coursive !

Le spectacle est encore une fois à la hauteur. Sous la coque de la nacelle, l'eau est parcourue d'éclairs vif-argent. Quand le *Wakaroa* s'est approché suffisamment, tout le monde s'est exclamé en même temps :

« Des dauphins ! »

Il y avait là au moins cinquante individus qui s'amusaient à bondir dans les vagues !

Nous nous sommes enfoncés vers le sud à leur poursuite, laissant la Sardaigne sur notre gauche. C'était comme s'ils avaient décidé de nous faire escorte… ou de faire la course avec nous. Hélas ! quelques minutes après, nous les avons perdus de vue et avons dû poursuivre seuls notre route, sans nous douter qu'elle croiserait à nouveau celle des dauphins, dans des circonstances nettement moins gaies…

 ZOOM SUR LES DAUPHINS, ÉCRIT PAR FATOUMATA

Le dauphin commun, ou dauphin à bec court, se rencontre dans toute la Méditerranée, surtout dans le sud et l'ouest du bassin occidental, et dans le sanctuaire Pelagos. Mesurant 2 m, pour un poids de 100 kg, c'est un nageur très rapide : il atteint facilement une vitesse de pointe de 50 km/h. Les dauphins se déplacent en groupes de 50 individus et plus. On les trouve plutôt près des côtes. Curieux et joueurs, ils n'ont pas peur des voiliers (ni des dirigeables en rase-mottes !) et peuvent passer de longs moments à jouer dans l'étrave des bateaux.

Nous étions en train de mettre la table pour le dîner (ou plus exactement, de nous disputer pour savoir qui mettrait la table). Tout à coup, une formidable détonation a déchiré l'air, tel un coup de tonnerre, nous faisant tous sursauter. Sauf que le temps n'était pas du tout à l'orage. Nous sommes tous restés figés sur place, l'oreille aux aguets, tendus dans l'attente d'une autre explosion. Quand elle a retenti, mon cœur a fait un bond dans ma poitrine. Oubliant de nous disputer, nous nous sommes précipités sur le pont extérieur.

Le spectacle qui nous attendait était beaucoup moins réjouissant que tout à l'heure.

Il y avait deux gros bateaux, autour desquels s'agitait un groupe de dauphins. Les mêmes que ceux aperçus plus tôt ? Cette fois, les cétacés n'étaient pas en train de jouer mais de se sauver ! Un troisième coup de tonnerre a retenti, répercuté et amplifié par l'eau.

« Mais on leur tire dessus ! » s'est écriée Vai.

Pas de doute, c'étaient bien des coups de fusil que l'on avait entendus. On pouvait même, à présent, distinguer la silhouette du marin assassin penché au-dessus du bastingage, le bras prolongé par son arme. À notre grande horreur, l'homme a levé la tête et nous a aperçus. Le bras tendu dans notre direction, il s'est mis à hurler des paroles incompréhensibles, mais dont le sens était très clair... Notre présence dérangeait !

À travers le hublot de la cabine de pilotage, Sofia a fait signe aussitôt à Tematai de remonter. Celui-ci a hoché la tête et nous avons senti le ballon gagner de l'altitude.

Sofia a encore adressé une question muette à Skip : elle a fait décrire des cercles à son poing serré, levé à hauteur de la tempe. En langage universel : « Est-ce que tu as filmé ? » Le pouce dressé, Skip a fait signe que oui, c'était dans la boite.

« Mais on ne peut pas les laisser s'en tirer comme ça ! a repris Fatou.

– C'est trop dangereux de s'attarder dans les parages, a dit Sofia. Ces pêcheurs sont surement dans l'illégalité et nous faisons des témoins gênants. »

Selon elle, il s'agissait d'un thonier et de son re-morqueur. Le fait qu'ils se trouvent dans ces eaux, en cette période de reproduction et donc de pêche interdite, n'était pas bon signe.

Un dernier coup de fusil a résonné. Dirigé contre les dauphins... ou contre nous ? Nous ne nous sommes pas attardés pour le savoir.

« Skip a tout filmé, nous a rassuré Sofia. Dès notre arrivée, je préviendrai les autorités algériennes. »

En attendant, la seule chose à faire, c'était de passer à table. Mais personne n'avait beaucoup d'appétit. Pour détendre l'atmosphère, Macodou a lancé une blague :

« En entrée, soupe d'ailerons de dauphins ! Des amateurs ? »

À présent, c'est sa blague à lui qui tombait « platte », comme disait Kwanita...

📷 ZOOM SUR LES DAUPHINS MENACÉS, ÉCRIT PAR FATOUMATA

La diminution des ressources en petits poissons (le menu des dauphins) et l'activité croissante de la pêche sont une menace pour les dauphins communs. Même s'ils ne sont plus chassés dans cette partie du monde, comme dans certains pays, ils peuvent être tués par des pêcheurs, volontairement, car ils représentent une concurrence, mais surtout accidentellement, pris dans les filets dérivants. Ces filets, déployés sur des kilomètres de longueur et une profondeur de 10 à 30 m, capturent aussi bien les poissons que les cétacés, les tortues ou les oiseaux de mer. Dans les années 1960, des millions de dauphins sont morts, piégés par les filets dérivants. Cette technique de pêche est aujourd'hui interdite mais provoque chaque année encore la mort de milliers de dauphins. Ceux-ci ont presque failli disparaitre de la mer Noire et sont menacés en mer Ionienne. Enfin, les dauphins sont très sensibles à la pollution chimique. En 1990, un virus causé par la pollution a tué plus de 6 000 dauphins.

4

DOUNIA

6 septembre, matin. Notre arrivée à Tabarka, hier soir, n'est pas passée inaperçue. Nous avons jeté nos amarres sur la plage, près du port de pêche, provoquant aussitôt un attroupement.

L'excitation de notre arrivée à Tabarka a un peu effacé la mauvaise impression de l'après-midi.

Est-ce que je vous ai dit que le *Wakaroa* pouvait aussi bien se poser sur l'eau, à l'ancre, que sur la terre ferme ? En effet, il dispose de filins d'amarrage pouvant se fixer dans la roche.

Nous avons donc atterri sur une plage près du village des pêcheurs. Ceux-ci nous ont accueillis avec des mines ébahies : évidemment, ils ne devaient

pas voir tous les jours un dirigeable se poser sous leurs fenêtres ! Les enfants voulaient tous nous aider aux manœuvres d'amarrage.

Une petite fille s'est détachée du lot pour se présenter avec un sourire : Dounia ! L'auteur de notre appel au secours. Elle n'en revenait pas que nous ayons répondu à son message. Et encore moins de nous voir déjà arriver ! Aussitôt, elle nous a invités à prendre le repas du soir chez elle.

Sur le chemin, elle était intarissable. Dans un très bon français, elle nous a raconté sa ville : son histoire, ses habitants, leur vie basée sur la pêche (de plus en plus difficile) et le tourisme (de plus en plus important).

« Qu'est-ce qu'on pêche par ici ? a demandé Vai.

– Le mérou, la langouste… Mon père m'a dit qu'avant, le poisson était si abondant qu'il faisait vivre tous les pêcheurs. Aujourd'hui, il est plus rare, alors il faut aller le chercher en pleine mer, avec des bateaux plus gros et du matériel plus couteux. Mais les pêcheurs d'ici ne peuvent pas se le permettre.

– Alors de quoi vivent-ils ? s'est inquiétée Kwanita.

– Beaucoup travaillent dans le tourisme, employés dans les grands hôtels. Il y a aussi la plongée sous-marine et la récolte du corail.

– Le corail ? a répété Chen.

– Oui, le corail rouge, c'est un matériau précieux qui sert à la confection de bijoux. Il y en avait beaucoup dans la région. Mais comme pour le poisson, les réserves s'épuisent et il faut aller le chercher plus loin, et plus profond. »

ZOOM SUR L'OR ROUGE DE MÉDITERRANÉE. ÉCRIT PAR FABRIZIO

Le corail est un animal microscopique, qui constitue des colonies en forme de rameaux ou d'arbres, soutenues par un squelette solide. Il se fixe sur les fonds rocheux ou les parois des grottes, et pousse très lentement, de 2 à 8 mm par an. Le corail rouge est très recherché en bijouterie, en Italie, en Algérie, en Tunisie. Autrefois, on pouvait récolter des coraux hauts de 1 m, à des profondeurs de 30 ou 40 m. Mais la surexploitation et la lenteur de sa croissance ont fait du corail rouge un matériau rare et très convoité. Aujourd'hui, il faut aller le chercher à des profondeurs de 100, 150 voire 200 m, et donc disposer de navires équipés de moyens ultraperformants : sondeurs, caméras téléguidées.

Nous sommes arrivés chez Dounia. C'est une petite maison de pêcheurs dans une ruelle tout près du port. Son père, Ahmed, avec qui elle vit seule, nous a accueillis gentiment, nous serrant la main l'un après l'autre. C'est là que j'ai remarqué quelque chose d'étrange…

Lorsqu'il a pris la main de Kwanita, elle a eu un petit sursaut. Elle s'est crispée, les yeux dans le vague, et elle est devenue toute pâle. Il y a eu un long moment de gêne, jusqu'à ce qu'Ahmed retire sa main. Alors Kwanita a semblé sortir subitement de son rêve éveillé.

Je croyais que j'étais le seul à avoir remarqué. Mais, un peu plus tard, j'ai vu que Sofia mettait la main sur l'épaule de Kwanita. Inquiète, elle semblait l'interroger du regard. Kwanita a souri d'un air absent et détourné les yeux.

Trop bizarre, si vous voulez mon avis !

Ahmed avait préparé un plat de boulettes de sardines frites. C'était trop bon ! Puis il a servi le thé à la menthe dans de jolis verres décorés d'arabesques. Dounia a commencé à parler de la colonie de phoques sur l'île de la Galite. Colonie, c'est beaucoup dire, vu qu'elle ne compte que trois ou quatre individus. Ou plutôt, « comptait ». Car, depuis quelques semaines, les gens du coin ont remarqué qu'on voyait de moins en moins souvent les mammifères marins. Et ils ont commencé à se demander s'ils n'auraient pas définitivement quitté la région. Mais pour quelle raison ?

« Et si nous allions faire un tour du côté de la Galite, demain matin, a suggéré Sofia. Est-ce que vous seriez d'accord pour que Dounia nous accompagne à bord du *Wakaroa* ? »

Tout à coup, Ahmed, si gentil pendant tout le repas, a complètement changé. Son visage s'est fermé, et il a répondu sur un ton sec :

« Pourquoi vous voulez aller là-bas ? Il n'y a rien à voir sur la Galite, rien que des rochers déserts ! Je vous conseille de rester à Tabarka et de profiter de la plage.

– Nous ne sommes pas venus pour la plage, a répliqué fermement Sofia, mais pour nous intéresser aux phoques de la Galite ! »

Devant la résolution de Sofia, Ahmed a semblé se radoucir. Il a jeté un regard vers sa fille, qui semblait le supplier des yeux.

« Mmm, a-t-il grommelé dans sa barbe, je suppose que je ne peux pas vous en empêcher. Mais je vous aurai prévenus, il n'y a rien à voir là-bas. »

Le repas s'est terminé sans autre accrochage mais l'atmosphère est restée un peu pesante. Nous avons été bien contents de retrouver le chemin de la plage.

Durant tout le chemin du retour, et une fois à bord du *Wakaroa*, Kwanita est restée étrangement silencieuse.

De plus en plus bizarre…

ZOOM SUR LE PHOQUE MOINE DE MÉDITERRANÉE. ÉCRIT PAR FATOUMATA

Le phoque moine est l'espèce de mammifères marins la plus menacée d'Europe. Victime de la chasse, de la pollution et de la dégradation de son habitat, il est en danger d'extinction partout dans le monde. Autrefois abondant en Méditerranée, il a disparu des côtes françaises, puis de Corse, de Sardaigne, et d'Italie. Il n'en reste plus aujourd'hui qu'entre 500 et 600, dans l'Atlantique (à Madère, au Maroc et en Mauritanie), et dans le bassin méditerranéen (en Lybie, et surtout en Turquie et en Grèce).

5

UN PETIT ORPHELIN

JOURNAL DE BORD DE SOFIA

6 septembre. Je suis passée à la capitainerie du port pour alerter les garde-côtes de notre rencontre avec les pêcheurs soupçonnés de pêche illégale (et de tuerie de dauphins !). Puis nous avons décollé en direction de la Galite. Dounia, qui nous avait rejoints, faisait partie des passagers.

RÉCIT DE FABRIZIO

La Galite n'est pas une île, mais un archipel de plusieurs îles. Seule la principale est habitée. Tematai a posé le *Wakaroa* dans une petite crique au sud du Galiton, un îlot inabordable au sud-ouest de l'île principale. C'est dans cette zone protégée qu'habitaient les phoques moines. D'après Dounia, ils avaient élu domicile dans les grottes sous-marines. Pour ne pas effrayer les animaux (s'il en reste !), Sofia a demandé à Tematai de s'ancrer à distance du littoral. Nous continuerons à la nage.

Le *Wakaroa* est entièrement équipé pour la plongée sous-marine, et dispose même d'un compresseur. Mais pour ne pas déranger les phoques, nous avons plongé en apnée. Quand je dis « nous », cela veut dire tout le monde sauf Macodou, Tematai… et Chen. Hier soir, quand nous étions couchés, il m'a avoué qu'il ne savait pas nager. Ne pas savoir nager, à son âge ! Il m'a demandé de garder son secret, et j'ai promis.

Une fois équipés, Sofia, Vai, Fatou, Kwanita, Dounia et moi, nous nous sommes mis doucement à l'eau par la plateforme arrière.

Tout de suite, je prends la tête, décidé à arriver le premier au rivage. Soudain, je sens quelque chose qui s'agrippe à moi. Paniqué, je me retourne… Ce n'est que Sofia qui se cramponne à l'une de mes palmes. Du plat de ses deux mains, elle me fait signe de ralentir. Ne pas faire de bruit, OK, compris…

Nous voilà enfin à proximité du rivage. Nous allons explorer cette portion de la côte. Sofia met un doigt sur sa bouche pour nous rappeler le silence. Nous plongeons par équipes, tour à tour : Kwanita et Dounia avec Sofia, et Fatou, Vai et moi ensemble. Sur un signe du pouce, Sofia fait signe à Kwanita et Dounia de la suivre.

Nous mettons la tête sous l'eau pour suivre des yeux leur descente. Une minute plus tard, elles remontent. Sofia secoue la tête : rien par ici.

Nous palmons jusqu'à la grotte suivante. C'est à notre tour de plonger : Sofia compte sur notre expérience de la plongée, à Vai et à moi, et nous rappelle de garder un œil sur Fatou.

La grotte est petite… et déserte. Nous remontons, déçus, même si nous savons qu'il y a une chance pour que les phoques aient effectivement quitté l'île. Nous poursuivons notre exploration de la côte en alternant les plongées. Sofia nous montre en passant des branches de corail rouge. Je comprends l'intérêt que suscite « l'or rouge » chez les pêcheurs, les marchands et les joailliers : c'est magnifique !

Arrivés au nord, de l'autre côté de l'île, nous avons fini par perdre presque tout espoir de retrouver la trace des phoques. Je commençais à ressentir la fatigue de ces apnées répétées. C'est alors que nous avons fait notre découverte…

C'était notre tour de plonger. La paroi de la falaise s'enfonçait profondément sous l'eau. Nous allions remonter bredouilles lorsque Vai, qui me précédait, a tendu le bras. Sans nous attendre, elle s'est mise à palmer vers le fond, où une tache noire signalait l'entrée d'une grotte. J'ai regardé vers Fatou, qui m'a fait signe qu'elle manquait d'air. Pouce vers le haut, elle m'a indiqué qu'elle devait

remonter. J'ai hésité à suivre Vai mais j'ai pensé à Sofia qui nous faisait confiance et suis remonté avec Fatou.

« Où est Vai ? » demande aussitôt Sofia.

Je lève les bras en signe d'impuissance.

« Restée en bas. Elle a trouvé une grotte. »

Nous avons attendu dans un silence inquiet que Vai nous rejoigne. Et attendu, et attendu… Voilà qu'elle ne remontait pas ! Sofia avait du mal à cacher son anxiété.

« Fabrizio, tu vas redescendre avec moi, a-t-elle dit dans un souffle. Les autres, vous attendez ici. »

Nous sommes descendus le long de la paroi rocheuse. Arrivés à l'endroit où Vai avait disparu, j'ai tendu le bras et nous nous sommes enfoncés plus profondément.

L'entrée de la grotte sous-marine était juste un peu plus bas. Nous nous sommes engouffrés… J'ai essayé de ne pas penser aux risques de rester coincés et de se noyer. Heureusement que j'avais déjà fait de la spéléologie, sinon j'aurais paniqué ! Puis le conduit a commencé à remonter tout doucement et à s'élargir, avant de déboucher à l'air libre. J'ai pris une grande bouffée d'oxygène et j'ai regardé autour de moi. Nous étions dans une caverne souterraine aux murs voutés.

« Par ici ! »

J'ai tourné la tête en direction du cri.

À côté de moi, Sofia a poussé un gros soupir de soulagement. D'un surplomb de roche formant une sorte de plage, Vai nous adressait de grands signes. Nous avons nagé vers elle mais quelque chose clochait : comme si elle se désintéressait de nous, Vai nous tournait le dos. Elle était agenouillée près d'une masse sombre que j'ai d'abord prise pour un rocher. Mais la masse sombre s'est mise à bouger.

Vai a tourné la tête vers nous. Elle avait les yeux rouges, comme si elle avait pleuré.

« On dirait qu'il est blessé », a-t-elle dit d'une toute petite voix.

J'ai regardé de plus près la petite chose tremblante qui me dévisageait de ses grands yeux noirs apeurés, par-dessus les moustaches ornant son museau arrondi.

Apparemment, tout ce qu'il restait de la colonie de la Galite, c'était ce bébé phoque apeuré.

« Il est très maigre et très affaibli, a remarqué Sofia. Surement un orphelin. Sa mère a dû être tuée… Ou bien quelque chose l'aura effrayée. Il arrive qu'une mère abandonne son petit lorsqu'elle se sent menacée. Comme il ne sait pas encore nager ni se nourrir seul, il meurt.

– Il faut le sauver ! s'est écriée Vai. Le prendre à bord du *Wakaroa* !

– D'accord, mais ça ne va pas être facile de le ramener à la surface. Et encore moins de regagner le *Wakaroa* à la nage tout en le portant. Il doit peser une dizaine de kilos.

– J'ai une idée ! suis-je intervenu. Tematai pourrait piloter le *Wakaroa* jusqu'ici, et pendant ce temps on fabriquerait un brancard !

– Mmm, je crois bien que c'est la seule solution, a reconnu Sofia. Alors remontons sans perdre de temps !

– Pas moi, a dit Vai. Je vous attends ici ! »

Bien sûr, Sofia n'a pas été d'accord. La marée pouvait monter dans la grotte… Comment savoir quel niveau l'eau atteindrait ? Mais Vai n'a rien voulu savoir. Elle a fait quelque chose d'étrange : s'allongeant à plat ventre, elle a plongé ses deux bras dans l'eau et fermé les yeux pendant plusieurs secondes. Et s'est mise à sourire ! Puis elle s'est redressée et a dit, très sure d'elle :

« La marée est descendante. »

Jamais vu quelque chose d'aussi bizarre ! Mais le plus bizarre, c'est que Sofia a hoché la tête et n'a même plus essayé de discuter.

« On revient le plus vite possible », a-t-elle simplement dit.

Pas possible ! Je n'en revenais pas que Sofia ait cédé aussi facilement à Vai…

J'ai pris une bonne goulée d'air et j'ai suivi Sofia sur le chemin du retour.

Nous avions commencé notre remontée lorsque, soudain, j'ai entendu un ronronnement assourdi au-dessus de ma tête. Levant les yeux, j'ai distingué la forme ovale, familière, de la coque d'un bateau. Une coque trop petite pour être celle de notre nacelle.

Non, ce n'était pas le *Wakaroa* venu à notre rencontre et guettant notre remontée…

Lorsque nous avons sorti la tête de l'eau, c'était pour tomber nez à nez avec une demi-douzaine de pêcheurs pas vraiment amicaux. Ou plutôt, carrément hostiles. Surtout l'un d'eux…

« Je vous avais dit de ne pas venir trainer dans le coin, a fait Ahmed d'une voix sombre. C'est une zone protégée, ici, pas un endroit pour touristes.

– Mais un endroit pour les pêcheurs, peut-être ? l'a défié Sofia.

– Je vous conseille de ne pas vous attarder ici, a répliqué Ahmed. Vous pourriez avoir un accident, et il n'y aurait personne pour venir à votre secours…

– Et vous, vous ne craignez pas d'être dénoncés pour pêche illégale ? a insisté Sofia. À moins que ce ne soit pas le poisson qui vous intéresse, mais une marchandise plus précieuse encore ? »

À ces mots, le père de Dounia est devenu tout rouge. Il s'est tourné vers sa fille et a marmonné entre ses dents :

« Tu viens avec nous, on rentre.

– Mais papa…

– Tu viens, je te dis. »

Il a hissé Dounia à bord. Les larmes aux yeux, notre nouvelle amie nous a jeté un dernier regard mi-désolé, mi-implorant. Puis le bateau a fait demi-tour pour s'éloigner dans un rugissement de moteur.

Kwanita et Fatou avaient l'air effrayées. Moi, j'étais surtout impressionné par la façon qu'avait eue Sofia de tenir tête aux pêcheurs. Apparemment, notre maitresse, si calme et si douce, a la moutarde qui lui monte au nez dès qu'elle flaire l'injustice.

« Où est Vai ? a demandé Fatou, d'une voix inquiète.

– Elle va bien, elle nous attend dans une grotte sous-marine. Mais je vous raconterai tout cela en chemin, il faut regagner le *Wakaroa* sans tarder. Vous devez être frigorifiés d'avoir passé tout ce temps dans l'eau. Pour gagner du temps, nous allons couper à pied à travers l'île, plutôt que de la contourner à la nage. »

Nous avons nagé jusqu'à une petite plage. Nos palmes à la main, nous avons commencé l'ascension des flancs escarpés et pelés de l'ilot, semés ici ou là d'arbres isolés et de broussailles. Une question me trottait dans la tête.

« Qu'est-ce que vous avez voulu dire tout à l'heure, par "une marchandise plus précieuse encore"?

– Je ne crois pas que ce soit le poisson qui attire les pêcheurs par ici, mais le corail, bien plus rentable. Leur bateau n'était pas équipé pour la pêche. De toute façon, la zone est interdite. Pour les phoques qui habitaient ici, le résultat est le même : la perte de leur habitat. »

Tout en pensant au bébé phoque orphelin, abandonné dans sa grotte et mourant de faim, je serrais les poings de colère.

📷 ZOOM SUR LA DISPARITION DES PHOQUES. ÉCRIT PAR FATOUMATA

Autrefois, les phoques se reproduisaient et mettaient bas sur les plages. Mais, dérangés par l'homme, ils préfèrent aujourd'hui les côtes rocheuses sauvages et abruptes. Ils se réfugient dans des grottes sous-marines, pour se reposer et donner naissance aux petits.

La naissance se produit entre mai et novembre, après 9 à 11 mois de gestation. Le nouveau-né mesure moins de 1 m et pèse entre 10 et 20 kg, pour atteindre 80 kg au bout de 2 semaines !

Malheureusement, la mortalité est très importante : 1 jeune sur 2 meurt avant d'être sevré. Les grottes sous-marines sont sauvages, mais exposées aux tempêtes. Lorsque le niveau d'eau monte, le bébé, qui ne sait nager qu'au bout de quelques heures après sa naissance, peut alors être emporté. Il arrive aussi que la mère, si elle se sent en danger (dérangée par des bruits de moteur par exemple), se sauve en abandonnant son petit.

6

UN BÉBÉ PHOQUE À SAUVER

6 septembre. L'opération de sauvetage s'est bien déroulée : nous avons désormais un petit passager de plus à bord !

Après dix minutes de marche, nous avons atteint le phare qui domine l'ile. Cela faisait plaisir de retrouver la forme ronde du *Wakaroa*. Sofia a fait de grands gestes des bras, dans l'espoir que Tematai ou Chen nous aperçoive.

Une petite silhouette s'est agitée dans le nid-de-pie : c'est comme cela qu'on appelle le poste d'observation situé tout en haut du dirigeable. On y accède par une échelle de coupée dont les barreaux sont fixés directement au flanc du ballon. Ce n'était pas difficile de reconnaitre Chen : il passe la plupart de son temps dans le nid-de-pie, les yeux rivés à une paire de jumelles. Chen a toujours l'air d'être ailleurs quand on lui parle. Mais là, à son poste favori, on peut compter sur lui pour garder l'œil ouvert. Tant mieux pour nous : apparemment, il nous a aperçus, car la petite silhouette est aussitôt descendue de son perchoir pour regagner la passerelle et alerter Skip. Bientôt, les ancres sont levées et le *Wakaroa* tourne sa proue vers nous, en route pour nous récupérer. Bien vu, Chen !

« Allons-y, a fait Sofia. Tematai ne pourra pas accoster, à cause des rochers, mais il peut nous faire gagner de précieuses minutes. »

Nous nous apprêtons à entamer notre descente lorsqu'un cri de Kwanita nous arrête net dans nos pas.

« Regardez ! Là-bas, vous voyez ce que je vois ? »

Elle pointe son doigt vers le nord-ouest, où deux navires sont ancrés à quelques encablures. Même sans jumelles, nous reconnaissons des bateaux de pêche. Peut-être même s'agit-il du thonier et de son remorqueur survolés hier ?

« Je croyais que ces eaux étaient interdites à la pêche ? ai-je dit.

– Elles le sont, a répondu Sofia. Mais, visiblement, tout le monde ne le sait pas… ou choisit de l'ignorer. »

Décidément, pour des eaux protégées, les parages de la Galite sont plutôt fréquentés !

Nous dévalons la pente caillouteuse aussi vite que nous le pouvons. Moi, je suis avantagé par mon expérience de randonnées sur les pentes des volcans. Je cours comme un cabri !

« Attention ! m'a crié Sofia. Ne va pas te tordre une cheville !

– C'est bon, j'ai l'habitude ! »

Il ne nous faut pas plus de cinq minutes pour atteindre la rive sud. Le *Wakaroa* nous y attend déjà, à une distance confortable des rochers. Quelques brasses plus tard, nous mettons le pied sur la passerelle.

Pendant que le *Wakaroa* fait le tour de l'île à petite vitesse, à couvert des falaises pour ne pas alerter les marins de l'autre côté (au cas où ce seraient les mêmes qui nous ont déjà tiré dessus), nous confectionnons un brancard artisanal à l'aide d'une couverture à laquelle nous cousons des sangles.

Pour la seconde fois, nous nous mettons à l'eau.

Sofia a reconnu l'endroit et, à nouveau, nous plongeons, elle et moi, accompagnés de Fatoumata. Ainsi, avec Vai, nous sommes quatre pour tenir les bords de la couverture.

Vai nous attend assise en tailleur, une main posée sur le flanc de l'animal. Il faut croire qu'elle avait raison pour la marée, car l'eau a découvert une plus grande surface rocheuse, ce qui laisse davantage de place pour y tenir tous.

Lorsqu'elle voit le bébé phoque tout amaigri et effrayé, Fatoumata en a les larmes aux yeux.

« Le pauvre… Il a l'air si fragile. »

Mais elle se ressaisit vite pour nous aider à le faire glisser sur notre brancard improvisé.

En sentant toutes ces mains l'agripper, l'animal commence à se débattre et à gémir comme un jeune chiot. Il se met à trembler du museau à la pointe de la queue. Il gigote tellement qu'il est impossible d'avoir une prise solide.

Alors, Fatoumata fait quelque chose d'incroyable : elle pose une main à plat sur la fourrure de l'animal, ferme les yeux et se met à fredonner tout bas un air dans une langue que je ne connais pas. On dirait qu'elle chante une berceuse à un enfant pour l'endormir.

Et c'est exactement l'effet qu'a sa chanson sur le petit phoque. Il ne s'endort pas, non, mais il cesse de trembler, et il devient tout calme. Nous regardant de ses grands yeux noir de jais, il se laisse désormais manipuler sans plus faire d'histoires.

Décidément, ces filles sont TROP bizarres !

Dans un silence appliqué, nous nouons les sangles pour que le bébé phoque ne puisse pas se dégager pendant le transport.

« À trois, on lève tous ensemble, dit Sofia. Une, deux, trois. Hissez ! »

Délicatement, chacun tenant un des coins de la couverture, nous faisons glisser notre précieux paquet à l'eau et regagnons la sortie de la grotte aussi vite que nous pouvons.

Lorsque nous atteignons la surface, Chen et Kwanita nous accueillent avec des bravos et des applaudissements. Tematai et Macodou, penchés par-dessus la coursive, tirent l'animal à bord.

Opération « sauvetage du bébé phoque » réussie !

7

PLONGÉE DE NUIT

7 septembre. Hier soir, à la demande des enfants, nous avons effectué une plongée de nuit, Vai, Fabrizio, Tematai et moi. J'aurais dû refuser mais une partie de moi avait envie de savoir ce que trament ces pêcheurs.

Fatoumata a donné son premier repas au bébé phoque, à l'aide d'un biberon improvisé. Elle nous a dit qu'elle habitait sur une réserve pour animaux blessés ou perdus. Apparemment, s'occuper de petits orphelins comme Farouk, ça la connait. Eh oui, Farouk, c'est comme cela que nous avons prénommé notre bébé !

Tout le monde est tombé amoureux de Farouk, avec ses grands yeux noirs qui lui donnent un air étonné. Et avec Fatou, il est entre de bonnes mains. Vai et moi, nous avons laissé les autres faire des risettes à Farouk et nous sommes allés parler à Sofia.

Ça n'a pas été facile de la décider. Tout d'abord, elle n'a rien voulu entendre : trop dangereux.

« Laissons la police se charger de ces histoires, a-t-elle dit d'un ton sans appel.

– Mais la police ne bougera pas sans preuves ! s'est exclamée Vai.

– On ne fera rien d'autre que jeter un œil, promis, ai-je ajouté. Et peut-être prendre une photo ou deux… Si on nous surprend, on pourra toujours dire qu'on faisait une plongée de nuit pour observer le corail rouge. »

À force d'arguments, Sofia a commencé à se montrer un peu hésitante. Au fond, je crois bien qu'elle aussi avait très envie de savoir ce que faisaient ces bateaux dans les parages.

Mais ce qui l'a convaincue pour de bon, c'est lorsque Tematai a proposé de nous accompagner. C'est un excellent plongeur, et deux adultes pour encadrer une plongée de nuit, ce n'est pas de trop. En plus, si jamais on était surpris par des pêcheurs, Tematai représentait un argument « de poids » : personne n'oserait jamais nous chercher des ennuis avec un quintal de muscles nageant à nos côtés.

Une fois équipés, nous nous sommes mis à l'eau. Nous avons nagé tous les quatre en surface pour économiser notre air, en essayant de ne pas faire trop de bruit avec nos palmes. Arrivés à portée de voix des bateaux, Sofia nous a fait signe de nous préparer à plonger. À son signal, nous avons vidé nos gilets stabilisateurs et nous nous sommes laissé descendre. Nous avons allumé nos torches et nagé en direction des masses sombres dessinées par les coques des deux navires suspects.

Tematai et Sofia ouvraient la route, Vai et moi suivant le faisceau lumineux de leurs torches.

Pour tenter de convaincre Sofia, je lui avais dit que j'avais déjà fait plusieurs plongées de nuit. En réalité, c'était ma première… J'avais le cœur qui battait à cent à l'heure ! La nuit, sous l'eau, on se sent vraiment perdu.

Passant sous la coque des bateaux, nous avons nagé jusqu'à la poupe. C'est là que nous avons fait notre découverte : deux énormes cages remplies de thons, nageant dans toutes les directions et se cognant aux grilles comme des fous, leurs dos renvoyant des éclairs vif-argent dans la lumière des torches.

Selon Sofia, la pêche au thon est interdite en cette saison de reproduction. Pas de doute, ces marins du dimanche étaient bel et bien dans l'illégalité ! Mais pourquoi, après avoir pris les poissons dans leurs filets, les pêcheurs ne les avaient-ils pas tués, au lieu de les enfermer dans des cages ?

À côté de moi, Sofia prenait des photos, sans oublier les plaques d'immatriculation du thonier et de son remorqueur.

Tout à coup, un bruit de moteur a déchiré l'eau, agitée de remous. Une masse sombre s'est profilée au-dessus de nos têtes, venant se ranger tout contre la coque du bateau de pêche. Des éclats de voix ont été répercutés par l'onde.

Sofia nous a fait signe de l'attendre tandis qu'elle remontait pour jeter un œil. Dans sa combinaison foncée, elle devait être à peu près invisible.

Mais si elle était invisible, alors… moi aussi !

En me voyant crever la surface de l'eau à sa hauteur, Sofia m'a fait les gros yeux derrière son masque. Puis elle a reporté son attention sur les nouveaux arrivés ayant grimpé à bord du thonier.

Sur le pont, les deux hommes ont été accueillis par les pêcheurs avec des embrassades et des grandes claques dans le dos. Ils semblaient très bien se connaitre.

C'est alors que j'ai remarqué que les deux nouveaux venus étaient en uniforme… Des garde-côtes !

Sofia m'a fait signe de redescendre. Tous les quatre, nous avons regagné le *Wakaroa*.

Une fois à bord, Sofia a laissé éclater sa colère.

« On peut ranger l'appareil photo, cela m'étonnerait que toutes ces preuves nous soient très utiles !

– Pourquoi ? a demandé Vaiana, qui n'avait pas été témoin de la touchante scène de retrouvailles entre les pêcheurs et les garde-côtes.

– Les deux hommes sur le pont, c'est à eux que j'ai parlé à la capitainerie ce matin. Ce sont des douaniers. Ils ont fait semblant de m'écouter. En réalité, ils sont de mèche avec les pêcheurs, ils ne feront rien contre eux.

– Ils sont surement payés par les pêcheurs pour fermer les yeux », ai-je conclu.

Sofia était très remontée :

« Puisqu'on ne peut pas compter sur les douaniers, nous nous débrouillerons seuls. Demain, debout à l'aube. Si les navires lèvent l'ancre, nous les suivrons ! »

📷 ZOOM SUR LA PÊCHE ILLÉGALE. ÉCRIT PAR VAIANA

Le thon rouge de Méditerranée est un poisson très prisé par les consommateurs de nombreux pays. Avec la mode des sushis, son prix a grimpé à des hauteurs jamais atteintes. En janvier 2011, un thon rouge de 340 kg a été acheté par des restaurateurs japonais au prix record de 300 000 € ! Mais, trop pêchées, les populations de thons sont aujourd'hui menacées. L'Europe a dû imposer aux pays méditerranéens des règles et des quotas (des limites à la quantité autorisée de thons pêchés). Les dates d'ouverture de la pêche sont aussi très restreintes : un mois avant la période de reproduction. Mais certains pêcheurs ne respectent pas les règles : ils pêchent en dehors de la période autorisée, et capturent des poissons trop petits, qui n'ont pas atteint leur maturité sexuelle. Certains de ces poissons sont capturés vivants pour être revendus dans des fermes d'élevage, et ne pourront jamais se reproduire à l'état sauvage.

8

SAUVETAGE EN PLEINE MER!

7 septembre, matin. Au réveil, mauvaise surprise: les deux navires avaient disparu. Et à notre arrivée à Tabarka, deuxième mauvaise surprise!

Ce matin, à l'aube, Sofia est retournée à la nage sur l'île, pour guetter les bateaux des hauteurs. Malheureusement, elle est revenue avec une mauvaise nouvelle:

« Ils ne sont plus là, ils ont levé l'ancre pendant la nuit!

– Ils ne vont quand même pas s'en tirer comme ça? s'est offusquée Vai.

– Je vais faxer les photos à la douane européenne, avec les numéros d'immatriculation. Les deux navires naviguent sous pavillon turc. Peut-être les douaniers européens parviendront-ils à les intercepter sur la route du retour… »

Selon elle, les pêcheurs sont payés pour alimenter des fermes d'élevage en Turquie. En capturant les thons durant la période de reproduction, ils font ainsi d'une pierre deux coups : les femelles accouchent de leurs bébés en captivité. Ceux-ci sont ensuite engraissés et vendus à l'étranger. Ils ne pourront pas se reproduire à l'état sauvage. La population des thons rouges de Méditerranée est donc menacée.

Il n'y avait plus rien d'autre à faire que retourner à Tabarka, dire au revoir à Dounia. Notre mission était terminée ici.

Restait le problème de Farouk. Si on le relâchait dans la nature, il serait incapable de se défendre et de trouver sa nourriture. Sofia avait peut-être une solution :

« Je sais qu'il existe un centre de secours pour les phoques perdus ou blessés sur l'île d'Alonissos, en Grèce. Là-bas, ils sauront s'en occuper.

Fatoumata a serré « son bébé » très fort dans ses bras :

« Ça veut dire que Farouk va rester encore un peu avec nous ?

– On dirait bien… » a acquiescé en souriant Sofia.

Nous avons pris le chemin du retour, un peu rassurés à l'idée que tout allait peut-être s'arranger. Une heure après, Tabarka était en vue.

Nous étions trop impatients d'apprendre la bonne nouvelle à Dounia et de lui présenter notre petit protégé! Le seul rescapé de la Galite. Aussitôt les manœuvres d'amarrage terminées, nous avons couru tous les cinq à travers les ruelles du village de pêcheurs, jusqu'à la maison de Dounia.

Mais là, une deuxième mauvaise nouvelle nous attendait : la porte était barricadée. Nous avons frappé mais personne n'a répondu à nos coups.

« Vous cherchez Dounia ? » a-t-on entendu dans notre dos.

C'était Norah, une amie de Dounia. Je l'ai reconnue tout de suite : le soir de notre arrivée à Tabarka, elle jouait sur la plage avec elle.

« Elle est partie.

– Elle est allée faire une course ? a demandé Fatou. Ou bien elle est à la pêche avec son père ?

– Non. Partie pour toujours. »

Quoi ? Dounia, partie sans nous dire au revoir ? Sans attendre de connaitre le résultat de nos recherches sur la Galite ? C'était impossible !

« Mais où est-elle partie ? » a encore demandé Fatou.

Norah se tortillait sur place, hésitant à répondre.

« Tu peux nous le dire, tu sais », a dit doucement Kwanita.

La fillette se balançait d'un pied sur l'autre, ne sachant pas si elle devait nous faire confiance. Kwanita a posé doucement sa main sur son bras et fermé les yeux, le front plissé, comme si elle faisait un effort intense de concentration. Puis elle a murmuré :

« Elle est sur un bateau. Elle va sur une ile et… oh non ! Elle est en danger ! »

Un peu effrayée, Norah a fini par lâcher timidement :

« Elle est partie sur un gros bateau, ce matin, pour Lampedusa. »

Nous nous sommes regardés sans comprendre ce qu'elle voulait dire. Mais tout à coup, j'ai entendu Kwanita murmurer :

« Je le savais… »

Est-ce que j'avais bien entendu ? Kwanita était au courant du départ de Dounia et elle ne nous en avait rien dit ?

« Vite, il faut se dépêcher ! a insisté Kwanita. Dounia est en danger… »

Nous avons regagné le *Wakaroa* à toute vitesse, sans chercher à comprendre davantage. Sofia, elle, a cru Kwanita sur parole. Elle a aussitôt décidé de se lancer à la poursuite du mystérieux navire.

« Fabrizio, va aider Tematai à lever l'ancre, on décolle ! »

La seule à ne pas être d'accord, c'était Fatoumata. Elle s'est mise à protester :

« Mais… Farouk ! Je croyais qu'on devait l'amener en Grèce ?

– L'île de Lampedusa se trouve sur la route de la Grèce. Nous n'aurons pas à faire de détour. »

ZOOM SUR LAMPEDUSA. ÉCRIT PAR KWANITA

Lampedusa est une petite ile italienne qui compte moins de 6 000 habitants. Elle fait partie de l'archipel des Pélages, et c'est le point le plus au sud du territoire italien. Située entre la Tunisie et la Sicile, plus proche de l'Afrique que de l'Italie, sa proximité avec la Tunisie et la Libye en fait une voie d'entrée pour les immigrés nord-africains qui veulent tenter leur chance en Europe.

Le bateau sur lequel avaient embarqué Dounia et son père avait quelques heures d'avance sur nous. Mais, comme l'a rappelé Sofia, dans les airs, nous étions les plus rapides.

Nous avons survolé la Tunisie en direction du sud-ouest, par-dessus des montagnes escarpées puis des étendues arides, aux portes du désert. Mais personne n'avait tellement le cœur à s'extasier sur ces magnifiques paysages. De temps à autre, je jetais un coup d'œil en coin vers Kwanita, qui se rongeait les ongles d'angoisse. Je me remémorais les mots prononcés plus tôt ce matin : « Je le savais… Dounia est en danger ! » Que savait-elle de plus que nous ? C'était la deuxième fois qu'elle se comportait de façon étrange.

À l'heure du déjeuner, les appétits étaient dans les tongs. En passant au-dessus de Monastir, au sud du Golfe d'Hammamet, nous avons dit au revoir à la Tunisie.

Macodou a tenté de nous remonter le moral avec l'un de ses proverbes énigmatiques :
« Il y a quelque chose de plus fort que l'éléphant, c'est la brousse ! »
Une heure plus tard, la voix de Chen a résonné dans l'intercom reliant le carré au nid-de-poule, où il s'était à nouveau perché pour faire le guet.
« Je les vois ! Droit devant. On dirait qu'ils ont mis un canot à la mer ! »
Nous nous précipitons tous sur la passerelle, tandis que Tematai fait descendre le *Wakaroa*. Nous apercevons de vieilles connaissances : le thonier et son remorqueur. Encore eux !
Et, en effet, un canot à rames a été mis à l'eau. Vue d'ici, l'embarcation ressemble à une coque de noix. Elle se dirige vers le sud, tandis que le thonier et son remorqueur ont poursuivi leur route plein est.

Sofia semble hésiter sur la conduite à tenir : poursuivre les pêcheurs illégaux, ou escorter la petite barque ? De l'autre côté de la vitre séparant la coursive de la cabine de pilotage, Tematai l'interroge silencieusement du regard. Sofia se tourne vers Kwanita, qui semble lui adresser une prière muette. En soupirant, Sofia tend son bras vers la barque.

À mesure que nous approchons, il devient évident que le canot est trop petit pour supporter autant de passagers : il doit y avoir au moins vingt personnes à bord, serrées comme des sardines en boite.

« Elle est en danger… » Soudain, je comprends ce qu'a voulu dire Kwanita. Dounia se trouve à bord du canot, avec son père et d'autres malheureux qui cherchent à gagner Lampedusa. Ce doit être l'île dont on distingue le rivage un peu plus au sud. Mais ils en sont encore loin.

Et tout à coup, c'est la catastrophe. Soulevé par une vague de fond, le canot s'incline dangereusement. Un des passagers panique et veut se lever… La barque chavire, tous ses occupants se retrouvent à l'eau !

Nous sommes juste au-dessus d'eux maintenant. Horrifiés, nous voyons une forêt de bras s'agiter, battant l'eau dans des mouvements désordonnés.

« Elle ne sait pas nager ! gémit Kwanita. Je le savais, elle va se noyer.

– Il faut se poser ! Vite ! hurle Sofia en direction de Tematai.

– Pas le temps ! dit Vai. Le temps qu'on amerrisse, il sera trop tard. »

Et avant que Sofia ait pu l'en empêcher, elle enjambe le garde-corps… et saute à l'eau, pieds joints en avant, bras le long du corps !

Le *Wakaroa* a beau s'être rapproché, elle a dû faire un plongeon d'au moins quatre ou cinq mètres ! Et pourtant, elle fend la surface de l'eau sans une éclaboussure !

Lorsqu'elle reparait, elle agite la main dans notre direction pour nous signaler que tout va bien. Aussitôt elle se met à nager vers une petite silhouette qui se débat en faisant de grands moulinets des bras. Dounia ! Vai passe ses bras sous ses épaules et nous fait signe à nouveau.

Tematai a posé le *Wakaroa* aussi près du canot retourné qu'il a pu sans prendre le risque de heurter les hommes à la mer (apparemment Dounia est la seule enfant à bord).

« Les bouées, vite ! » s'exclame Sofia en dénouant l'un des huit flotteurs de secours répartis le long du bastingage.

Aussitôt, chacun s'active à détacher une bouée pour la lancer vers les naufragés. Sofia saute à l'eau pour aider les plus en difficulté.

Je n'hésite pas une seconde : je plonge à mon tour, imité par Kwanita et Fatou.

BUONA FORTUNA, DOUNIA!

8 septembre. Le drame a été évité de justesse, hier. Nous avons recueilli les passagers les plus effrayés et remorqué les autres dans le canot, retourné et éco- pé, jusqu'à Lampedusa où le comité d'accueil nous attendait!

Dounia a eu une sacrée frayeur! Elle était trop heureuse de nous retrouver. Apparemment, elle ne savait pas elle-même qu'elle partait en voyage. Elle n'a même pas pu dire au revoir à ses amis.

Fatoumata a pris Dounia dans ses bras pour la consoler. Puis elle a fait les présentations:

« Farouk, voici Dounia. Dounia, je te présente Farouk, le dernier habitant du Galiton. Nous l'emmenons en Grèce, où il va trouver de l'aide, et peut-être une nouvelle famille. »

En voyant la petite boule noire se déplier pour ramper vers elle, Dounia a fondu en larmes. Des larmes de joie cette fois. Comme s'il la connaissait depuis toujours, le bébé phoque est venu frotter son museau tout contre ses jambes.

Le père de Dounia aussi a eu très peur. Dès qu'il a mis le pied à bord du *Wakaroa*, il s'est effondré en nous remerciant environ mille fois. La tête entre les mains, il a raconté comment ils en étaient arrivés là : le poisson qui se faisait de plus en plus rare, la pauvreté qui poussait les pêcheurs à chercher ailleurs une vie meilleure.

« En Italie, Dounia aura un avenir », a-t-il dit.

Bizarrement, je n'arrive pas à lui en vouloir. Tout ce qu'il a fait, c'était pour sa fille.

Et Sofia ne s'était pas trompée : ce que lui et ses amis pêcheurs cherchaient du côté de la Galite, ce n'était pas le poisson, mais bien le corail, l'or rouge qui devait payer leur billet de départ :

« La moitié pour le capitaine du bateau qui avait accepté de nous transporter illégalement jusqu'à Lampedusa, l'autre à vendre à notre arrivée, pour nous aider à démarrer notre nouvelle vie. Mais cette moitié est maintenant au fond de l'eau… »

Sofia a voulu savoir pourquoi le capitaine les avait débarqués si loin de leur destination.

« Je l'ai entendu parler sur le pont. Il avait peur que la douane européenne contrôle son navire. Les douaniers avaient été avertis qu'il remorquait des cages pleines de thons pêchés illégalement. Il ne voulait surement pas être accusé de transporter des clandestins en prime ! »

Évidemment, on savait tous qui avait averti les douanes du trafic de thons : Sofia.

À cet instant, Tematai a passé la tête dans le carré, pour annoncer dans son français inimitable :

« Je eu message douaniers. Ils arrêtent thonier et capitaine. Tout le thon retourne dans mer ! »

Encore une bonne nouvelle !

Une chose est sure : le *Wakaroa* est nettement moins rapide sur mer que dans les airs ! Notre remorque nous a bien retardés. Bilan : il nous a fallu encore une heure pour parcourir les derniers milles jusqu'aux côtes de Lampedusa.

Enfin, nous sommes arrivés. Et bien sûr, nous étions attendus…

Une foule de gens se pressait sur le quai pour assister au débarquement des clandestins. Ceux-ci ont aussitôt été pris en charge par les *carabinieri*, les policiers italiens.

Dounia avait de nouveau les larmes aux yeux. Elle avait l'air complètement perdue et s'accrochait au bras de Fatoumata, refusant de la quitter. Sofia s'est avancée vers les policiers, et a dit en italien :

« S'il vous plait, laissez-la dire au revoir à ses amis. Deux minutes, c'est d'accord ? »

Ils ont accepté et, chacun notre tour, nous avons embrassé notre amie. Tout le monde avait le cœur gros de la voir s'en aller pour on ne savait où.

Dounia a promis de donner des nouvelles sur sa nouvelle vie. Puis, son père l'a prise par la main et elle a dû suivre les autres. Dans ma tête, je lui ai souhaité « *Buona fortuna per il futuro* ». Bonne chance pour l'avenir…

« Que va-t-il lui arriver, maintenant ? a demandé Vai en reniflant.

– Elle va être conduite dans un centre d'accueil. Après cela, j'imagine que sa demande d'asile sera étudiée. Peut-être Dounia et son père auront-ils la chance de pouvoir rester en Italie et commencer une nouvelle vie… »

Deux policiers en civil se sont approchés de Sofia et lui ont demandé si elle acceptait de répondre à des questions concernant les circonstances du naufrage, et elle a dû les suivre jusqu'au commissariat.

Dès qu'elle a été partie, les journalistes se sont jetés sur nous pour nous poser des dizaines de questions et prendre des photos de nous. On aurait dit un *remake* de la cérémonie de départ.

J'adore être une star. En tout cas, je crois que ce soir il va y avoir de quoi alimenter le blog…

📷 ZOOM SUR LES CLANDESTINS. ÉCRIT PAR FABRIZIO

Chaque année, des milliers de clandestins venus de Tunisie, de Lybie et d'Afrique de l'Est s'entassent dans des embarcations légères, pour une traversée dangereuse vers l'ile de Lampedusa. Parfois, cela finit très mal : en 10 ans, on estime que quelque 13 000 personnes ont perdu la vie lors de ce voyage en mer.

Avec les révolutions de 2011 en Tunisie et en Libye, le rythme s'est accéléré : entre janvier et mars 2011, 20 000 clandestins ont tenté leur chance. Ils sont hébergés dans des centres d'accueil en attendant d'obtenir un statut de réfugié et des papiers.

De là, ils gagnent l'Italie, la France, l'Allemagne ou la Grande-Bretagne, où ils vont travailler pour rembourser les contrebandiers qui les ont aidés à traverser. Aujourd'hui, Lampedusa compte plus d'immigrants clandestins que d'habitants.

10

IL FAUT SAUVER FAROUK !

JOURNAL DE BORD DE SOFIA

9 septembre. En route pour la Grèce. Les enfants sont un peu tristes depuis leurs adieux à Dounia. Et une nouvelle source d'inquiétude est venue aggraver leur moral : l'état de santé de Farouk…

RÉCIT DE FABRIZIO

Nous avons fait route au nord-est, direction la Grèce. Nous sommes passés au-dessus de l'île de Malte mais nous volions trop haut pour voir quoi que ce soit. De toute façon, aucun de nous n'était d'humeur à observer le paysage.

La soirée a été tristounette, après le départ de Dounia. Et le petit déjeuner encore plus morose.

La matinée, elle, a été calme et studieuse : nous avons avancé nos reportages pour le blog, un peu délaissés en raison des derniers évènements.

J'étais en train de rédiger le compte-rendu de notre halte à Lampedusa quand Fatoumata est rentrée dans le carré en larmes. J'ai pensé qu'elle faisait encore un gros caprice, mais non, pour une fois c'était sérieux.

Nous avons tous fait cercle autour de Farouk, étendu sur la plateforme arrière. Depuis hier, il refuse de s'alimenter. Fatou a tout essayé : le bibe-ron, la bouillie de poisson, mais rien à faire. Sofia l'a examiné sous toutes les coutures. Elle a palpé son abdomen, pincé sa peau et scruté ses yeux.

« Qu'est-ce qu'il a ? a sangloté Fatou. Est-ce qu'il va mourir ?

– Il est déshydraté, et il a des problèmes pour ré-guler sa température. Je crois que le stress de sa capture y est aussi pour quelque chose.

– Est-ce que c'est grave ? a insisté Fatou.

– Disons qu'il faut arriver sans tarder à Alonissos. L'état de Farouk est très sérieux, et il a besoin de soins urgents. Je vais demander à Tematai de faire aussi vite que possible et, s'il le faut, nous volerons toute la nuit… »

Juste à ce moment-là, Sofia a été interrompue par le son de la cloche…

En regardant à bâbord, j'ai eu un coup au cœur.

Le ciel au nord était obscurci par un immense pa-nache de fumée grise ! J'ai lancé un regard pani-

qué à Sofia. J'ai vu qu'elle aussi avait compris…
Je n'ai pas eu besoin de lui demander quel était
ce bout de côte qu'on apercevait : j'avais reconnu
la pointe sud du triangle que forme la Sicile, et
la côte est qui s'allongeait au-delà, se déroulant
jusqu'à Taormina. Ma ville, à présent noyée dans le
nuage de cendres, au pied de l'Etna.
L'Etna entré en éruption.
J'ai repensé au sentiment que j'avais eu au sommet du volcan, une semaine auparavant. La sensation, le pressentiment que quelque chose allait
se passer. Et puis j'ai pensé à mes parents, à ce qui
avait pu leur arriver.
« C'est toi qui décides, Fabrizio », m'a dit Sofia.
Le choix qu'elle me proposait était simple. Si
simple, et si difficile à la fois : soit poursuivre notre
chemin et avoir une chance de sauver Farouk. Soit
obliquer vers le nord mais condamner le bébé
phoque à une mort certaine.
« Oh, s'il te plait, Fab, je ferai toutes tes tâches pendant une semaine, m'a imploré Fatou. Je suis sure
que tes parents vont bien.
– Qu'est-ce que tu en sais, toi ? » ai-je rétorqué.
Bravo ! J'avais réussi à lui faire à nouveau venir les
larmes aux yeux.
« Elle a raison, est intervenue Kwanita. Tes parents
vont bien…
– Et comment tu le sais, toi ?
– Parce que sinon, je l'aurais v… Je le sais, c'est
tout, ne me demande pas pourquoi…

– C'est facile à dire, ce ne sont pas tes parents! »
Tematai était sur le pas de la porte. Visiblement, il attendait les instructions de Sofia. Et Sofia attendait que je me décide.

Jamais je n'avais eu de décision aussi difficile à prendre! Mes yeux allaient de Farouk, si fragile, à Fatou, suppliante, à Sofia, imperturbable, au nuage de cendres, menaçant… avant de se poser à nouveau sur le bébé phoque, comme s'il pouvait m'aider à trouver la solution de ce dilemme.

Tout à coup, une sonnerie caractéristique a retenti, provenant du carré: on cherchait à entrer en communication avec nous. Nous nous sommes précipités pour voir qui voulait nous parler. En haut de l'écran, tout le monde a pu lire: « Appel de M. Ridolfi ». Mon père! Tematai a cliqué pour accepter la communication et le visage de mon père s'est affiché. Nous étions en ligne.

« Papa! Tu vas bien? Et maman?

– Tout va bien, a-t-il répondu. L'éruption était mineure et n'a causé aucun dégât sérieux. J'ai lu dans le blog que vous survoliez la région. Je me suis douté que vous verriez le nuage de cendres. J'ai aussitôt tenu à vous rassurer.

– Attends, papa… avant que tu me racontes, j'ai une chose à faire. »

Je me suis tourné vers Tematai et je lui ai crié:

« Skip, direction la Grèce, pleins gaz! »

Tandis que mon père commençait à raconter en détail l'éruption, nous avons pu entendre le ronflement des moteurs qui enflait et senti très nettement la poussée du *Wakaroa* s'arrachant à plein régime.

📷 ZOOM SUR LES VOLCANS DE MÉDITERRANÉE, ÉCRIT PAR FABRIZIO

Le sud de la Méditerranée est au cœur d'une zone sismique très active. L'Italie est particulièrement exposée, car elle est parcourue sur toute sa longueur par une zone de « subduction ». Cela signifie que deux plaques tectoniques entrent en collision : la plaque africaine et la plaque eurasienne. Cette zone passe également sous la Sicile. Les îles Éoliennes, au nord de celle-ci, sont nées de l'affrontement entre ces deux plaques. Les séismes sont donc nombreux dans la région. Le volcanisme y est aussi très actif : le Stromboli, sur l'île du même nom, est actif en permanence depuis 20 000 ans : on compte une éruption toutes les 20 minutes. L'Italie compte un grand nombre de volcans, dont 4 encore actifs : le Vésuve, le Vulcano, le Stromboli, et bien sûr l'Etna, le plus grand volcan en activité d'Europe.

Le compte-rendu de mon père m'a complètement rassuré. Et, en passant au-dessus de Zákynthos, l'une des iles les plus à l'ouest de la Grèce, j'étais à nouveau calme. Mais la vue de ces criques aux plages de sable blanc, de ces falaises plongeant dans la mer, m'a aussitôt transporté en Sicile, sur l'autre bord de la mer Ionienne. L'idée que mon ile et mes montagnes, mes parents, mes copains se trouvaient de l'autre côté de cette mer me serrait le cœur.

Tout l'après-midi, nous avons survolé la Grèce continentale, un paysage incroyable de montagnes, de golfes, de détroits et de péninsules. La Grèce est un pays aussi montagnard que marin. On survole un pic abrupt et, passé le sommet, on s'aperçoit qu'il plonge dans la Méditerranée. La mer n'est jamais loin.

Pourtant, toute cette beauté n'avait aucun intérêt pour nous. Tout ce qui comptait, c'était de gagner cette course contre la montre pour sauver Farouk. Skip poussait le *Wakaroa* autant qu'il le pouvait. Et, miracle, en début de soirée, nous avons atteint les bords de la mer Egée ! Il était temps, car la nuit commençait à tomber.

Le parc marin d'Alonissos, dans l'archipel des Sporades, est la plus grande réserve marine protégée d'Europe : il s'étend sur une trentaine d'iles, dont seulement sept sont habitées. Certaines sont interdites aux touristes : seuls les scientifiques y ont accès.

C'est sur l'une de ces îles que nous avions rendez-vous avec Xenia, une jeune biologiste du centre de secours pour les phoques. Prévenue par radio de notre arrivée, elle est venue à notre rencontre.

« Bonjour, a-t-elle fait gaiment. Je suis Xenia. Bienvenue en Grèce ! »

Ses yeux se sont posés sur notre protégé.

« Alors, c'est toi, le fameux Farouk qui cause tant de soucis ? lui a-t-elle demandé, comme s'il pouvait répondre. Nous allons bien prendre soin de toi, ici ! »

Nous avons utilisé notre brancard improvisé pour le transporter jusqu'au centre où il a retrouvé des bébés phoques, orphelins comme lui. Certains ont perdu leur mère, d'autres ont été abandonnés ou se sont perdus lors de tempêtes.

Pendant qu'un vétérinaire s'occupait de Farouk, Xenia nous a fait visiter le centre. Elle nous a proposé de nous installer ici pour quelques jours et Sofia a accepté. Ainsi, nous pourrons suivre jour après jour les progrès faits par Farouk. Et aussi avancer un peu notre travail, avant de repartir pour l'Afrique.

 **ZOOM SUR LES BÉBÉS PHOQUES. ÉCRIT PAR FATOUMATA**

Les femelles mettent au monde un petit tous les 2 ans. Le bébé reste dans le ventre de sa mère entre 9 et 11 mois. À sa naissance, il mesure de

80 à 100 cm, et pèse entre 10 et 20 kg. Il possède alors un pelage d'aspect laineux et de couleur noire, qui s'éclaircira avec l'âge. Il est allaité pendant 6 à 8 semaines, après quoi sa mère l'abandonne. La mortalité est très importante, à cause des tempêtes, qui emportent les bébés avant qu'ils sachent nager. 1 jeune sur 2 meurt avant d'être sevré. Parfois, c'est la mère qui disparait trop tôt. Une nourrice peut alors prendre le relais de l'allaitement, si le bébé a la chance d'appartenir à une colonie comme celle des Sporades.

Le parc marin d'Alonissos recueille chaque année des dizaines d'orphelins. Après une période de convalescence, lorsqu'ils sont assez gros, ils sont relâchés dans la nature. Mais le rôle des biologistes du parc ne s'arrête pas là. Les petits sont marqués et contrôlés régulièrement. Les scientifiques ont même installé des caméras dans les grottes sous-marines, afin de les surveiller.

11

UNE RÉVÉLATION

17 septembre. Farouk a trouvé une maman d'adoption. Toute l'équipe du centre de secours, tombée sous son charme, est aux petits soins pour lui ! Fabrizio, lui, est aux petits soins pour Chen…

« Allez, tu peux y arriver !
– Tu savais que la noyade est la quatrième cause de décès accidentel après les accidents de la route, les chutes et les intoxications ? Et elle vient au premier rang des accidents de sport, devant le vélo, et chaque année…
– Oublie un peu ton encyclopédie et garde ton souffle ! »
Depuis trois jours, j'essaie d'apprendre à nager à Chen. Lorsqu'il a lu sur le blog que j'avais trahi son

petit secret, il a piqué une de ces colères ! En guise de punition, Sofia m'a imposé de lui donner des cours de natation. Autant apprendre à nager à un fer à repasser !

Quelques mètres plus loin, Farouk aussi apprend à nager. Et il comprend plus vite que Chen… Il est complètement remis de ses émotions, à présent. Une femelle l'a pris sous sa nageoire et lui fait découvrir son nouvel environnement. Xenia dit que, dans quelques semaines, lorsqu'il aura emmagasiné assez de graisse pour survivre dans la nature, il sera relâché dans le parc. Il trouvera sans doute refuge dans l'une des nombreuses grottes surveillées par les biologistes du centre au moyen de caméras.

Ces quelques jours de repos nous ont permis de terminer et de publier sur le blog tous nos reportages, ainsi que mon journal. Ouf, c'était du travail ! C'est Vai qui prendra la suite pour raconter nos aventures.

Le mystère reste entier sur notre prochaine destination.

Il y a un autre mystère que j'aimerais bien résoudre…

En remontant à bord, je n'y tiens plus. Je vais frapper à la porte de la cabine de Sofia.

« Entre, Fabrizio ! »

Pas possible, est-ce qu'elle voit à travers les portes maintenant ?

Sofia est assise devant le minuscule bureau qui occupe un coin de sa cabine. Elle a son ordinateur portable ouvert. Elle est en communication satellite avec un homme, que je reconnais tout de suite : c'est le Dr Garnier, le président de SOS Planète. C'est lui qui nous a reçus en entretien, après avoir sélectionné nos dossiers. Et lui qui a répondu à la plupart des questions lors de la conférence de presse.

« Regardez qui nous rend visite, docteur », dit Sofia. Elle tourne le portable vers moi et me prend par la main pour m'attirer vers l'écran. Aussitôt, je ressens un drôle de fourmillement remonter le long de mon bras.

« Quelque chose te tracasse ? demande Sofia, qui semble lire dans mes pensées.

– Non, c'est juste, je me demandais… »

Et je m'interromps, par peur de paraître ridicule.

Des images de notre aventure me reviennent, comme dans un film : Kwanita, qui prédit les évènements et semble lire dans les pensées. Vai, « la sirène », aussi à l'aise dans l'eau que sur terre, capable de sentir le mouvement des marées sur sa peau. Fatoumata et son don évident avec les animaux.

« Je crois que je sais ce qui te tracasse, intervient le Dr Garnier. Et je crois que je peux t'aider. Pour cela, je vais te raconter une petite histoire… Il y a très longtemps, les hommes vivaient en harmonie avec la nature. Pour survivre, ils avaient développé une sorte d'intuition, de sixième sens si tu veux. Certains avaient reçu un don plus développé, qui leur permettait de lire dans les éléments naturels, de communiquer par la pensée avec d'autres personnes, et même d'entrer en rapport avec les animaux. Je les appelle "les Naturels". Avec le temps, cette faculté a disparu. Ou plutôt, on la croyait disparue. Mais en étudiant le sujet, j'ai découvert que ce don naturel subsistait chez une minorité d'individus, parmi ceux qui étaient restés en contact très proche avec la nature. Comme vous cinq… Et, d'après mes recherches, ce don se développe vers l'âge de dix ans… »

Je repense à l'impression bizarre que j'ai eue au sommet de l'Etna, juste avant mon départ. Comme si j'avais su, « senti » plutôt, que le volcan allait entrer prochainement en éruption. Ce n'était pas la première fois que j'avais ce genre d'impression.

« Vous voulez dire que tous les cinq… nous avons un don ? Mais comment avez-vous su ?

– Je crois que la réponse à cette question se trouve juste à côté de toi… »

Je regarde vers Sofia, qui me sourit. Tout à coup, je comprends :

« Sofia aussi possède un don, n'est-ce pas ?

– Celui de déceler le don chez d'autres "Naturels", oui… Et de vous aider à le développer…

– Je préfère parler de "talent", dit notre maitresse. »

Est-ce que ce voyage allait nous aider à révéler nos "talents", comme dit Sofia ? Si c'est le cas, notre tour du monde nous réserve sans doute encore bien des surprises. Cette idée me rend encore plus impatient de découvrir ce qui nous attend dans la suite de notre voyage.

« Avant que tu rejoignes les autres, poursuit le Dr Garnier, je voulais te féliciter pour ton journal, que j'ai lu avec intérêt. Et bravo pour cette première mission ! À ce propos, j'ai reçu un autre appel au secours. Il a mis plusieurs jours à me parvenir, car il était envoyé d'un village isolé dans le désert. Il vient de Bacar, un garçon qui vit en Mauritanie. J'ai posté sa lettre sur le blog. Je te charge de prévenir les autres. »

Encore un peu assommé par cette avalanche d'informations, je rejoins le carré, impatient de lire la lettre de Bacar. Je ne suis pas le seul… Tout le monde se masse devant le grand écran, tandis que je me connecte au blog. L'appel au secours nous attend en page d'accueil :

L'APPEL AU SECOURS

Chers Globe Report'air,
Bonjour, je m'appelle Bacar et j'habite en Mauritanie, dans un village au milieu du désert. J'aide mon père, qui est agriculteur et éleveur. Ce n'est pas facile, car dans la région nous manquons beaucoup d'eau. Parfois, l'eau amène des maladies. Mais, depuis quelque temps, le problème s'est aggravé. Des chèvres ont été retrouvées mortes, de nombreuses personnes

sont tombées gravement malades. J'ai peur que ma famille décide de partir s'installer ailleurs. Je ne veux pas quitter mon village, mais je n'aurai sans doute pas le choix. Dans le journal, j'ai lu un article qui parlait de vous. Il disait que vous alliez venir en Afrique. S'il vous plait, si vous passez par la Mauritanie, aidez-moi !

Votre ami, Bacar

ÉPILOGUE
ATHÎO, FAROUK !

📓 JOURNAL DE BORD DE SOFIA

19 septembre. La première partie de notre voyage s'achève. Nous partons ce matin en direction du continent africain, à la découverte du désert.

📓 RÉCIT DE FABRIZIO

Athîo. C'est comme ça qu'on dit au revoir en grec. Nous avons donc dit « *athîo* » à Xenia et toute l'équipe du centre de secours. *Athîo* à Farouk aussi. On a tous eu un pincement au cœur en le laissant derrière nous. On avait l'impression de l'abandonner. Mais, bien sûr, sa vie est en Méditerranée, avec les siens. Et puis, il sera protégé ici, dans le parc marin.

Tandis que nous laissons l'île d'Alonissos derrière nous, je fais le bilan de cette semaine de folie, au cours de laquelle nous avons sauvé plusieurs clandestins, un bébé phoque… et trois tonnes de thons! Pas mal pour un début, non?

Nous avons aussi appris à nous connaitre, avec nos qualités, et aussi nos petits défauts. Maintenant, je sais qu'il ne faut pas parler à Fatou tant qu'elle n'a pas pris son petit déjeuner…

Nous avons aussi dit adieu à une nouvelle amie, Dounia, et à notre mascotte, Farouk.

Nous partons pour la Mauritanie et le désert du Sahara. Après toute cette eau, cela va être étrange de ne survoler que des étendues arides.

Prochaine étape: l'Afrique!

Renee:

All Hail the Queen

Renee:

All Hail the Queen

Brandie Davis

www.urbanbooks.net

Urban Books, LLC
300 Farmingdale Road, NY-Route 109
Farmingdale, NY 11735

Renee: All Hail the Queen

ISBN 13: 978-1-64556-145-3
ISBN 10: 1-64556-145-3

First Mass Market Printing January 2021
First Trade Paperback Printing February 2019
Printed in the United States of America

10 9 8 7 6 5 4 3 2 1

Distributed by Kensington Publishing Corp.
Submit Orders to:
Customer Service
400 Hahn Road
Westminster, MD 21157-4627
Phone: 1-800-733-3000
Fax: 1-800-659-2436

Renee:

All Hail the Queen

Brandie Davis

I dedicate this book to the love of my life, Donnell.
My heart beats for you.

Acknowledgments

First and foremost, I would like to thank God for all my gifts and blessings. You continue to bless me and steer me toward my dreams, and for that, I am forever thankful. I love you. Donnell, I thank God for blessing me with you, and I am truly and deeply in love with you. Thank you for being who you are, and for always being by my side. Mommy and Daddy, your love has never gone unnoticed and is the reason my eyes have a twinkle. Thank you for all you've done.

Crystal, my ace, my homie, thank you for always pushing me and believing in me. Chucky, because of you, I understand the importance of exercising my brain by reading. Mike, your kind heart is what always shines the brightest. Big Cory, you are not only my brother but also my friend. Gina, thank you for your shoulder and for always being supportive. Christian, the sky is the limit, and with your talent and potential, you will reach the stars. Lil Cory, you are the sunshine in my life. Angel, I am glad to call you my nephew. You make my puzzle of nieces and nephews complete. Kyra, my little diva, your personality and creativity are what this world is missing. Desiree, even before you were born, you had my heart.

Chapter 1

Nightfall is when New York comes alive and the city is at its best. Billboards and building lights shine so brightly, you'd never guess the sun is missing. The streets are jam packed with children of the night, loud and full of energy, ready to party the night away. This is the city that never sleeps. It watches everyone who steps foot in its concrete jungle and sucks them in.

However, during this summer night, the city was surprisingly quiet and peaceful. Only a handful of people were out and about. Cars zoomed by but didn't make a sound. It was eerie, as if the world had come to a halt and felt Renee's rage.

Like a queen, Renee sat on her throne and looked out at all of New York from her terrace. Her Manhattan penthouse supplied her with the view she needed to marvel over what was hers. Her eyes danced across the sky, then made their way down to the very streets she flooded with cocaine. Renee had entered a game labeled "boys only" and had taken it over with ease. Her rage and emotionless soul made it possible for her to enter a man's game and conquer it without apology or regret. However, tonight it wasn't about that. Tonight the betrayal she felt didn't come from the streets, but from home.

Her slender fingers were wrapped so tightly around the glass holding her Pinnacle and cranberry juice, it was bound to shatter. Renee looked into the night and wondered where the one man she had given her heart to was. After she had revealed to Julian three days prior that she had aborted their child, he'd cut off all forms of communication with her. He hadn't been taking her calls, coming by, texting, or doing FaceTime with her. The way he'd cut her off, you'd think they had no history whatsoever.

Renee finished the last of her drink and poured herself another glass of vodka, minus the cranberry juice, from the bottle at her elbow. She took it to the head. Liquor had been her best friend through college. The more Julian ignored her, the more anger surged through her and ripped her soul apart. Life wasn't fair. It was cruel and hurtful, and all Renee could ask was, *Why*?

Yes, she had aborted their child without his knowledge, but she didn't understand why he was throwing such a tantrum. On many occasions, Renee had voiced that she didn't want kids. She wasn't mother material, and she knew it. Renee attended meetings with her connect, not with teachers. She flooded the streets of New York with the purest coke the state had ever seen, and no child deserved to have a callous queenpin as a mother. Motherhood entailed warmth and selflessness, things Renee didn't possess.

She had lost those good qualities a long time ago and, in the words of Omarion, had an icebox where her heart used to be. So why act as if she could be Clair Huxtable when she knew she couldn't? Julian knew all of this, including the fact that Renee was a selfish individual who showed interest only in herself. So why be surprised that she'd had an abortion?

Renee abandoned her glass and started to drink the vodka from the bottle. She thought about how true the saying "It's lonely at the top" really was. Although she was cruel and insensitive, she cared for Julian. He had been there for her when the rest of the world had walked out, and he had remained loyal to her throughout the years. For that reason, his disappearance left a bitter taste in her mouth.

She drank the last of the vodka and stood up to get a better view of the city. She looked far out into Manhattan, until she could see nothing but buildings and darkness. She ran her fingers through her hair like a comb. Renee was losing her mind, but her pride wouldn't allow her to break down and feel the pain she was really experiencing. She would sleep in an empty bed that night, and even though she would never acknowledge it, that was what scared her the most. A lone tear threatened to fall from her eyes, but she fought against it. No tear had touched her cheeks in five years, and they weren't about to now. She stood there, frozen in place, while her blood ran cold and her nails dug into the railing. What Renee wanted was a normal, healthy life, but she found it difficult to admit this even to herself. She longed to have a husband and kids one day, but more importantly, she wished for the ability to let go of what had damaged her since childhood. Obtaining pure happiness would be her happily ever after, but it was conquering her demons that made it all unattainable.

He'll be back, was all she thought. *He has to.*

Chapter 2

Three half-dressed females in their mid-twenties stood in front of Barnes & Noble and watched as Jared left the bookstore and headed toward his truck. The women couldn't stop staring at the six-foot-three, muscular brown-skinned brother with tribal tattoos running from the left side of his neck all the way down to his wrist. His serious, thuggish appearance made women want to sink in their claws and bite him.

"Damn, he's fine," one of the females said, loud enough for Jared to hear.

He paid them no mind. He jumped in his truck and threw the two anger-management books he'd purchased on the passenger seat. He could spot a gold digger a mile away and steered clear of them all. Jared didn't believe in paying to play. If he didn't have enough game to win a female over without going for broke, she wasn't for him. After he looked down at his wristwatch and saw it was time for work, his eyes darted over to the tattoo across his wrist that read JANAE and he sucked his teeth.

"I got to get this shit removed," he mumbled to himself. Jared placed his watch higher up on his wrist so it completely covered the tattoo.

The car door across from him flung open just then, and a skinny dark-skinned dude with a baby face and a head full of waves flopped down in the passenger seat and landed right on the books. Feeling the hard covers beneath him, he jumped up and tossed the books on the backseat.

"Damn. You see them fine-ass females over there?" he asked as he eyed the threesome.

Jared didn't bother following his friend's stare; he knew he was talking about the females posted in front of the bookstore.

"Leave them alone, Waves. They're nothing but paper chasers."

"Those are the best ones. They'll do anything for a dollar." Waves nearly broke his neck while trying to get a better look at the females. One of the girls, whose shorts had once been a pair of pants and who wore no bra, blew him a kiss. He nearly went wild. "Scratch that. Make that fifty cents."

Jared laughed and started up the truck. There was never a dull moment with Waves. The two had grown up down South and had been best friends since junior high. Since as far back as Jared could remember, Waves had been a comedian. He lived off being the center of attention, so he was always cracking jokes and making people die of laughter. In high school, he had been crowned class clown and had worn his title with pride.

The joy Waves brought others was the distraction he needed from his pain. It made it possible for him to survive in a world he felt abandoned in. At the age of ten, his mother had walked out on him and his father. It had torn him apart and had made him feel like a motherless child. Five years later, she had turned her life around and started a brand-new family. She had remarried, had had a baby, and had landed the job of her dreams. She'd had everything she could ever want, but one thing had been missing from this fairy-tale life: Waves. So she'd tried to step back into his life and make him feel a part of her new family by taking him on vacations with her new family and flying him out to New York whenever she could.

Waves was thrilled to have his mother back in his life, but deep down inside, he resented her for leaving in the first place. He'd welcomed her back with open arms, but he refused to live with her. That was something he just couldn't do.

Waves got comfortable and watched the world go by while he and Jared drove through Brooklyn. After a while, his stomach started to growl, so he focused his attention on an approaching Burger King.

"Yo, let's head to Burger King right quick."

"Nah, we got to get to work."

Waves looked down at his Rolex, then back up at Jared. "Oh, hell no! Listen, I know you want to fuck Renee and shit, but I ain't going to her house earlier than I need to. We have an hour till we're due at her crib, so if we ain't gonna eat, I suggest we hit up a strip club or something."

Jared shook his head. There wasn't a day that went by where Waves didn't mention how mentally unstable he believed Renee was or how he knew Jared had a thing for her. Working twelve hours a day, six days a week, as Renee's home security guard had caused Waves to form a negative opinion of her. To him, she was a cold woman with no conscience or emotions. She never smiled, never laughed at anything he said, and never even bothered to speak.

Waves and three other men, including Jared, were on her home security team. Jared was the only one who looked at her with lustful stares tinged with romance.

Jared always denied his attraction to Renee, but Waves knew the truth. His best friend's eyes revealed that he wanted more than just sex; he wanted to give Renee his heart.

"We're going to Renee's," Jared announced.

Waves looked at his friend and shook his head. "Real talk, I can understand why you're feeling shorty. She's bad as hell. But, son, she ain't for you."

Jared looked at his friend from the corner of his eye. When Waves saw he had Jared's attention, he continued speaking.

"With all the shit you went through growing up, you need yourself a good girl, not a woman who outranks you and whose government name you can't tell your parents."

Jared stopped at a red light but kept his eyes on the street. He didn't like what he was hearing, but he understood it all. Renee was not your ideal woman. Men didn't flock to women who hid behind an alias and could have them killed in the blink of an eye. In the streets, Renee was known as Jordan, a man no one saw, but everyone feared. Jared knew that everything Waves had said was the truth. He had lived a hard-knock life and needed a good girl. Something as simple as having a crush on Renee could send his life spiraling out of control. However, it was too late. He had feelings for her, and he was already in too deep.

Twenty minutes later, Jared and Waves arrived at Renee's penthouse and knocked on the door. For five minutes, they waited in the hall for someone to answer. They were heated when a fat brown-skinned dude, with so many diamonds on that it was blinding, opened the door with a toothpick in his mouth. He looked at Jared and Waves, flung the door all the way open, and walked away.

Jared's hands balled into fists. He had never liked Slice, and on countless occasions, he'd wanted to punch he could say any and everything to anyone and get away with it. If it were up to Jared, he would be dead and stinking by now. But because Slice was third in command and had been Renee's close friend since high school, Jared let him live. So until Renee gave the word, Jared would sit in the cut, watching his prey.

After closing the door behind him and Waves, Jared watched Slice make his way over to the living-room couch and continue playing *NBA 2K19* on PlayStation 4. Jared followed him into the room, sat down on the love seat, and cracked open one of the anger-management books he had purchased not even two hours ago. Massaging his temple with his left hand, he looked at Slice and knew he would need to soak up every word the authors wrote.

He was on page five on the first book when Renee stormed down the stairs. Her Chinese red silk robe flowed in the air as she quickly passed by the men in her living room without bothering to speak. Jared's eyes followed Renee until she disappeared into the hall. When he turned away, he saw Lyfe, the O.G. of the crew, staring at him. He hadn't noticed Lyfe when he walked in. Then again, no one noticed Lyfe.

Waves walked into the living room just then, chomping down on a bag of Lay's potato chips. He flopped down on the couch, and half of his body landed on Slice. Slice paused the video game, and with a screw face, he pushed Waves off him.

"Fat boy, what you do to Renee? Why she so pissed?" Waves asked as he munched on a potato chip.

"Fuck you, you skinny bastard! I ain't do shit!" Slice un-paused the video game and continued to play. He couldn't stand Waves. In his eyes, Waves played too much and purposely tried to push his buttons.

Waves sat beside him and watched the steam leave Slice's head. He took pleasure in making Slice miserable. "Nah, seriously, fat boy, why she so pissed?"

Slice didn't answer right away; instead, he held himself back from strangling Waves. "I don't know why, you piece of shit," he finally spit. "You know Renee don't say shit about anything. It probably has something to do with Jay. He hasn't been seen in over two weeks."

Jared's eyes got low, and he started biting the inside of his cheek. He didn't want to admit it, but he disliked hearing that Julian was the reason Renee was in such a funk. Their relationship had brought Jared to a dark place and had made him despise Julian twice as much. His eyes darted around the room. When they landed on Lyfe, Jared saw that he was staring at him again.

Lyfe knew exactly what was on Jared's mind. He never spoke, but he noticed everything. There was a time when Jared didn't understand why the old man was still in the game. Really, what could he do? He was frail, and his hair was damn near all gray. He looked so fragile, you'd think one touch would break him. However, after working with Lyfe for only one week, Jared had realized why Renee had him on her team. He was a beast, and he had no problem laying his murder game down.

Lyfe had been in the game since Jared was in diapers. For years, he had worked for Renee's close friend Metro, a kingpin who had handed down his crown to Renee when he retired. Because Lyfe hadn't been ready to leave the game alone, and probably never would be, Metro had put Lyfe on to Renee. Metro had believed she needed someone experienced and trustworthy on her team. The streets were what Lyfe was good at, so going from a kingpin to a queen had not been an issue.

Jared was torn out of his thoughts concerning Julian, Renee, and Lyfe when Renee came storming through the living room again. As quickly as she came in, she left and headed up the stairs. Seconds later she slammed her bedroom door. Jared couldn't help but think how gorgeous she looked in her silk robe. Whenever she wore it, he'd steal a look at her legs. They were always shiny and looked so soft. Things like that made showing up to work worthwhile.

Waves shook his head. "Dude needs to hurry up and resurface, because she's about to pop a blood vessel."

Jared sank farther into the love seat. *Nah. That motherfucker needs to stay wherever the fuck he's at*, he thought.

For a few minutes, no one spoke, each man lost in his own thoughts. While Lyfe, Waves, and Slice thought about random things that held no importance, Jared thought of the one thing that had dominated his thoughts for the past few months: how he wanted Renee all to himself and Julian out of the picture.

Chapter 3

As Julian sat in first class, with a glass of Hennessy in his hand, his bloodshot eyes told the story of a man who hadn't slept in days. If you looked closely, you could see the fury that dwelled deep within the shadows of this soul. Renee telling him that she aborted his child had crushed him. For days, he had cried within the privacy of his home. His pain had soon turned into anger and had grown with every day that passed.

The image of Renee sitting behind her huge cherry-wood desk, breaking the news to him, was embedded in his mind. They had sat in her office, talking about the abortion as if it was business instead of something personal. The setting alone angered him and had led him to believe she couldn't have cared less about what she'd done. Her voice had been cold and ever so calm. She had never broken eye contact or given the slightest hint that she was disturbed by her actions.

Julian took a sip of his drink. He looked in the glass and knew he would soon need a refill. He knew his drinking had gotten out of hand since Renee told him the bad news, but he didn't care. He needed the alcohol, depended on it. It was the only thing that he knew would numb his pain. Renee had pushed him to his breaking point. It had gotten to the point where all he did was drink. This past week, he had sat in his Miami Beach house, his place of refuge, and had talked to himself and consumed alcohol. He downed the rest of his drink now and frantically looked around for a flight attendant to take his drink order.

"She's getting your drink now," said a female voice.

Julian looked over and saw a beautiful woman looking at him. She had honey-brown straight hair that touched the center of her back, hazel eyes, and skin the color of caramel. She reminded him of Renee. The only difference was, Renee's hair was shoulder length and black.

The thought of Renee sent Julian into a trance. He could see her angelic face staring back at him. Her bright, almond-shaped hazel eyes and dimpled smile made him weak in the knees, but the longer he stared at her, the more he saw her for who she really was. She was a rocklike creature with no emotions. This was the woman he had stood by for years and had allowed to eat away at his soul.

As if a hypnotist had snapped his or her fingers, Julian snapped back to reality. He looked at the stranger, the beautiful woman, who was speaking to him. She hadn't noticed that Julian had temporarily zoned out.

"I could tell by the way you looked at your glass when it was getting low that you wanted another, but you seemed to be in a daydream when the flight attendant walked by. So I took the liberty of ordering you the same of what you had. I hope that's okay," she said.

Julian's face softened. Being in the business he was in, he trusted no one and questioned everything. Her reason for ordering him a drink seemed legit, so he let it go.

"Yeah, it's cool," he said, turning his head to look at her. Then faced forward and drifted back into his own little world.

The woman continued to stare, as if she was examining him. Julian could feel her eyes burning a hole into the side of his face. His features hardened. He wasn't in the mood for a conversation with some chick who was obviously trying to pick him up. He turned toward the woman, his frustration written on his face.

"What?" he said.

"Would it kill you to say thank you?"

The woman's stare was so hard, Julian felt like she was challenging him. Her boldness took him by surprise. One second she appeared to be a nice, sweet woman. And the next, she was a controlling, "don't take any mess from anyone" type of woman.

This broad must be out of her damn mind. I'm so stressed, I could choke her ass and easily get off by pleading temporary insanity.

The two had a staring contest that neither intended to lose. Julian was on edge. The smallest thing could push him over and cause him to take all his frustrations out on an innocent person.

Holding a drink in her hand, the flight attendant stepped in front of him just then, blocking his view of the woman. "Here you go, sir. Here's your Hennessy."

Julian took the glass out of the perky flight attendant's hand and said, "Thank you." He looked at the woman across from him and smiled.

The woman knew what he was doing. He wasn't saying thank you to the flight attendant to be polite; he was letting her know he'd say it to anyone except her. Moreover, he was making it clear that her straightforwardness and demand for respect did not and would not faze him.

The flight attendant waltzed back into coach, and Julian got comfortable in his seat. After lying back, he closed his eyes and thought about how the moment he landed in Jamaica, he would put in motion his plan for Renee to let go of her past so they could be in a real relationship. He smiled. He couldn't wait for the whole "friends with benefits" thing they had going to end. He wanted more, needed more. Life would be complete when their relationship flourished and grew to the highest level.

Renee was so traumatized and hurt by her past, she had become emotionally detached, wanting none of the happiness and joys life had to offer. For years, starting at the age of twelve, she had been raped by her stepfather, while her mother had stood by and done nothing but verbally abuse her. Through it all, Julian had stood by her side and had patiently waited for the day she opened her closed heart to him and they became a couple.

From the first day he laid eyes on Renee, he'd known she was the woman he was destined to grow old with. But the longer he'd waited for her depression to wear off, the more cold and withdrawn she'd become. Believing that one day everything would change, Julian had held on to hope. But when Renee had told him she aborted their child, a child he never knew she was pregnant with, he had lost it. All his patience had gone out the window. He had decided he would have her and the family he'd always wanted right then and there. There would be no more waiting. He knew exactly how to get Renee to let go of her past and look forward to their future. He would eliminate the cause of her pain by unleashing the world's most skilled assassin to wipe her stepfather and her mother off the face of this earth.

Julian looked out the small window, at the clouds, and grinned. Soon everything he had ever wanted would be his. When he looked away, he locked eyes with those of the woman who'd ordered his drink. She'd been staring at him the whole time. Julian's jaw tightened.

She doesn't give up.

Once again, the two stared at each other for what felt like forever. Julian's blood began to boil, and he felt himself getting hot. When he noticed his hand squeezing his glass with enough force to shatter it, he tried to calm himself down.

This is not the time. Stay focused.

Julian was not one to be challenged, but normally, he was cool, calm, and collected when he handled issues. He would eliminate the enemy after stripping them of their pride and confidence. However, due to the fact that he was on an emotional roller coaster, he now envisioned harming this aggressive woman. He quickly dismissed the thought. Her immaturity was not worthy of attention. He gave her his famous Colgate smile, turned away, and went to sleep.

Julian's eyelids opened and shut numerous times before staying open to observe his surroundings that reminded him of his location. He stretched his arms and legs out and fell right back into the same thoughts that had escorted him sleep.

"It there anything you'd like, sir?" the stewardess inquired.

Attempting to respond, Julian opened his mouth; however, instead of words leaking out, a yawn escaped. "Damn, I'm sorry. I'll have a rum and Coke, please."

She smiled, and before fetching his order, checked in with the other first class passengers. Julian stood and stretched some more until he felt and heard the bones in his back crack. Every move he made drew additional attention to his full bladder and the increasing discomfort.

An extremely thin woman wearing floral patterns and heels that added to her already towering height left the bathroom just as Julian reached for the door handle.

Relieving himself, Julian let out a sigh, feeling his bladder shrink down to size. The space and cleanliness offered by the restroom made Julian comfortable enough not to avoid touching anything, and if he had, not to retreat and dip himself in a vat of sanitizer. He slapped the toilet lid down, and after washing his hands, splashed some water on his face and watched as drops slid down face into the sink. Some droplets moved faster than others, forcing Julian to struggle while trying to keep up with each of the movements.

Julian looked into the mirror, where he saw the ob-noxious young woman he'd encountered earlier. She was staring back at him, and the door behind her was closed.

He turned around and placed his vision on not a reflection, but on the actual person and spit out, "What the fuck are you doing in here?"

Julian did not receive a verbal response but a physical and aggressive answer. The young Renee lookalike ap-proached him, wrapped her arms around him, and pulled him into her; then she covered his lips with hers. Julian grabbed the top of her arms and squeezed. Without giv-ing full force, he tried pushing her away, which was nothing but a waste because she fought against him by sinking herself deeper into him to the point her breasts were planted into his chest.

"You now can tell yourself you fought me. Are you done yet?" she let out in between kisses.

Julian pulled his face from her and allowed himself to look her over, starting from her eyes, leading down to her legs. When he back-tracked and their eyes met, she smiled and nodded, cheering him on to make the leap. In his eyes, her youth caused him to see the Renee he'd fallen for years prior—the girl he'd lost when she was violated and her heart turned to ice. He missed that girl, along with the hopes he'd had for their future.

I want her back, his conscience told him.

Julian gripped her by her waist and sat her on the sink. His hands tugged at her clothing and removed it all piece by piece. Julian went to unbuckle his jeans.

"That's what the fuck I'm talking about," she encouraged just as his jeans fell.

Chapter 4

Page sat at the checkout desk, watching patrons skim the bookshelves, trying to decide on which books they would take out. Her eyes followed random people as she tried to pinpoint which genre each one preferred. She cleverly figured out that three out of five people were into urban fiction, mysteries, and romance. The library had been open for only an hour, so only a handful of people skimmed the stacks in search of books.

As she watched people roam around aimlessly, she saw a female who appeared to be in her early twenties and was dressed in skinny jeans and a tank top. She stood at least six feet tall and had legs a mile long and glistening chocolate skin. Anyone would believe she had walked down countless runways and was in fashion magazines worldwide. The woman walked into the black experience aisle, and Page watched her search for a book. She began to guess which author she'd choose.

Let me guess, she's a Zane kind of girl. On second thought, I'ma go with Nikki Turner.

After watching her for two whole minutes, she realized something about the young woman looked familiar. Just then a middle-aged woman with three books approached Page and handed over her library card. Page proceeded to check out the material, but she never took her eyes off the young woman. As soon as Page placed the middle-aged woman's book receipts inside the novels, the young woman turned around and looked Page right in the eye. That was when it hit her. A slight grin came across Page's face as she watched the young woman prance up and down the aisles. She couldn't care less about choosing a book. She just wanted to catch Page's attention, and now she had.

Well, well, well, if it isn't the ghost of Christmas past, Page thought.

She watched the young woman walk out of the black experience aisle and head farther back, toward the general fiction section. With every step she took, she stared at Page, until she disappeared into the aisles reserved for authors whose last name started with the letter *P.*

Page didn't sweat it. Instead, she concentrated on taking care of the people checking out items. Five minutes later, however, the young woman was in front of Page, with a wide smile across her face.

"Ain't this a bitch? Who knew that I would bump into Page in a library? Isn't it a small world?" she said.

Page recognized game, and it didn't matter what size, shape, or form it came in. Page was sure Janae had done her research by going back to their old neighborhood in Brooklyn and finding out where she worked.

"So, Page, tell me, how's your sister? Where is she resting her head at nowadays?"

Page grinned. She leaned on her elbows and looked Janae in the eye. "I don't know. I'm not my sister's keeper."

Janae leaned in closer to Page. "That's funny," she whispered. "Because I am my sister's keeper."

Page sat back and folded her arms. *That shouldn't be hard, considering she's dead.*

"Let's cut to the chase and cut the bullshit," Janae said. "I came back to Brooklyn to find your sister, but to my surprise, I heard old girl up and left after I moved. What's up with that? Guilty conscience?"

Page grinned. "Guilty conscience? Now, why the hell would she have that?"

"Well, I don't know . . . If I killed someone, I'd consider that reason enough. Especially if I got away with it. Wouldn't you?" Janae searched Page's eyes for answers.

"I can see not much has changed. You're still hung up on your sister's death. But I have to tell you, Janae, it isn't nice of you to go around accusing people of murdering Leslie."

The comment shocked Janae. She was surprised that Page was even insisting that her own sister wasn't guilty of Leslie's murder, and that she, Janae, should have been over it by now.

"Enough of this shit!" Janae hit the counter with her fist.

An elderly lady was ready to approach Page and check out her books, but after Janae's outburst, she walked right over to the next available clerk.

"My mother committed suicide last month because she could no longer deal with the fact that her eldest daughter had been murdered. Your sick bitch of a sister had my sister Leslie raped, murdered, and left in the dumpster like a piece of garbage. I want that bitch's head!" Janae noticed that her voice had risen. She looked around, then turned back to Page and regained her composure.

She went on. "She took my sister's life in our old neighborhood, so that's exactly where I'm going to take hers. But that little slut's making it hard for me to do. It seems like she vanished into thin air or something. No one knows were old girl's at. It's like she never existed. So, I'm telling you now, if that bitch don't show her face around here and soon, bodies are going to start dropping. And when I say *bodies*, I mean yours and your family's." Janae was fuming. She had tried not to draw attention to herself, but she'd failed miserably. Everyone was watching.

Page laughed. In no way was she intimidated by or afraid of Janae's threats. You see, Janae had become fearless after the death of her sister. Page, however, had been born that way. She was the most coldhearted, deranged person anyone could meet, so threats like this meant nothing to her. Nothing scared her.

Page laughed so hard, her coworkers and patrons all turned her way. She waved everyone off and apologized for the interruption. Then she noticed library security heading toward Janae. Her loudness and her banging on the counter had made people uncomfortable.

"She's leaving. Don't worry," Page called out to the guards.

They stopped dead in their tracks and waited for Janae to be on her way.

"She better show up soon, because I'm back for good," Janae spit. She pushed a book so far across the counter, it fell into Page's lap.

After Janae left, Page looked down and read the title of the book in her lap. It was Jodi Picoult's novel *My Sister's Keeper*.

Hours after Page's encounter with Janae, she sat in the employees' lounge at the library, drinking Coca-Cola heavily spiked with vodka. She was furious. Although she found Janae's threat to kill her if her sister didn't resurface hilarious, a little voice in her head constantly nagged her. It told her there was no reason why she should let Janae live after she had threatened her life. Sometimes Page heard voices in her head. They were constant, and they pushed her to do the unthinkable. From time to time, she thought about going and talking to a therapist, but the more she thought about it, the more she saw nothing wrong with the thoughts running through her mind. Therefore, she saw no reason to fix what she honestly believed wasn't broken.

Page truly did not care that Janae wanted to put her sister six feet under. Page hated her sister, so for someone to make such a threat did nothing for her. What bothered her was that *she* was threatened.

Page sat in the booth at the back of the lounge, sipping her drink, and thought of ways to get rid of Janae. Did she really believe she could come back, sling around threats, and get away with it? Page mused. While Page considered multiple ways to lay Janae down to rest, it hit her. The person that she was planning to kill was not the same fourteen-year-old stick figure from across the street. For all she knew, Janae could be a ruthless contract killer with myriad connections and more bodies under her belt than the morgue, and Page might be totally oblivious to the fact. Page might be crazy, but she was far from stupid. If she was going to get herself into something, she wasn't going to walk into it deaf, blind, and dumb.

She needed information on Janae, and she needed it fast. As soon as the thought crossed her mind, a high yellow–skinned girl with fire-red hair walked into the lounge. She walked over to a group of people sitting at a round table and began to converse with them. Moments later she glanced over and saw Page, alone at a booth. Page gave the redhead a look that had business written all over it.

Bingo! Page thought. *Here goes my little information machine. Just put one quarter in her and she dishes out all the dirt.*

The redhead nodded at Page. She said a couple more words to their coworkers and then made her way to the back of the lounge. Page smiled. She knew that everything she needed to know was literally walking her way. Tina was the queen of gossip and knew almost everything there was to know about people in New York. She was very selective about the people she gave information to, and when she did, she made sure they came out of their pockets. She limited the people she gossiped with so that she wouldn't be dragged into any unnecessary problems.

Tina saw dollar signs when she looked at Page. She was sure that since Page's sister had magically disappeared, Page would want to hear any information that came her way. Page's and Janae's sisters had been archenemies while in high school. Because of this, Page's sister was a suspect in Leslie's murder. However, the evidence showed that Page's sister, Renee, wasn't the culprit, and for that reason, the police had left her alone. Everyone believed the young girl was innocent, everyone except for Janae. She was sure that Renee had taken Leslie's life, so when she got wind of the fact that Renee had up and left without a word, she was even more certain that it was true.

Tina kept her ears to the streets, and she'd been dying to hear anything about the whereabouts of Page's sister, in order to make a dollar. Little did she know, Page couldn't have cared less if her sister was lying out on a beach somewhere or was dead in an alley in Brooklyn. As long as she was away from Renee, Page was happy. The only reason she associated with Tina was that Page wanted to make sure her sister *remained* missing, and she wanted to hear it first if Renee ever did resurface. Now that Janae was back, and was throwing around threats, Page knew Tina would come in handy in more ways than one.

Tina approached Page with a friendly smile and sat down across from her.

"What's up, Page? I haven't seen you in a minute." Tina's bright red hair was blinding. Every time Page saw her dye job, she couldn't help but think there was no way Tina wouldn't be pegged as a gossiper.

"Well, that's because I haven't needed any info," Page answered honestly.

Tina whipped out her iPhone and responded to a text message. "Yeah, I heard about Janae coming to the library. I'd heard she was coming through *next* week. That's why I didn't rush to tell you. I don't know how it got under my radar that she had switched up and was coming through today."

Page smirked. "You know, just for that slipup, I'm not paying you the full two hundred." Page's right eyebrow rose like the Rock's when he gave "the people's eyebrow."

Tina took a deep breath, frowned, placed her iPhone back in her pocket, and nodded.

Page went on. "I told your ass, as soon as info hits your ears, it should hit mine. Now, for that slipup, your ass lost out on money." Page spoke sternly and harshly, daring Tina to challenge her.

Tina just nodded her head again and remained silent. If it weren't for the money, she would have no dealings with Page. She knew everything about everyone, except for Page, and that creeped her out. No one was squeaky clean.

"Now, what else do you know about Janae?" Page asked.

Tina sat up straight, preparing to tell Page all she knew, hoping that the news she had was good enough to get at least some of her money back.

"You already know about her leaving Brooklyn and moving to Jersey with her parents after Leslie's death. Well, according to my sources, life in Jersey wasn't any better than life in New York. I just found out that Leslie's death fucked Janae up so much, she's been talking to someone professionally since she arrived in Jersey. I think she's on meds. She's so fucked up in the head.

"Janae wasn't the only one going through hell over her sister's death, either. Her mother also saw a therapist, but she took the death a lot harder. Last month she committed suicide by keeping their car running in the garage, with the doors and windows shut. She left a suicide note, saying that she had tried, but she couldn't live another day without her oldest daughter. She prayed that God would forgive her, and she apologized to Janae."

Page's face scrunched up. *Damn. This chick is good. How the hell she find out what the suicide letter says? This hasn't even been on the news. I'm not paying her enough for this shit.*

"I know fine threads when I see them. When and how did she come into money?" Page straightened out her short-sleeved dress and ran her fingers over her newly waxed eyebrows.

She worked in a library, but her mother had money and kept her fly at all times. Her mother's boutiques were doing really well, so well that they were in the process of opening a third one in Manhattan. For a twisted soul, Page was a gorgeous young woman. At the age of nineteen, she had an hourglass shape, a mocha complexion, and a low haircut that Halle Berry used to sport. Her presence demanded all eyes on her.

"That's what I was getting to. Months before her mother's death, Janae wound up meeting this guy from Brooklyn. Things got hot and heavy fast, and now she's stuck on homeboy like glue. He's paid. He supplies her with nothing but the best, and he even moved her in with him."

"It's all starting to make sense. Move in with the dude from Brooklyn and get a better chance at revenge. I feel her, gangsta," Page responded.

Tina nodded her head. "Yup. But I wouldn't say she moved in with him just to seek revenge on your sister. I hear she's so sprung over dude that even if he lived in Alaska, she would have followed him."

"What's dude's name and address, and what's his occupation?"

"That, I don't know. All I know is he resides in Brooklyn and is paid. The best info that I got on him is how he takes care of her every need, took her in when her mother died, and that she's madly in love with him. So in love that she put some chick in a coma who was staring at him while they were walking down the street together."

Once again, Page's right eyebrow went up. "A coma? Chick really became gangsta, huh? Tell me how many bodies she has under her belt."

"I don't know. I just heard that she's beating the hell out of anyone who even looks at her man."

"What company does she keep?"

"I'm not sure about that either." Tina felt herself losing more and more of her money. "If you're talking about anyone and everyone she associates herself with, I can't say."

Damn. She has never asked this many questions before. Something must be up, Tina thought.

Page sat quiet for a minute, pondering if there was anything else she needed to know.

"One more thing, since you can't tell me dude's name, occupation, or home address . . ." Page paused, giving Tina a look that clearly said, "You fucked up." "Can you at least tell me who he associates himself with?"

Tina put her head down and shook it, answering no.

No? Homegirl can tell me that Janae's seeking professional help and what her mother wrote in a suicide note, but she can't tell me who homeboy chills wit'? Page mused.

Page shook her head. "Get on your A game, Tina. You're missing out on some serious loot, and I'm not talking about a measly two hundred dollars."

Page finished her drink and then got up. She went into her purse, pulled out bills, and threw 150 dollars on the table. Without further comment, she left the booth and headed for the door. Her heels clicked against the tile on her way out.

Chapter 5

Janae sat on the floor at the side of her bed, with her face in her arms. The tears on her face had dried up, and she felt as if she no longer had a tear left in her body to release. When she looked up at her night table, the clock read 4:00 a.m. She bit down on her lip, desperately trying not to cry all over again. Her boyfriend had yet to return home.

I refuse to think that he's still at work.

Janae sat up straight, laid her head against her bed, and closed her eyes. At that moment, she was willing to do anything in order to calm down. Before she knew it, she was asleep.

Five hours later, Janae woke up in bed, dressed in the same clothes she had had on the day before. She had a headache from all the crying she'd done the night before, and it took a second for her to remember what had actually taken place. As she lay there, everything slowly started to hit her.

She turned to her right and saw Jared lying on his stomach. His face was turned away from hers. The second she saw him, tears slid from her eyes. She wiped them away, sat up, and started to nudge him. The longer he took to wake up, the harder she nudged.

Jared turned to face her and finally opened his eyes.

"Where were you last night?" she asked, her voice cracking slightly.

"What?" Jared's eyes were open, but it was obvious no one was home.

Janae spoke louder. "Where were you last night!"

"At work." Jared stretched his body out.

"Then why didn't you get home by two thirty in the morning?"

"Because work lasted longer than usual. The office had a party and trashed the place."

When Janae met Jared, she had been led to believe that he was some rich kid who was given everything on a silver platter by his parents, who were both lawyers. This explained why he was loaded and lived in a nice brownstone in Brooklyn. Yet the truth of the matter was that he was not getting money from his parents, but from working for Renee. He had never told Janae what he really did for a living, and after they moved in together, he'd lied and told her that he'd got a job doing maintenance in an office building at night so he wouldn't be so dependent on his parents. This was the perfect lie, especially since working for Renee required a lot of late nights. Janae had never questioned him until recently.

"I saw you driving down the street yesterday morning. I saw you do all you could to avoid me. You damn near killed yourself in the process," Janae remarked.

Jared looked at her like she had lost her mind. But he thought, *Damn! She saw me? I know I pulled a 007, but I was that noticeable?*

Yesterday was the first of the month, and Jared and Waves had picked up Renee's money from the local pharmacies she did business with. Whether if it was by way of fake paper or digital prescriptions called in by dirty doctors, druggies got whatever they wanted out in the open. Jared had driven and had listened to Waves rant and rave over how cold he thought Renee was. But while Waves had spoken, all Jared had been able to think of was how smooth Renee's legs were and how she bit down on her lip when she was angry.

While in his fantasy world, Jared had noticed Janae walking down the street, and he'd immediately broken into a U-turn. He'd nearly caused an accident, one that would have resulted in him killing himself and Waves, just to avoid being seen by Janae. He knew that if she'd seen him, she would have grilled him about why he was out in the street, instead of home, sleeping.

"I don't know what you're talking about," Jared said as he grabbed the TV remote.

Before he got a chance to turn on the TV, Janae took the remote out of his hand and placed it on her night table.

"Yes you do. Tell me, shouldn't you have been home, sleeping? Why are you out running around in the morning when you get home late from work? When I left in the morning, you were still in bed. What were you doing? Waiting till I left before you got up and headed out?"

The more Janae spoke, the more annoyed Jared became. He really felt she was digging into this more than she needed to. It didn't help that she saw right through Jared. He had known she had a doctor's appointment yesterday morning, and he had purposely waited for her to leave before he did. He'd do anything to avoid being interrogated.

"Janae, you're tripping. Ain't no one avoiding you, and yeah, I did leave out early yesterday morning. So what? I had a couple of things to take care of before I went to work."

"I bet you did. So what's her name?"

"What?"

"You heard me. What's her name? No man would pull a stunt like that unless he had a trick in the car with him. So tell me, who is she?"

This chick is really buggin'. Her ass is getting all paranoid on me.

"Just be real. Who is she? Because I'm telling you right now, she only wants you for your money. She doesn't love you like I do, and she damn sure don't need you like I do. What you have to realize is, I'm the only one you need, just like you're the only one I need. I don't even know why you work. Your parents can pay your way. Plus, I got some money my mom saved up for me before she died, so we're okay. All you need to do is quit that job, and we can always be together. I can't stand sleeping alone. I need you by my side to make me feel safe."

This is the shit I'm talking about, Jared told himself. *She's too damn needy. How do you tell someone to quit their job so that you can spend more time with them? What type of selfish shit is that?*

When Jared first met Janae, she'd been nothing like the way she was today. She'd been a true ride-or-die chick, a gangsta, a no-holds-barred kinda girl. They'd met at the ferry while Jared was keeping an eye on one of Renee's investments. After exchanging numbers, they'd had a couple of dinner dates, and the two of them had hit it off and become inseparable. After a couple of months, Jared had really started to believe that she was the one for him. Granted, Janae knew absolutely nothing about who Jared really was—she hadn't even known his real name until recently—and still, their relationship worked. Jared was a private man. The business he was in required him to be nothing else.

However, after two months of living with Janae, Jared had slowly started to regret it. She had become needy, paranoid, and jealous. He had thought it was cute that when they first met, she was protective and would hurt females who even looked at him. But over time it had become too much. She would blow his phone up every hour, search his pockets, and wait up until he got home in the wee hours of the morning. She was smothering him.

He knew that she had just lost her mother, and that her father had disappeared after the suicide, so he was aware that Janae was going through some rough times. But he couldn't take the way she treated him. She was digging her claws into him, and he could feel the scratches.

Shorty's gonna make me lose my mind if she keeps this up. I can predict that I'ma get rid of her soon, he thought now.

Jared got up and stood at the side of the bed. His brown complexion complemented his broad shoulders and his chiseled chest. He made his way to the bathroom.

"Where are you going?" Janae called.

Jared stopped and looked over at the clock. It read 2:00 p.m. "Out." He didn't have to be at work for hours, but he wanted to get away from Janae as soon as possible.

After Jared went in the bathroom, Janae leaned her head against the headboard. When she looked down at her clothes, she remembered she had never changed the night before.

I remember whenever I used to fall asleep without changing into my pajamas, he would change my clothes for me and place me in bed. He doesn't even bother to do that anymore, probably because he's undressing the next girl, she thought.

Fifteen minutes later, Jared walked back into the bedroom. Then he left like a bat out of hell, without even saying goodbye to Janae. She just sat there on the bed, hurt and confused. Janae had become so needy and protective of Jared because he had actually made a commitment by moving her in with him. She didn't want to lose him, like she had her family. She knew that he was unaware of her sister's death, and the fact that she even had a sister to begin with, so Jared could not possibly understand the pain she was going through. Janae felt like she had a curse over her head. Everyone she loved died.

Her father was still alive, but in her eyes, he was dead. Instead of them mourning their loved one's death together, he had disappeared to God knows where after her mother died. Traumatized, Janae was scared someone would come and take Jared away from her. He was the only person she had left, so when she stepped into her new home with him, she'd made herself a promise: over her dead body would she let someone take Jared away from her or allow him to leave her.

Thoughts of Jared with another woman and of her deceased family members floated in her mind. Before she knew it, she jumped off the bed and started trashing the entire place. She threw clothes, dresser drawers, plates, chair cushions, and pots and pans all over the place. After a half hour of throwing things nonstop, Janae had exhausted herself, and she collapsed on the living-room floor. Within minutes, she fell asleep, like a child who had had a long tantrum.

Two hours later, Janae woke up in the middle of the garbage can she had once called her living room, and was introduced to broken glass, upturned chairs, cracked picture frames, and other detritus lying all over the floor.

Her head was spinning, and she didn't feel any better than when she had first trashed the place.

She got up and headed to the bathroom. From the medicine cabinet, she took out a bottle of One A Day vitamins, and then she left the bathroom, walked into the dining room, and poured the powdery white substance out of the vitamin bottle, onto the dining-room table. She divided the cocaine into four thin lines and then sniffed each line back to back until she had cleaned the table. High and numb to any feeling, she eventually started to clean the house, acting like nothing had ever happened.

Chapter 6

Page sat at a table in the prison's visiting room, her palms sweating, her legs shaking, and her heart beating a mile a minute. She was so excited yet nervous to see the love of her life. She wondered if he looked the same. Page was ashamed to admit it, but she hadn't been to see him in months. She had been forced to buckle down in order to maintain her 4.0 GPA at college. If there was one thing he had drilled into her, it was the importance of an education.

Page tapped her fingers on the table and waited for him to enter the room. She was so anxious to see him, she didn't trust what she'd do when he entered. She yearned to touch him, yearned to feel his succulent lips against hers, and wanted nothing more than to stare in his eyes and hold his hand, but she knew this couldn't happen. Touching of any kind was not allowed, so instead there would be nothing but lust and pure temptation once he sat across from her.

Page looked around the room at all the inmates with their loved ones. She caught a few sneaking feels, while others were heavily engaged in conversation. She bit down on the inside of her lip in order to hold back tears. She didn't know how she was doing it, didn't know how she was waking up every day and functioning without him by her side. She missed him and wanted him home.

This man was her air; she needed him to live. And she felt drawn to him like a vampire to blood. Page turned away from the inmates and their families and was greeted by Curtis and his infectious smile.

"Baby girl," his baritone voice boomed. Curtis stood in front of her in his orange jumpsuit, with a smile so bright, it brought out his mocha-colored skin.

"Daddy!"

Page shot up and went to hug her father. She stopped in her tracks when she remembered she couldn't. The guards looked at her, and immediately her heart broke. Her eyes met the floor. Curtis noticed her change in attitude, and his smile widened.

"Baby girl, don't let them get you down. In a month these motherfuckers will have no say over what I do." Curtis stood there, confident and unaffected by his inability to have physical contact with his daughter.

Page nodded her head, and they both sat down. As he got comfortable in his seat, Page noticed how much his appearance had changed. His hair was now sprinkled with gray, and all the weight that he lost had been replaced with muscle. He even had a twinkle in his eye, which let the world know he wasn't allowing prison to bring him down. Although she was proud to see him in such good shape, it sadden her that her disappearance for eight months had had little effect on his life. Curtis sat with his hands folded on the table and his body leaned forward.

"How's my little girl doing? You're looking more and more like your mama. We sure as hell made a pretty girl."

Page blushed. She liked it when her father called her his little girl and complimented her. Words like that proved she was irreplaceable.

"I'm good. One more year and I'll have my bachelor's. Not to mention, I'm maintaining my four-point-o GPA." Page smiled, but seconds later, the smile began to dissolve. "I'm sorry I haven't been to see you. It's just that . . ."

Curtis put his hand up, signaling for her to stop speaking. "You got your head in them books. Keep doing what you're doing to get that diploma, and don't worry about coming to see me. We don't need another beautiful airhead in this world."

Page ran her hand along the side of her short haircut, pleased with the fact that he had noticed her beauty.

He went on. "You're on the right track. You must get your brains from your sister. You know she always did good in school."

Page sat back in her seat. Her body tensed up as rage surged through her. The mere mention of her sister sent her flying off the handle, but she contained herself and didn't say or do anything. Instead, she listened to him speak.

"She's one smart girl, the smartest girl I have ever known. And, boy, oh boy, was she beautiful." Curtis licked his lips.

Curtis pictured his stepdaughter Renee exactly how she looked when he'd last seen her. Her hazel eyes, smooth skin, and pouty lips were embedded in his mind. She was his forbidden fruit, the reason he was in prison. But still, he couldn't help but want her. Renee was all the motivation he needed to survive his bid.

Almost every night, Curtis dreamed about Renee: the sound of her voice, the way her tears would roll down her cheeks and he'd lick them up. He craved her body and knew the best was yet to come. Years had passed, and she was no longer a teenager but a grown woman. Curtis had to see how she'd turned out. He wanted to find her and continue what he'd started. Renee was his, and he wanted to remind her of that. He had loved many women in his day, but none had made him feel the way she did. He didn't know what it was, but she had cast a spell on him, and he was forever hers. Curtis had one month left in prison, and he wanted Renee's face to be the first one he saw when he got out.

He stared off into space now, thinking about the innocent young girl's body and the fact that he had taken her virginity. It was a moment he'd cherish forever.

Suddenly, he snapped out of his thoughts, and a hint of madness filled his eyes. Within a second, Curtis had gone from being cool, calm, and collected to desperate. "Have you heard anything? Do you know where Renee is?"

He was so desperate to hear Page's answer, he didn't notice the menacing glare she gave him. Page was seeing red. In a snap of a finger, their conversation had gone from being about her to being about Renee, the story of her life. She cocked her head to the right and imagined herself losing it. For as long as she could remember, she had wondered what it was about Renee that drove people crazy, especially her father. What was it that Renee had that she didn't? Whatever it was, why couldn't she get it?

In a trance, Page stared at her father, the man she would die and bear children for all in one breath. In that moment, her heart broke. After all these years of her visiting him, loving him, and being on his team, even when his own wife wasn't, he still chose Renee over her. He chose the very person who had landed him in this hellhole, then had run away.

"Page!" Curtis's voice was loud, and his fist banged down on the table. The sound bounced off the walls.

All eyes were on them in an instant, and Curtis looked like a crazy animal waiting for his raw meat to be thrown to him. At that moment, Page realized how much he truly loved Renee.

"Bookend! Keep it down!" the guard shouted.

Curtis was breathing heavily, but after hearing the guard yell out to him and seeing the attention he was drawing, he slowly began to calm down. He couldn't let his visit end without getting an answer.

Page was broken inside, but she hid it. "Never let them see you sweat" was her motto. She smiled and shook her head.

"No, Daddy, there's still no word." She leaned forward, pretend sadness filling her eyes, her hand inches away from his. "I wouldn't be surprised if she's dead."

Page never thought she'd say this, but she took joy in seeing the pained expression wash over her father's face. It was the highlight of her visit. When he thought of Renee, he needed to associate her with pain. It would make it a lot easier for him to let go. For the remainder of the visit, they didn't bring Renee up again. They talked about small, meaningless things. It was obvious the thought of Renee being dead had crushed Curtis. That was exactly what Page wanted her to be, dead in his eyes.

During their talk, Page continued to play her position as the supportive, loving daughter that she was. She knew he loved her. Now all she had to do was turn that fatherly love into a romantic one, and the thought of Renee being dead into a reality.

Chapter 7

With a face full of tears, Page sped down the highway at eighty miles per hour, with total disregard for her life and the lives of others. Her nerves were shot, and her emotions were at an all-time high. Even with Renee out of sight, she still held the key to Curtis's heart.

That bitch isn't even his biological daughter, and still he wants her ass! What the fuck ever happened to blood coming first?

Page's hands shook violently, making it almost impossible for her to retain a firm grip on the steering wheel. Images of Curtis flashed before her, and her body temperature rose. She wanted him, needed him, and craved him. She imagined reaching her sexual peak when he entered her. This was a game of pleasure, a scavenger hunt for the ultimate orgasm, and Curtis was the key to instant gratification.

Page licked her lips. She imagined how sweet he tasted, and pictured her nails penetrating his back and her screaming out in ecstasy. Page's dream was to bed her father and become his world. She'd slept with many men, only to picture her father's face on theirs. Her sex was psychotic, and there were rules to her sexcapades. If they wanted to play, they had to allow her to call them Curtis and dominate the whole experience.

Page went into a trance whenever she had sex. In her mind, the man she was with was Curtis. She became so lost in the fantasy that she could actually smell his scent and would beg for more. On countless occasions, when she came off her high and was reminded that the men she allowed in her temple were not Curtis, she would lose it. While on top of the men, she'd spit in their face, and the moment she saw them about to react, she'd grab the box cutter from under her pillow and hold it to their neck.

There was always fear etched in the eyes of those men. Naked and on top of them, she'd hold the blade so close to their neck that trickles of blood would stain the white cotton sheets and darken the soft multicolored blankets. The moment they did, she was ready for another round.

"Fuck me," she would whisper in their ears, all while pressing the blade farther into their neck. Beneath her, each and every man trembled. A few would sweat, one cried, but the majority of them obliged.

Page refused to accept reality. She refused to believe that once again, her dream of being with Curtis was simply that, a dream. As she thought now of Curtis and how she yearned to be with him, Renee's face flashed before her eyes, and she slammed down on the brakes. Her body flew toward the windshield, and when she thought she was seconds away from kissing it, her seat belt slammed her back into her seat.

"Ahhh!" she screamed. "I'm tired of this bitch! I want her motherfuckin' head! I want her dead!"

Page's face was beet red, and fresh tears graced her cheeks. She looked like a warrior, with her smeared mascara racing down her cheeks. Like a trained boxer, she punched the steering wheel, trying her best to let out all her frustration. The horn honked with each blow, and people driving by would slow down a little to watch her tantrum, but she didn't care. All she cared about was winning the heart of a man who was in love with her sister.

Eventually, Page exhausted herself and took deep breaths. She sat, wide-eyed, and stared out the window. Punches eventually turned into slaps, which reverted to punches.

Why can't it be me? Why couldn't he have picked me?

As she fought to catch her breath, Page's memory ran away with her.

Page's eyes shot open. She had had a bad dream, and was too frightened to fall back asleep. At the age of six, she found comfort in her favorite blanket, so she frantically searched her bed for it. On the floor, it lay in a pool of its own fabric. Page snatched it up and held it against her chest.

"I want Daddy," she said aloud.

Curtis was the only person who could make all her bad dreams go away. He would come into her room and tell her countless stories until the nightmare was pushed out of her head and replaced with fairy tales.

On the verge of searching for her father, Page realized that her bladder was full and decided to take a detour to the bathroom. While rubbing her eyes and walking out of the bathroom, she saw her father slip into Renee's room. She rubbed her eyes again, trying to get rid of the sleepiness that tried to conquer her. She slowly walked over to her sister's door. Curiosity got the best of her, so she placed her ear against the door and listened carefully.

Page heard what sounded like muffled whimpering and her father constantly repeating, "You're so beautiful, so beautiful."

She heard Renee's bed squeaking, so she placed her hand on the doorknob and slowly pushed the door open a tiny bit. Through the crack, she could see her father positioned between her sister's thin, trembling legs. A rainbow-colored sock was stuffed in her mouth, and with one hand, he held both her hands over her head while he forced her legs open with his knees and free hand.

The moonlight hit Renee's face, and Page could see her tears as clear as day. One by one, they fell from her cheeks and onto the carpeted floor. Page didn't see the pain and the cry for help that seeped from Renee's eyes. All she saw was her father's contorted face. His eyes frequently rolled to the back of his head, and his mouth was agape. However, it was more than her father's erotic facial expressions that made Page believe he was in heaven. It was his heavy breathing and focused demeanor that confirmed her assumptions.

Back then, Page didn't know what her young body was feeling, but watching her father have sex with her half sister made her want in. She wanted her father to caress her, to kiss her, and become one with her as he was with Renee. She wanted to make him happy.

After that night, Page would listen to Curtis rape Renee and, once in a blue moon, have sex with her mother. It seemed that he had a thing for everyone in the house except her, and it was starting to piss her off. With each day and year that passed, her hatred for her mother and her sister grew. They had what she wanted. Page was Daddy's little girl, and she wanted to show him how much she loved him, but he never gave her the chance, no matter how much she flaunted her sexuality.

Once she was old enough to understand the art of seduction, Page started dressing and behaving provoca-

tively around her father. She'd bend over, ever so slowly, to give him a show. She'd leave her bedroom door wide open when undressing. Her antics got her no attention. All Curtis ever told her was to put some baggier clothes on and to close her bedroom door when she was changing. Curtis just wasn't interested, and Page didn't understand why.

She was living in a house with women she hated, and she was suffocating. Depression clung to her and wouldn't let go. In Page's mind, her mother was no better than Renee; they both were slutty, weak women who had something neither deserved. The only pleasure Page received while living in that house was from her mother degrading Renee. It was entertaining to see her mother verbally abuse her sister. In fact, it was entertainment at its finest. She'd listen to Renee cry almost every night, while locked up in her room, praying to God, asking Him why her mother hated her so much and calling out for her father. She probably hoped that if she called out for him enough, he'd magically appear and take her away from everything that hurt.

To hear Renee sounding so weak made Page stronger, and she thrived on that. The only thing she couldn't shake was her mother's love for her. Sheila had never hid the fact that Page was her favorite. She gave her the world, and it made Page nauseous. She could deal with receiving the material things, but the talks and the maternal affection were where she drew the line. She would never like a woman who slept with her man.

Page had managed to convince herself that Curtis needed time and would soon come around and realize that although she was young, she was the woman for him. Page's dreams were shattered when Curtis was arrested and sentenced to ten years for raping a minor. Renee had pressed charges and had had him torn from their home. That was when things really got bad. Not only did Sheila continue to verbally abuse Renee, but from time to time, she would also beat her.

Renee was a prisoner within her own home. A month after she graduated from high school, she disappeared. No one knew where she went, and honestly, no one cared. Sheila didn't even bother to file a missing person's report. The way she saw it, Renee was a thorn in her side that had finally been removed.

Page was pleased with Renee's disappearance, and she was ecstatic when Sheila came waltzing in with her new boyfriend, who was twenty years younger than her. In Page's mind, now that Renee was MIA and her cheating heifer of a mother had a boyfriend, Curtis was sure to run right into her arms. All Page had to do was stand by her man while he was incarcerated and wait for him to return home and kick Sheila to the curb. Everything was unfolding nicely without her even having to do anything, or so she thought.

Page couldn't stop the tears from falling from her eyes as she sat in her car. They were like track runners racing for the finish line. She hadn't known how obsessed Curtis was with Renee until today. The look in his eyes had verified that he'd do everything in his power to find her once he was released, but Page wouldn't and couldn't allow that. She wiped her tears away and looked into space, murder a recurrent thought. After throwing out the idea to Curtis that Renee could be dead, and after seeing his reaction, she knew what she had to do. The only thing that could stop his love for Renee was death.

She had to find Renee and kill her before Curtis got out of prison. He wouldn't rest until Renee was in his arms, and this would demolish Page's mind, body, and soul. Brokenhearted and lonely, Page would soon become riven with hate, and this she couldn't allow. She had to make her dream come true, and she had only one month to get rid of the one person standing in her way. One month to put her one and only sister underground.

Page gazed in the rearview mirror and saw that she looked a mess. She dug in her purse and pulled out tissues and cosmetics. After dapping her eyes and reapplying her makeup, she stared at herself in the mirror.

"Stop crying, bitch," she said aloud. "We have a cunt to kill and a man to get."

She smiled at herself in the rearview mirror.

"That's my girl," she said happily to her reflection. "It's crunch time, baby. No more tears. And for now, fuck killing Janae. We have to get to Renee before she does."

Chapter 8

"She doesn't know. I haven't told her."

Crouched down, hidden behind the wall that separated the living room from the dining room, Renee listened to a tearful Sheila's discussion with her friend Ms. Pam.

"Sheila, how could you not have told the child?"

"I don't know how. How do you tell a ten-year-old this?"

Renee poked her head out. Ms. Pam moved from the love seat she sat on to the full couch and plopped down next to her friend. Ms. Pam's chubby hand stretched across the coffee table and plucked a single tissue out of the rectangular tissue box. She gave it to Sheila.

"It's been a week. Where does she think he is?"

Sheila dried her cheeks with the tissue, then rolled it into a small ball, which she covered with both hands. A tiny sob seeped out of her mouth. She swallowed, then cleared throat. "A medical convention."

Ms. Pam pursed her lips. She crossed one leg over the other, crossed her arms, and turned her head in the opposite direction to Sheila.

"Don't give me that, Pamela. You're not a mother. You don't know how difficult this is." Sheila tossed the tissue ball on the coffee table.

"I'm not a mother, but I am a woman who lost her father at a young age, and I'll tell you this much. Had *my mother waited a week to tell me my father had passed away, I'd have been pissed the hell off."* She got up from her seat. Her red and cream sandals slapped against the wooden floorboards as she walked away.

"I'll tell her soon!" Sheila hollered.

Renee leaned against the wall. Her heart fell to the tips of her toes, and her stomach roiled. She shut her eyes, balled her small hands into fists, and repeated over and over in her mind, It's not true. It's not true. He's at a convention. He's not dead. *Then the waterworks started, making it harder for her to believe what she heard held no truth.*

She opened her eyes, looked up and, through tears, made eye contact with a pale-faced Ms. Pam. Ms. Pam's mouth dropped. Her lips formed a lot of words; however, none fell out except for two.

"She knows."

Renee buried herself deeper under her blanket as painful memories constantly played in her mind.

"Remember that paper you helped me write on the Cold War? I finally got my grade. I got an A." Renee beamed. *"I'll be getting my report card soon, and I'm predicting all As."*

A cool breeze started blowing, and Renee folded her arms.

"Mommy said we're going to Disney for spring break, but I don't believe her." She ripped a piece of grass out of the ground and threw it to the side. *"I don't think I'll ever believe what she says after she lied to me about you."* Renee pulled strands of grass out of the ground and tossed them aside. *"I wish you were here."*

"Renee!" Ms. Pam walked as fast as she could through the grass without falling in her high heels. With each step she took, her stilettoes stabbed the ground.

"How did you get in here?" Renee asked.

Huffing and puffing, Ms. Pam told her, "You don't want to know." She used her hand to fan her face, then rested it on her chest to catch her breath. "Have you been here since four?" Ms. Pam looked down at her watch. It read 11:00 p.m. "Your mother and I were worried sick!"

"Yup. Did Mia tell you where I was?"

"Her mother did. She told us she dropped you off here because you told her Sheila had asked her to. She was under the impression that your mother was meeting you here in the cemetery."

Renee didn't respond. She just continued staring at the tombstone. Ms. Pam straightened out the purple polka-dot sheet Renee sat on. She kicked off her heels and sat down beside her. For some time neither of them said anything. They both just stared at Daniel's grave and read over and over the tombstone's inscription.

Renee broke the silence with her words. "I just don't understand." Before Ms. Pam could chime in, Renee continued, "I just don't understand death." Renee's head shook softly.

"I felt the same way when my father died."

"Your father died?" Renee turned to face Ms. Pam.

"Yup. It was the worst day of my live. I was a daddy's girl, just like you."

"How did you get over it? How did you make it stop hurting?"

"You never get over it, and it never stops hurting. It only becomes easier to cope with," Ms. Pam explained. "Don't fight so hard to ignore and understand your feelings right now, Renee. Take this time to mourn."

"That's the thing. I don't know how!" Renee's watery eyes begged for answers.

"Do what you feel like doing. If you feel like crying, cry. If you feel like screaming, scream. Hell, if you feel like dancing in the middle of a rainstorm, do it. Just don't deny yourself the opportunity to feel."

"Do you want to know how I really feel?"

"That's why I'm here."

"I feel broken, I feel gypped, and I'm angry all the time." Renee gave a weak smile. *"And I feel trapped, because I have a mother who doesn't even love me."*

Ms. Pam's gaze dropped. *"Renee—"*

"She doesn't care about me."

"That's not true."

"Then why are you here and not her!"

A gush of wind rushed past both Renee and Ms. Pam and caused the hair on their arms to rise. Renee directed her attention away from her mother's friend and back to her father.

"Your mother has a lot of issues. That is obvious. But I guarantee she loves you. She just has no clue how to show it."

Renee folded her arms and fell silent.

"How did you manage to stay in here for so long without getting caught?" Ms. Pam quizzed, looking from left to right.

A sly smile crossed Renee's lips. *"You don't want to know,"* she answered.

Ms. Pam playfully shoved Renee. She stood up. *"We better get going."*

Renee touched the tombstone. *"Five more minutes."* She looked up at Ms. Pam. *"Please."*

Ms. Pam sat back down beside Renee. *"Hi, Daniel. It's Pamela."*

Renee took a deep breath and shut her eyes in an effort to will the memories away. For three days, Renee had lived in darkness within the four walls of her bedroom. Sweaty and depressed, she resembled the fiends who bought her poison. Her hair was a bee's hive, her eyes were sunken in, and dried-up blood stained her lips due to them cracking so badly.

Renee couldn't take it. Today marked the fifteenth anniversary of her father's death, and she couldn't come to terms with it, couldn't accept that once her father passed, her life had turned into a nightmare she couldn't wake up from. Every year that passed was a blow to the heart, and just the thought of her father no longer being around choked the life out of her. This year was worse. This year Julian had left her to battle her demons alone.

It'd been three weeks, and Julian still hadn't shown his face or contacted Renee. She could feel the coldness he was blowing her way, and she was sure she'd caught frostbite. Julian locking her out of his life had left Renee feeling lonely and lost. She covered her face with her hands and lay paralyzed, trying her best to fight off the pain. With Julian absent, Renee didn't know how she'd get through this day. In her mind, she had officially lost the two most important men in her life. She saw no need to go on.

Each year, on this day, Renee allowed her vulnerability to show and her pain to speak. Like the good man Julian was, he had been right there, cradling her in his arms while whispering all the right things in her ear. The two had fallen in love as teenagers. Renee and her family had moved from Miami to Brooklyn after her mother remarried, and there she had met Julian.

Three houses down from Julian's, Renee and her family had unpacked and prepared to try to fit into the new neighborhood, but they would never fit in. What took place in that house would transform every person, inside and out.

A month after Renee settled into the family's new home, Julian had walked past her house, only to see this magnificent beauty sitting on her porch steps, crying her soul out. He'd asked what was wrong, and her answer had shocked him. "My stepfather rapes me," was what she'd told him, her eyes drowning in a sea of pain, begging him to save her. It was the first time she had said it out loud, and she'd said it to a stranger in a strange place. At that moment Julian fell hard for Renee, and he vowed to be her knight in shining armor.

Although their first encounter had been drenched in heartache, Julian never mentioned it when they were walking down memory lane. Instead, he turned the memory into a fairy tale and told Renee how the moment their eyes met, he knew she was the one. Tangled in his arms, Renee would mourn her father's death and wish she could turn back the hands of time. Julian gave her the strength and love she needed to get through the day. It was his touch and soothing voice that made Renee fight the demons of her past. She was traumatized and scarred, and she missed him terribly right now.

Her father's death and her abusive childhood had turned her into a coldhearted monster. Unable to let go of what was, when she became an adult, she created her alias, Jordan, and set out to wreak mayhem on the streets of New York. She wanted everyone to feel her pain, so she had made the streets take a never-ending ride down misery lane with her.

Few had ever seen the ruthless person responsible for pumping cocaine into New York, so people automatically assumed Jordan was a man. Only those who worked directly with Renee and had seen the inside of her home knew she was the person behind the name. This no-face alias of hers kept her protected and under the radar. And hers was a close-knit circle, which guaranteed her more insurance for longevity in the game.

Renee was a queenpin sitting on millions now, but no amount of money could ease the constant anger she felt toward her past. Renee had demons that she couldn't shake, and she had allowed them to swallow her whole and crush her heart. She stared into space now and turned the pages of her life in her mind. Her father would turn in his grave at the sight of her; she was a monster, a black-hearted beast with no conscience. She was nothing he had envisioned her being. Before he died in that five-car pileup on the highway, he had had great dreams for his baby girl. His love for his daughter had trumped everything. Even as a successful heart surgeon, he had still found time for his Ree-Ree. She was the reason he had stayed with her mother; he'd been the bandage to a broken family.

Renee had been ten years old when he passed. Her world had crumbled when he died, and the little that was left of it had shattered when her mother remarried, exchanging vows with a man who would steal Renee's innocence, virginity, and happiness. Renee was lost in a sea of confusion over why her childhood had been such a nightmare. She had many unanswered questions, such as why her mother had stayed with a man who continuously raped her child, why she'd been bullied, why friends had been so hard to come by, and why her father had disappeared for days at a time before he died. Life had been hard, and it had left Renee scarred. But instead of searching for answers to all her questions, she let her despair control her.

Renee rolled over on her side and felt the empty space in her bed, the spot reserved for Julian. She took a deep breath. She was far from being the woman that he wanted, but she knew one thing: she knew that she was the woman he needed. With Julian's disappearance, flashbacks of her father vanishing for days at a time invaded her thoughts, and she pushed them to the back of her mind. Anger took over once again. Renee didn't know what to do with this thing called life, but if she didn't figure it out soon and get past her rage, she'd be doomed.

Two days later . . .

Renee opened her eyes and felt like she had been hit by a ton of bricks. Her soul was broken, and her heart was punctured. Lying in her bed for days had done nothing to ease the pain of losing her father and enduring Julian's disappearing act. She pulled herself out of bed and walked over to her vanity table. Leaning the palms of her hands on the table, she stared at herself in the mirror. She didn't know the woman who looked back at her, and she didn't care to meet her. The longer she looked, the more she hurt. She was lost within a world she had created, and she didn't know how to get out of it, didn't know how to walk out of the darkness and into the light.

Renee closed her eyes and then opened them and stormed away from the mirror. She couldn't stand the sight of her own face, and she couldn't conjure up the strength she needed to move past the pain and into happiness. She was weak, and in her mind, weak people had no place in her life.

She jumped in the shower, dried off, and threw on a diamond-studded black tank top, dark blue skinny jeans, and a black, fitted hat. Then she went out on her terrace. It was late afternoon, and the cool summer breeze graced her skin as she sat on the terrace. She knew it was time to end her mourning for the year and continue doing what she did best: ignoring her pain and allowing her misery to wreak havoc on the world. She looked down at the busy streets of New York City, and her eyes followed a guy riding his motorcycle, weaving in and out of traffic.

Smiling, Renee walked into her bedroom and reached into her nightstand. She pulled out her Harley-Davidson keys. When she made her way downstairs, Slice was in the living room, playing her PlayStation 4. The screams of a crowd coming from the console indicated that he was playing *NBA 2K19*. Lyfe sat alone in a corner, playing a game of chess. When they heard her open the coat closet and retrieve her helmet, both men looked at her with confusion. Renee hardly, if ever, left the house. It was something she just didn't do. She ran the streets behind closed doors and sat on her throne, looking pretty. So now that she wanted to leave, with dark circles around her eyes, and bags so heavy that they threatened to pop, all eyes were on her.

"Where you going?" Slice questioned, but Renee didn't answer. She just continued to grab her belongings, and then she made her way toward the door.

Slice paused the game and stood up. "Renee!" he called out.

Still, she didn't answer.

He opened his mouth to call her again, but he stopped when he felt a hand on his shoulder. He turned around and saw Lyfe staring at him, his eyes and his firm grip telling him to leave it alone. Slice took his advice and shut up. He went back to his game.

Ten minutes after the front door shut, Lyfe was still staring at the door while clutching his cell phone. The calendar app was open, with the date from two days ago displayed on the screen.

Chapter 9

After forty-five minutes of riding around, Renee found herself in Brooklyn, over in East New York. She had had no destination in mind when she started out, and life had led her back to where she spent the bulk of her life. The mere sight of her old neighborhood brought back unforgettable memories. Three blocks from her old home, she looked across the street and saw Ms. Johnson, a sixty-five-year-old woman who had more men than Bill Gates had money. Renee watched her walk into the house with two men. She was wearing a black miniskirt and a tight spaghetti top.

Renee smiled. *Old Ms. Johnson still got it.*

Minutes later, Renee sat at a red light in front of her mother's house, a place she hadn't been to in years. The house hadn't changed; it still stood tall, with flowerpots filled with sunflowers on the porch, and roses and tulips surrounding the yard. She stared at the home, trying to find something, anything, that was different, but there was absolutely nothing different about it. To Renee, if there was nothing different about the outside of the home, then there was nothing different about the people inside it, and that angered her.

She thought about her sister, and instantly, her anger subsided. She looked up at the window to the bedroom that she knew belonged to Page, and she thought she

saw a shadow, but then she figured it was only her eyes
playing tricks on her. She hadn't seen her sister in years,
and as hard as it was for her cold heart to admit, she
missed her terribly and wanted nothing more than to get
off her bike and walk into the house.

However, entering that home would be like going
back in time, which was something Renee could never
do. Before another thought came to mind, she heard a
high-pitched woman's laugh. Renee looked over and saw
an older female with the physique of a model walking up
to the house with a male. Renee couldn't get a good look
at the guy's face. His head was turned in the opposite
direction, but she did look over his lime-green pants
and orange shirt before laying eyes on the woman who
caused her blood to boil. The sight of her mother after
all these years still enraged her. She followed her every
move now. You would have thought the woman was
twenty again by the way she was all over this young guy,
who could have been her oldest daughter's boyfriend.

As she stared at the couple, Renee entered her own
little world and relived the past.

*Why do we have to stay here again?" Julian dribbled
his basketball effortlessly and at such a high speed that
Renee's eyes could barely keep up with the ball.*

"I can't leave until she comes back."

"Where did she go?"

*Renee screwed up her face. "Don't know. Don't care."
A short brown-skinned guy walked past just then, pushing
a baby stroller. Renee sat right on the steps of her porch;
however, she felt completely separated from society. "I'm
stuck here in this shit hole. You can go."*

*Julian sped up his dribbling, his stare fixed on Renee.
"If you're stuck, then I'm stuck."*

Renee tried to suppress the smile creeping across her lips and failed. Her unwanted smile broke Julian's focus on dribbling. He smiled back, and the ball slipped out of his hands and tumbled inside Sheila's garden. It rolled over on an impatiens and a sunflower.

"My bad, Ree. I know your mother will blow her top if I mess up her flowers." He removed the ball from the garden and attempted to straighten the slightly damaged stems.

Renee walked over. "I got it," she announced. Julian stepped aside, and Renee stomped on the flowers. "Much better." She went back to the porch and sat down on the steps.

Shortly after the assassination of the flowers, a red convertible pulled up across the street.

"That is a bright-ass color red," Julian noted.

"Tacky as hell," Renee replied.

The driver's door opened, and Sheila stepped out. She speed walked from the car straight to her house.

"About time," Renee mumbled. She pulled her braids back into a ponytail and stood up, ready to go.

"Is your father home?" Sheila questioned.

"My father's dead, but if you're talking about that bastard you call your husband, he's not here."

With an open palm and stretched-out fingers, Sheila slapped Renee on the right side of her face. Her finger pointed in Renee's face as she told her, "You're going to learn to respect Curtis. Do you hear me!"

Renee kept her head in the direction her mother's slap had taken it in and didn't respond.

Sheila grabbed Renee's chin and turned her face to her. "Do you hear me!"

Still no response.

Sheila moved her hands to her daughter's cheeks and squeezed them forward until Renee's lips resembled a duck. "Do you hear me . . . ?" Sheila squeezed until her fingers hurt and Renee's cheeks reddened.

Unable to bear any more, Renee strained her mouth to utter, "Yes." Then she snatched her face away from Sheila's grasp and tried rubbing away the pain.

Sheila looked behind her and waved over at the red car. A bald-headed man dressed in slacks and a Hawaiian button-down shirt got out from the driver's seat and strolled across the street.

"Now, you stay here and be on the lookout for Curtis," Sheila instructed Renee.

"You said when you come back, I could go out. It's already nine o'clock, and I'm supposed to be home by ten," Renee explained with an attitude.

"Then I guess that means you're not going out," her mother hissed.

Hawaiian shirt stepped next to Sheila. He looked Renee over. His eyes trailed down her body and didn't reach her feet before Sheila snatched his hand and pulled him inside.

Renee crashed down on a porch step and covered her face with her hands. "I hate her," she said as she wept.

Julian pulled her into his arms. "Don't forget the plan. Keep doing your thing in school so we can get a scholarship to college and get the fuck outta here."

In between sobs Renee managed to push out, "Go to the park. Don't wait for me. I took enough of your time. I have to stay here, not you."

"If you stay, I stay."

The blaring sound of cars honking their horn behind her brought Renee back to reality. She looked up at the green light and made her motorcycle roar. She sped down the street and popped a wheelie. She couldn't believe she had seen her mother. She took her anger out on the road, doing eighty while weaving in and out of traffic. She didn't know where she was going. All she knew was that she had to get away before she did something she *wouldn't* regret.

Page saw Renee sitting outside, watching her house. She had no idea who she was or what she wanted, so she stood to the side of her bedroom window and looked at the stranger on the bike. She stepped farther from the window and hid behind her curtains when she thought the biker had caught her looking. Her first instinct was to whip out her switchblade, head out to the street, and take the biker out with one clean cut across the throat. But something told her to stand there and examine the biker. For all she knew, it could simply be someone admiring her mother's flowers.

They got a lot of that when people walked and drove by the house in the summer, but for some reason, this person didn't seem like a citizen admiring the flora. Page thought that perhaps it was Janae, or someone Janae had hired to watch the house, in hopes of spotting Renee. She shrugged it off. Janae could do whatever she pleased, but the second she stepped out of bounds and brought danger Page's way, it would be her life on the line. Minutes later she watched the biker speed off and pop a wheelie. Just then her mother, Sheila, and her mother's boyfriend entered the house, having noticed nothing.

As a child, Page was anything but normal. She was not your average little girl who desired to play with Barbie dolls and pretended to have tea parties. Instead, she was obsessed with sharp objects and intrigued by what they could do. When she was eight, she'd adopted the habit of playing with knives. She was fascinated with how they could cut through almost anything. She loved the fact that if used properly, knives caused humans to die *and* to suffer slow deaths, unlike guns, which could automatically put a person out of their misery.

In her backyard, when no one was watching, Page would gather ants and, one by one, cut off their small heads. She had always heard never to feed rice to birds, but whenever they landed in her yard, she would give it to them. She hoped they would die while in her presence. If they did, she would cut off their wings and legs.

Page was a lonely child. She never desired to play with other kids, because she found comfort in being alone with her thoughts. As she got older, she would place razor blades in her mouth and carry them almost everywhere she went. Her parents never noticed her odd behavior. They were too busy putting Renee through hell to notice that their baby girl was disturbed.

Now Page walked downstairs to the kitchen, where her mother and her boyfriend, Lincoln, who was twenty years younger than Sheila and was known for his multicolored wardrobe, were cooking. She stood in the doorway and watched the two interact with each other. Neither was aware that they were being watched. Sheila was stirring what smelled like spaghetti sauce, while Lincoln held her from behind. His hands were rubbing her sides and were on the verge of exploring her whole body.

Why can't it always be like this? She stays with her young-ass, multicolored boyfriend, while I get the one thing I have always wanted, Curtis. A man who can care for me, love me, please me, and who I can build a relationship and life with. Why must she be so stingy? Having her cake and eating it too.

Page nodded. She couldn't agree more with the voice in her head. She couldn't stand her mother and the fact that she was married to Curtis. For hours, she would listen to her mother's moans whenever Curtis found the time to please her. On several occasions, it had nearly driven her crazy and had made her want to slice her mother's throat. Now that Sheila was being greedy and was holding on to two men, Page couldn't wait for Curtis to be released, so that he could come home and kick her to the curb.

Page rolled her eyes and turned to walk away. The buffed wood floors squeaked beneath her feet. As soon as her back was turned, Lincoln turned around. His eyes lustfully scanned her body.

"Going somewhere, Page?" he said.

Page could have kicked herself a thousand times for allowing herself to be seen by Lincoln. She turned around but didn't speak.

"Hey, baby. How you doing? You're home early from work today." Sheila had a big smile on her face.

She turned Lincoln's face in her direction and fed him spaghetti sauce. The sight alone made Page want to vomit, so she didn't bother to speak. Instead, she just walked away and headed to the front porch to get some fresh air and watch the world go by. The sound of basketballs bouncing and girls jumping double Dutch blocks away, at the nearby park, filled her ears.

As much as people believed that Brooklyn was noth-ing but the hood, Page knew the truth. It was nights like this one that actually made her appreciate life. The breeze pushed the strands of hair out of her face, and the sound of bouncing basketballs actually soothed her.

I wish Curtis was here to share this moment with me. All would have been well if that bitch had kept her fucking mouth shut. Running around, screaming rape, when she knew she wanted it.

Page listened to the voice in her head talk about Renee. It was obvious the voice was hurt and needed to vent. Lost in her thoughts, Page didn't hear Lincoln come out of her house and step onto the porch. Her thoughts were interrupted when she felt hands wrapping around her thin waist. Instantly, she jumped and turned around.

"What the fuck you doing?" Page's words slid off her tongue like venom.

Given her appearance, she could easily be mistaken for a lady, but once she opened her mouth, the term *ladylike* quickly went out the window.

"Damn, girl. My bad. I couldn't help myself," Lincoln said with a smile.

Page rolled her eyes and turned back in the direction she was previously facing. She hadn't liked Lincoln since the first day she met him. She despised everything about him, from how he dressed to how he thought he was so damn slick. The dude was nothing but a clown in her eyes, and her skin crawled when she thought about what he and Sheila did in the privacy of her mother's bedroom.

"Damn, girl. You got one hell of a body."

Lincoln looked over every nook and cranny of Page's slim frame. She had the stature of a model, with her thin waist and long legs, but the assets of a video girl, with her protruding behind and well-developed breasts. His eyes dropped to her backside.

"You got nothing on your sister, but you'll do," Lincoln blurted out.

Page turned around and was face-to-face with Lincoln, their noses nearly touching. Her jaw was locked on the razor blade she held in her mouth, like a pit bull's jaw locked on its victim, making it nearly impossible for someone to loosen its grip. While staring Lincoln in the eyes, Page felt an unfamiliar taste in her mouth. *Blood.* In all her years of playing with razor blades, she'd never cut herself until now.

"What did you just say? Don't compare me to that bitch. It's the other way around. She has nothing on me."

Page's words were deadly. If spit had flown out while she spoke, Lincoln was sure it would've hit his skin and burned right through him like acid. He held his hands out in front of him, showing that he surrendered.

"Wow, little mama. My bad. No offense. It's just that I always had a thing for your sister. When she bounced, it damn near broke my heart."

Page gave him such a nasty look that if she willed it, it seemed as if Lincoln would turn to stone. "How the hell do you know her, anyway?"

Lincoln lowered his arms, happy that she seemed to have cooled off a bit. "I know her from high school. We used to kick it every now and then."

Kick it? This Gummi Bear–looking motherfucker is lying. As much as I can't stand the bitch, I have to admit that she has style. I know for a fact that she wouldn't be caught dead messing with this motherfucker. He just isn't her type.

"You and my sister used to kick it? Stop lying. That bitch would not have given you the time of day to wash her drawers, let alone chill with you. And as much as I can't wait to put that chick six feet under, I know she had some class and standards."

Page's hands were now on her hips, with all her weight on her right leg. If it was gum in her mouth instead of that blade, she would have looked like a straight-up chicken head.

Lincoln had an uneasy look on his face. He didn't like being disrespected. Yeah, he dressed a little different, and he wasn't your everyday guy that girls flocked to, but he was real. He actually did used to talk to Renee. They had never moved to the next level and become girlfriend and boyfriend, but they'd definitely been friends.

Lincoln had been an outsider in high school, and for some reason, he and Renee had become cool. He hadn't been a part of her, Julian, and Slice's clique, but he had formed a bond with them. From time to time, he'd hung out with Renee and just chilled. She'd accepted him, and that was all Lincoln ever wanted from someone.

It bothered him to hear Page butcher him right to his face, but what he found really interesting was her calling her own flesh and blood out of her name twice. She had even said that she couldn't wait to kill Renee. He didn't know what that was about, but he was going to find out.

"Fine, li'l mama. Your sister never even said two words to me. But, damn, you ain't got to call a brother out like that. Can't blame a brother for dreaming."

Page smirked. *I knew his ass was lying. He probably couldn't land Renee, so he's settled for the next best thing, my mother. Sick fuck. He'd do anything to get laid, even if it means running game on a woman nearly twenty years older than him, whose husband is locked up.*

"You didn't even have to admit it. I see right through you." Page walked over to a corner of the porch and played with the flowers in the pots. "Why are you out here, anyway? Shouldn't my mother be teaching your young ass your ABC's or something?" Page pulled a sunflower out of a pot and threw it off the porch.

"Come on now, P. Your mother ain't that much older than me. Besides, it ain't even that serious. We just hanging. I know about your pops being on lock. I'm just here keeping your moms company till he comes home."

Page looked at him and rolled her eyes, but Lincoln was telling her the truth.

He and Sheila had met one at a hole-in-the-wall bar in the city. Lincoln was drinking his life away that night, after finding out his girlfriend, Electra, had been cheating on him throughout their entire relationship. He felt stupid for actually having believed she was the one. When her lover had been offered a job out of state, she'd broken it off with Lincoln, telling him she was in love with the guy and was leaving with him. Hearing those words had hurt Lincoln so bad, he thought he would be better off if she had reached in his chest and ripped his heart out. At least that would hurt less. He went to the bar and told himself he'd drink till he couldn't drink any more.

After his third drink, he laid eyes on Sheila. She was sitting in a corner by herself, staring at him. Lincoln looked around the bar. He was sure she was making goo-goo eyes at someone else, because love sure wasn't in the cards for him. When she walked over to his table, it was clear she wanted him. Her hair was cut in a bob, her makeup was perfect, and her body was calling him.

He knew she was an older woman by the few visible wrinkles displayed on her face and the mature look in her eyes, but Lincoln wasn't going to let her slip through his fingers. There was something very familiar about her. That night they flirted and drank together, and before they knew it, they were in her bed, having sex. The next morning, when they got up, Sheila decided to lay all her cards on the table.

"Listen, I'ma level with you. I'm not looking for a relationship. My husband is in jail, and I just need someone to fool around with until he comes home. Are you cool with that? Because if not, it was fun and the door is that way."

Sheila's French-manicured finger pointed toward the door, and Lincoln was shocked. He was used to young girls, so when this grown, mature woman, who knew what she wanted and had no problem expressing it, laid it all out for him, he was ecstatic.

"No strings attached? We're just kicking it until your husband gets out?"

"No strings attached. This is nothing but a good time. And when my husband comes home, you go on about your business and continue doing what you were doing before you met me."

This was a no-brainer for Lincoln; the last thing he wanted to do was get into another relationship. A woman who told him he could screw her whenever he wanted without being in a committed relationship was his type of woman. It wasn't until he came back to the house the following week that he discovered she was Renee and Page's mother. It made sense why he was attracted to her: she looked like Renee.

"Besides, I told her I needed some air. But enough about Sheila. What's up with all the hostility toward Renee?" Lincoln told Page now as they stood on the porch. "Let me guess. Everybody thinks you're the ugly sister?" Lincoln laughed at his assumption.

"Please. Like I said earlier, chick ain't got nothing on me."

Yet again Page was reminded of the pedestal she believed Renee was put on. A pedestal she wanted to chop her down from. Renee got touched by Curtis and ignored by their mother, and now she was loved by losers like Lincoln. *Wherever she's hiding, I have to find her before Janae does. I have to be the one who ends her life.*

"If she has nothing on you, what's with all the anger?" Lincoln raised one eyebrow.

"It's a long story. Actually, it's none of your business." Page brushed past Lincoln and made her way into the house.

He watched as she walked up the stairs and vanished into the darkness.

Oh, trust me, it is my business, he thought.

Lincoln hadn't been lying when he told Page that he had a thing for Renee. The love that Lincoln had for Renee was the love that Steve Urkel had for Laura. It was everlasting and entailed an ongoing friendship, whether Renee knew about it or not. The day that Renee vanished, Lincoln was actually heartbroken. Even though he had never been as close to her as she was to Julian and Slice, he appreciated that she had decent conversations and hung out with him whenever she saw fit. Being the friendless and lonely individual that he was, he was forever in Renee's debt because of the attention she had shown him.

Lincoln couldn't shake the eerie feeling in the pit of his stomach that something wasn't right with Page. Sure, there were sibling rivalries, but the evil look on Page's face when she had spoken about Renee revealed that she harbored more than everyday anger toward her sister. This was not a case of Renee having been spoiled more than Page or having taken Page's clothes without asking. Pure hate had been written all over Page's face and had echoed in her words.

Lincoln was determined to find out how deep Page's hate for her sister actually ran and, more importantly, if she would really kill Renee. When he gathered enough information against Page, he'd find Renee and hand it over to her. No one knew where Renee was, but Lincoln knew where to start. High school, a time when he had had no one, could have been a nightmare for Lincoln, but Renee's friendship had made it bearable for him. That alone had earned Renee his loyalty. He'd never known how to thank her. Now he did.

A sly smile spread across his face.

Thank God I don't believe in burning bridges, he thought as he walked back into the house.

Chapter 10

The twenty minutes Renee rode around New York City after leaving her mother's house felt like forever. Seeing her mother had reignited the fire that burned within her and then transformed it into an inferno. Her heart had told her to show Sheila no mercy and run her over, rip her soul from her body, just as she had done to her child. However, the pesky humane part within Renee, the part that had kept her mother alive all these years, the part she figured she'd inherited from her father, had told her that she should keep riding and that Sheila's time would soon come. Renee allowed the wind to navigate and lead her to a run-down, hole-in-the-wall bar in the Village.

Bottom-feeders were lounging in the establishment, pushing smoke out of their mouths and downing beers with shots. An old, rusty jukebox lit up in orange spewed out songs from the fifties, while white men with tattooed arms and in sleeveless shirts and Holly jeans tapped their feet to the beat, and white women dressed in miniskirts, with cigarettes planted between their fingers, leaned against the bar. The only African American in the joint, Renee stood out like a sore thumb.

This should be fun, she thought.

Renee took a seat on a worn stool, ignoring the cotton that stuck out of it from where the leather had been sliced into.

Behind the bar, a large freckle-faced, redheaded man in a Woodstock Festival T-shirt kicked back two shots, one in each hand, and then asked Renee, "What will it be?" He used the back of his hand to wipe his mouth.

"Give me three shots of tequila."

"All right."

"Hey, Frankie. How about you give me one of those?" At the end of the bar, a red-faced middle-aged man who looked overdue for a hearty meal sat slouched over, his finger pointing toward the full shot glasses.

"No can do, Pete."

"Why the hell not!" Pete slapped the bar. His outburst turned heads.

Frankie sat Renee's shots down in front of her. "No cash, no booze. So either pay up or shut the fuck up!" he told Pete.

"Come on, Frankie. I'm this close to blowing my own brains out over here. Throw me a bone," Pete pleaded.

"What did I tell you!" Frankie almost made it over to Pete, but Renee's offer stopped him.

"Come on, Frankie. Throw the man a bone. You don't want your pretty floors covered in blood. It's no good for business." Renee finished off the third shot. Frankie's mouth opened. He was about to speak, but Renee spoke first. "I'll buy it. I heard you. No cash, no booze!" Renee pulled money out of her pocket and waved it around.

"Now we're talking." Frankie threw his hands up and marched over to the glasses.

Pete slid off his seat. He was a short man, but he moved fast to the vacant seat beside Renee. "Thank you, pretty lady. You saved my ass. I meant it when I said I'd blow my brains out if I didn't get a break."

Frankie gave Pete his drink. The glass hadn't sat on the bar for two seconds before Pete downed its contents. Frankie shook his head, and Renee moved her finger in a circle motion, indicating another round for her and her new friend.

"Blow your brains out? Shit, why would you want to do such a thing, Pete?" Frankie asked.

"Because I need a break, damn it. I haven't had one in months. I'm jobless, my wife left me, I'm down to my last fifty dollars, and my landlord's on my back. Offing myself has got to be better than this," Pete mumbled.

"Suck it up, Pete." Frankie sat four shots down in front of them.

Pete sat up a little in his seat, his fist in the air. "You don't know what's it like! You have no fucking idea!"

"Yeah, yeah, yeah." Frankie brushed Pete off while he walked down to the other end of the bar.

Renee pushed a shot over to Pete, and he took his drink. "He doesn't know," Pete repeated. "He doesn't know."

"I hear you. I hear you," Renee told Pete.

Pete nudged Renee in the arm. "You see this." She looked down and saw the revolver tucked in his pants. "Every day I'm a day closer to ending it all."

Renee smiled. "Frankie! We need more shots over here!"

Pete covered up his gun with his shirt.

Renee caught his eye. "Hey, Pete, you wanna play a game?"

An hour later Renee, Pete, and a friend of his, Jim, sat in a corner of the bar, at a round table. The lights flickered on and off. Minutes before, Renee had suggested a game of Russian roulette to Pete. It was her way of calling his bluff and demanding proof that Pete really wanted to meet his Maker.

"You challenging me or something, little girl?" Pete had growled, drunker now than when he first met Renee, and she'd seen how angry a drunken Pete really was.

"More like calling your bluff. A lot of people talk about killing themselves, but they don't have the balls." Renee had laughed in his face, the shot before here now vodka, not tequila.

"You're *challenging* me. Let me call my buddy Jim. Motherfucker's having a rough time too. I'm sure he'd like to get in on this."

"The more the merrier," Renee had said, smiling.

As the three of them sat at the table now, Renee held the revolver in her hand. "Okay, gentlemen, here's a little reminder about how this works." She released the cylinder on the revolver and showed its one bullet. "As you see, there's one bullet inside. We're all going to take turns spinning the cylinder and putting the gun to our head. We'll pull the trigger, and whoever wins dies." She closed the cylinder.

"Let's go. I'm ready!" Jim banged his fist down on the table. He was shaking, and his dilated pupils suggested to Renee that he was on something.

"Then let's get this show on the road." Renee spun the cylinder.

"Fuck that! I want to go first. Give it here!" Jim leaned over the table, his arm stretched out and his fingers wiggling for the gun. Renee laid eyes on the track marks on his arm. "Give it here!" Jim snarled, spit flying out of his mouth.

"All right, all right. She's all yours." Renee handed over the gun.

"He's been waiting a long time for this. Just needed a push. You know what I mean?" Pete commented. He was all smiles, his yellow teeth exposed.

"Bring it on! Ahhh," Jim yelled. Then he placed the muzzle against his head. Eyes open, he allowed no room for hesitation and went straight for the kill, pulling the trigger.

Renee's breath caught in her chest. She didn't notice she wasn't breathing until the sound of an empty chamber caused her to let out air.

"Fuck! Here, Pete. Go! The faster you go, the faster it's my turn again," Jim yelled.

Pete took the gun. He stomped his feet while he spun the cylinder. "Goodbye, stress!" He pushed the gun against his head, and before pulling the trigger, he told Renee, "Thanks for the drinks, pretty lady."

"Hey, what the fuck are you all doing!" Frankie screamed. The big man ran out from behind the bar and was coming their way when Pete pulled the trigger. Frankie rammed into Pete, knocked him off his chair, and both of them crashed against the floor.

"Fuck! Fuck! Fuck!" Frankie hollered. He got up off of Pete and looked him over, his adrenaline pumping so much and voices screaming so loud in his mind that he was unsure whether he had heard a gunshot or not. Both Renee and Jim were on their feet.

Spread out on the floor, the gun inches from his hand, Pete whimpered, his eyes on the ceiling. "Damn it! I'm still alive! Please no! Tell me it's a dream!"

***

God had to be with Renee, because not only did she live to talk about the bar Frankie had kicked them all out of, but by some miracle, she also didn't kill herself in a motorcycle accident while driving intoxicated. The hefty amount of alcohol in her system was sure to slow down her reflexes and take away any common sense. It took her ten minutes to get home, and after she stumbled to the front door, she fumbled with the keys in the door locks.

Ain't this something? These motherfuckers refuse to go in the keyholes.

After finally getting her keys into their proper locks, Renee stumbled into her home and knocked over the expensive glass statue that stood on a stand beside the front door.

"Damn it! I spent five thousand dollars on that!" Renee screamed.

As soon as the words left her mouth, Slice and Jared came running into the foyer with their guns drawn, ready to shoot. Renee had always taught the two to kill first and ask questions later. Thank God that for once they didn't listen to her. They just stood there, their weapons trained on her. Renee's eyes widened. The liquor brought out the childish, fearless side of Renee. After she realized that she could have been killed on the spot, a smile spread across her face, and she started to jump up and down, waving her hands in the air.

"Yeah! Yeah! That's what the fuck I'm talking about. Run up in here, ready to bust off!" she yelled.

Slice and Jared exchanged looks and lowered their guns. Slice slowly walked over to Renee, careful not to step on any glass, while Jared stared at her. Although her eyes were glassy and she was staggering all over the place, her intoxication added to the beauty he'd already seen in her.

Slice took a moment to examine her face. "Renee, you drunk?"

Renee looked at Jared and laughed. "This mother-fucker isn't the brightest lightbulb in the lamp store, now is he?" She continued to laugh at her own comment as Slice looked over at Jared and slowly shook his head.

Slice grabbed Renee's wrist and helped her step over the mess that she'd made. Normally, Renee would not let anyone touch her, but under the circumstances, Slice knew that she wouldn't put up a fight. In his mind, the real Renee had temporarily stepped out of the building and was not all there.

His grip tightened a little on her wrist as they walked across the foyer. This was the dumbest thing Renee could have done. Riding around New York while under the influence could have landed her in serious trouble. A woman in her position could not screw up, not once. Any heat that came their way was bad heat. What if she had done something stupid and the cops had got her? What then? Their whole operation would've been blown, leaving everyone broke and imprisoned. Just thinking of the countless things that could have gone wrong made Slice's blood pressure rise. His first and only love was money, so just the thought of it slipping through his hands gave him a rash.

Slice led Renee to the staircase and then watched her walk up the stairs. He didn't like the way things were go-ing. Julian had disappeared, and Renee was now leading with her heart instead of her head, angry that her partner had abandoned her and had left her to fend for herself.

In all honesty, Slice couldn't care less about their soap-opera drama. He wanted this money, and he believed that Julian's and Renee's immature behavior was putting that in danger. Slice's fist started to ball up. Renee was a close friend, had been his best friend since high school, but this was business, and she was fucking with his money.

"Dumb bitch! Getting all brand new because that motherfucker bounced," Slice mumbled to himself, sure that no one could hear him.

"What did you just say?" Renee slowly walked back down the stairs, toward Slice.

Jared started to feel funny. He knew something was about to happen.

When she reached the last step, she pretended to trip and fell on the floor. She grabbed her ankle, as if in pain. When Slice bent down to help her up, within the blink of an eye, she grabbed his revolver from its holster and pressed it against his forehead.

His eyes blew up, and he stared Renee straight in the eyes. He didn't know what to think.

This liquor making her straight bug the fuck out, he thought.

This wasn't Slice's first time having a gun pointed at his head, but it was his first time having Renee's gun pointed at his head. Never in a million years had he thought Renee, his boss, his best friend, would pull a gun on him. Fear was something that he was unfamiliar with. He feared no one, but for the first time in his life, he understood how the people whose lives he'd ended had felt when he had his nine pointed at their head, showing no remorse. Fear crept up his spine. This foreign emotion settled in.

Little did Slice know that Renee had no best friend, and if she did, he went by the name of Julian. Slice cut his eyes over to Jared, who just stood there, with his eyes locked on the scene, his arms crossed.

"He's not going to help you," Renee said. "Unlike you, he knows when to keep his mouth shut."

"Sorry," Slice told her.

"*Sorry*? You getting soft on me now? I've never heard that word leave your mouth before."

"Renee, I—"

"Shut up! Your punk ass said enough. You ain't so bad when a gun's at your dome, now are you? You think I'm getting all brand new? I'll show you brand new, motherfucker!"

Renee was heated. Her complexion was turning red, and her eyes were bloodshot. Murder was on her mind, and she craved the taste of blood. This night wasn't supposed to go like this. For one night, she was supposed to go out, act irresponsibly, and try to forget about the hardships she was enduring. She was supposed to let loose. She wasn't supposed to come home and be reminded that Julian had abandoned her, forgotten about her, and pushed her to the side. Wasn't supposed to be reminded of the fact that it was her fault he'd left. No, it was supposed to be a memory, a fact no one spoke about.

"Get on your knees," Renee growled. Slice needed to be taught a lesson.

"What?"

"You heard what the fuck I said."

Never in his life had Slice felt so embarrassed and disrespected. Renee was stripping him of his manhood and demolishing his pride. If you wanted to get back at a man, you had to strip him of everything that he was and make him feel less of a man. Slice swallowed. He was not in a position to rebel, so he did the only thing he could when his life was on the line: he got down on his knees. Renee kept the revolver pressed against his forehead.

Renee looked Slice in the eyes, and he knew what time it was. He saw her finger preparing to pull the trigger.

Should have stayed in his lane and minded his business, Renee thought.

Damn it! I'm about to be laid out by this bitch, the only person I trusted, the only person I vowed to protect and be loyal to. Feelings will get you killed! Slice thought.

Slice closed his eyes. In his mind, he said a quick prayer that God would open up the gates of heaven for him.

Click!

When Slice heard the loud click and still felt the muzzle of his own revolver pressing against his head, he knew he was still alive. He opened his eyes and saw Renee smiling at him.

"Don't you love a game of Russian roulette?" Renee said.

Beads of sweat dropped from Slice's face, and he looked over at Jared, who was in the same position he was in earlier, just standing there watching, with his arms folded against his chest.

I can't believe he would stand there while she killed me, Slice thought.

Renee laughed, put the gun away, and made her way upstairs. It was scary. The first time she'd walked up those stairs on this night, she had stumbled and had barely kept her balance. Now she walked with confidence and perfect posture, as if she were someone else, as if she possessed multiple personalities.

"I think I speak for all of us when I say, 'Learn to shut the fuck up,'" she said as she took the last step. When she reached the top of the steps, she turned back around. "By the way, you're fired."

That was the last thing Renee said to Slice before she retired to her quarters.

When she was out of sight, Slice jumped to his feet and speed walked to the dining room, where he got his hat, and then he was out the door.

Renee watched Jared over the surveillance cameras. He was doing his normal rounds, which consisted of a check of every room except for her bedroom and making sure the outside of the house was safe and secure, with his twin guns, one on each side. Renee was in her bedroom, with her lips wrapped firmly around a Newport, gazing at the cameras. She wasn't big on smoking. In fact, she hadn't smoked in years. But after seeing her mother today and then being disrespected by one of her loyal workers, she needed the cancer stick to ease her nerves. To be completely honest, it wasn't working, not one bit.

Renee blew smoke into the air. She watched as the huge cloud of smoke vanished and became nothing but a figment of her imagination. Glancing at the clock, she saw it was almost time for Jared's shift to be over. Whenever he was about to leave, he'd knock on her bedroom door and make his exit known.

Renee pressed a button, and the monitors went back into their appropriate place and were replaced by her flat-screen. She opened the glass doors to her terrace, walked out onto it, and got rid of the cigarette. It was unusually chilly for a June night, and Renee loved it. Cold weather always reminded her of herself—cold to the point of numbness. Seconds later, there was a knock at her bedroom door.

"Jordan, I'm leav—"

Before Jared could finish his sentence, Renee opened the door, in nothing but a floor-length black silk robe, red bottoms, and shoes. The robe was completely open, exposing every nook and cranny. Jared's eyes roamed over her entire body. Her caramel skin glistened due the moisturizer she had applied not even twenty minutes ago, and her skin twinkled, too, due to the hint of glitter the moisturizer contained. All of Jared's blood rushed from his head to his groin. Her B cup breasts were round and perky. He even admired her French-manicured toes. He wanted to devour her whole.

In all the years he had worked for Renee, this was the first time he'd seen the inside of her bedroom. He gazed past her and gave the room a once-over. It was definitely fit for royalty. The huge terrace, the king-size bed, the paintings, and the imported furniture screamed money. Renee didn't speak. Instead, she beckoned him to follow with her hand, and then she strutted toward the terrace, the back of her robe blowing in the wind that came in through the open glass doors. She looked like she was walking in slow motion. Jared took in every move she made, and stored it in his memory bank.

Renee made her way out onto the terrace and over to the railing, then turned and faced Jared, who had just closed the terrace doors behind him. She dropped her robe and red bottoms and kept her shoes on. Renee only had eyes for Julian, so she hadn't noticed until now how truly attractive Jared was. His coffee-brown skin and powerful physique confirmed that he was indeed the perfect person for Renee to lose herself in and possibly forget about the events of the day. She needed an outlet, and Jared was indeed the best fit.

Temptation ate away at Jared; he was like a fiend craving crack. She stood there in nothing but her heels, inviting him to have his way with her. At that moment, nothing mattered but conquering her body. He stepped toward her and stood so close, their noses touched and he could smell the honey-flavored mint she held captive in her mouth. Jared grabbed her by the back of her neck, and Renee dove in, her full lips taking Jared's. She pushed the mint into his mouth, and he happily took it and swallowed it, wanting nothing to be in their way.

Drinking, a game of Russian roulette, and smoking hadn't helped Renee shake unpleasant memories, and the confrontation with Slice had only stressed her out more. The only thing left to try that could clear her mind was sex. She needed to drown herself in a night of pleasure. She needed to conquer Jared's body and have the sexual control over someone that her stepfather had taken away from her many years ago. She needed to know what it felt like to conquer new territory and to make her mark on it.

Renee knew he was in a relationship, but she didn't know with whom. At that moment, she didn't care who was in the picture. That night was about her, and no one was going to ruin it. She needed to feel better, and at that moment, Jared's body was hers, and she was going to control it any way she saw fit.

The two kissed passionately. Renee couldn't get over the fact that he kissed her so affectionately yet with such force. He picked her up and sat her on the railing; it was then that she noticed how tall Jared was. She was not a short female, yet sitting on top of the railing put her eye to eye with him. His height turned her on and made her juices flow. She glanced down at the street below, which appeared to be miles away.

I never knew how nice the view was from here, she thought.

Renee wrapped her legs around him, and he tried his best to fit her whole breast in his mouth. His tongue danced across her nipple. Like a rebel, Renee leaned her body back, going farther and farther over the railing. Jared had a good hold of her, one hand gripping her breast and the other holding on to her back. He caressed her breasts and introduced her to heaven. She sat up and took his shirt off, but that was the last thing Jared allowed her to do.

He lifted Renee, took her off the railing and, with her legs still wrapped securely around his waist, pinned her up against the glass doors. With one hand, Jared fiddled with his pants, and his boxers dropped around his ankles. Jared guided himself inside her tight walls and nearly collapsed when he was taken over by pleasure. She clung to his penis like stockings on a woman's leg.

Jared's legs shook slightly, but he quickly recovered and regained his composure. He took control by grabbed on to her body and forcing her to move the way he desired. Whenever Renee tried to take over, he instantly turned the tables and made it about him. It started to rain, but the two didn't budge. They remained connected to each other while the rain washed over them. It wasn't until lightning came into the picture that Jared let Renee's feet touch the terrace again, and the two walked into the bedroom hand in hand. They left the terrace doors wide open. The wind blew the drapes into the room, and the lightning, like a huge night-light, lit up the place.

The two were intimate with each other until the sun came up. Renee could honestly say that this was the best sex she'd ever had. She had had multiple orgasms, and in the way he had caressed her and devoured her, he had made her feel like her body was a piece of the art. She hadn't conquered his body and dominated him like she'd planned, but Renee couldn't deny the fact that he had done an impeccable job. He had erased her bad day had made her forget for many hours that she was miserable and her life was in shambles. For a brief time, she'd felt normal, and life had been good.

Chapter 11

Without even glancing over at Jared, Renee grabbed her robe and threw it on. Her manicured feet hit the waxed hardwood floor as she stood up from the bed. It took her a second to catch her balance and walk correctly. Jared had put a hurting on her, and all she could do was smile as she walked out of her bedroom, careful not to wake him. It was chilly in her home, and goose bumps rose on her skin. The house was pitch black, and this would have made a stranger move with caution. However, Renee moved with ease, allowing the darkness to swallow her whole and shield her. She walked into the kitchen, retrieved a glass from one of her marble cabinets, and then grabbed the cranberry juice from the fridge. She stood at the island and poured herself some juice.

Click!

"Talk that shit now," said a male voice.

Renee placed the container of juice on the counter and let Slice jam his gun against the side of her head.

"I love when a motherfucker pops off at the mouth, but when the shoe is on the other foot, she folds up like a bitch." Slice held on to his gun for dear life, ready to shoot.

Renee laughed. "I love when a bottom bitch thinks they're on top."

Slice grabbed Renee by the arm and forced her to face him. He wrapped his hand around her throat and pointed his gun smack-dab in the middle of her forehead. "You think this is a game?" he sneered. "I'll blow your fuckin' head off!"

Renee didn't respond and she didn't blink. This *was* a game, her game, and she never lost.

Slice continued to rant. "What, you think I can't break you?"

He looked into her eyes and saw nothing. Not fear, not rage, nothing.

He went on. "You always thought you were a dude, always thought you were king, with all your money and shit. But I'll show you who is king. I'll remind your ass that you're nothing but a bitch!" Slice spit as he spoke, rage seeping out of his pores.

It angered him that Renee wasn't begging for her life and that he couldn't read her. He wanted control, and she wasn't giving it to him. Slice released her neck and stepped back a little. "Now, you get on your knees. Bow down to the king."

Renee's eyes turned into slits.

"Get on your knees," he repeated. "I'll show you who's the man."

With one hand, Slice began to unbuckle his belt, but Renee didn't move. She'd die before she allowed another man to sexually assault her.

"I said, 'Get the fuck on your knees!'" Slice slapped Renee across the face with the gun, and she fell to her knees.

The moment her knees hit the tiles, Slice's pants dropped and his penis was in her face. With the gun pointed at her, he took his free hand and grabbed Renee by her hair and forced her toward his crotch. He gritted his teeth, anticipating the pleasure. There were nights when he had heard Renee with Julian, and he knew her sex game was tight.

"Suck it, bitch."

Renee opened her mouth, preparing to bite his dick off and spit it at him, but before teeth could meet flesh, Slice's body dropped.

Renee looked up and saw Jared standing in the doorway. He held a smoking gun in his hand, with the silencer on. Renee stood. Slice lay dead at her feet, half of his head blown off.

For a moment no one spoke. Then Renee grabbed her glass of cranberry juice and headed out of the kitchen.

"What are you going to do about this?" Jared yelled at her back.

Renee stopped and looked back at him.

"If the respect is lost in here, then it's lost out there," Jared told her, gesturing toward the window with his head.

Renee licked her lips; the sweat from her top lip left her with a salty aftertaste. "Then I come out of hibernation."

Renee put her drink down on the kitchen counter and walked back over to Slice's body. She bent down and saw that pieces of his head were oozing onto the floor. "I'll be sure to make my first appearance at your funeral, so that I can spit on your grave." Renee turned Slice's head so that his remaining eyeball looked at her. "Fuck you, King. All hail the queen."

Later that morning, out on her terrace, Renee smoked three cigarettes within a matter of ten minutes and im-

bibed two glasses of vodka. Her nerves were right back
where they'd been before, and the fury inside of her
would not rest. Her leg shook, and from time to time,
her eye twitched.

Don't think about it. Don't think about it.

She inhaled deeply and trapped the smoke inside her
lungs for as long as she could before releasing it. Her
eyes, which felt heavy, begged her to rest. However, the
fear of seeing her past alive and in color kept her awake.
The cloud of smoke she'd just blown out was almost
invisible when she flicked the cigarette butt over the
railing and watched it fall to its death. She drank the last
of her liquor from the short, fat glass and then threw it
overboard as well.

Let it go. Let it go! she told herself repeatedly, but she
couldn't. The similarities were too strong, the memory
too dark, and the pain too deep to ignore. She could no
longer ignore the first time someone had failed when
trying to rape her. Her mind was forcing her to relive it.

"I gotta piss," Renee announced.

"Me too," Julian responded.

*Julian and Renee looked in the direction of the park's
bathrooms and saw the signs in red capital letters on
both the men's and the women's bathroom doors. They
read* CLOSED.

*"Damn. Even the women's bathroom is closed." Renee
swayed to the side and tried not to focus on her insistent
bladder.*

*Julian sucked his teeth. "I knew we shouldn't have had
that second Slurpee." He continued to look around until
he was staring at a quiet area filled with trees. "I'll be
back." He took a few steps away from Renee before she
pulled him back.*

"No! If I can't go to the bathroom, you can't go," she whispered. *"You're just ready to whip it out, aren't you?"*

Julian smirked. *"Don't blame me for being a man."*

Renee rolled her eyes. *"Let's go to the school. Summer classes are still going on, so it's open."*

"They're not going to let us in. We're not in summer school."

"Banks is on duty," Renee reminded him.

A wide grin jumped across Julian's face. *"Why didn't you say that to begin with? You're about to let me piss in the bushes and shit."* He laughed at his sense of humor. However, the silent treatment Renee gave him and her lips curling into a frown were reason enough for him to grow serious.

The instant Renee stepped foot back inside her high school, she was grateful for her straight As, which allowed her to enjoyed her summer break. Staring out a classroom window and listening to her classmates enjoy the nice weather was not her idea of summer. The front door closed behind Renee and Julian just as they approached the security desk.

Dressed in a light blue short-sleeved shirt and dark blue pants, Mr. Banks had his undivided attention on a small portable TV, which the two were sure he wasn't allowed to watch while on duty. Julian slammed his hands down on the desk and watched as their favorite guard jumped in his seat.

"I was watching the news!" he shouted without looking up. He cut the TV off and slid it inside the drawer. He was on his feet and straightening out his uniform when he finally made eye contact with both students.

"You know good and damn well that you weren't watching the news," Julian teased. His finger was

pointed at Mr. Banks, and on cue both he and Renee laughed.

"Lower your damn voices. Now, what the hell are you two doing here? You're not enrolled in summer school." Mr. Banks spoke in a hushed tone, but he made sure he added enough bass to his voice to remind the teenagers of his position of authority.

"Can we use the bathroom, Mr. Banks? The park's bathrooms are closed, and I don't think I can make it home." Renee spoke as politely as possible.

"Now, you know I can't let you past this desk," he told Renee. Then he turned to Julian. *"And unless you got to take a shit, I suggest you go find a tree and handle your business."* Mr. Banks plopped down in his seat, grabbed the white washcloth on his desk, and dabbed at the sweat sprinkled on his forehead. He scratched his head. *"Time to take these cornrows out,"* he said to no one in particular.

"Come on, Mr. Banks. We'll be real quick," Renee pleaded.

Mr. Banks ignored her and took his mini television out of the drawer.

"You owe me, B," Julian said.

Mr. Banks leaned back as much as the chair allowed and threw his thumb in the air. It pointed to the hall beyond. *"Be quick and don't get caught."*

As she and Julian rushed down the hall to the closest staircase, Renee heard Mr. Banks mumble, *"Motherfucker's too smart for his own good."*

"Why does he owe you?" she asked.

Julian held the stairwell door open for Renee. Together, they jogged up the steps. *"I caught him selling weed to a junior. I said I'd keep my mouth shut, but he'd be in my debt. Plus, he'd have to pay me two hundred dollars."*

They reached the second floor, and right before Julian stepped into the hallway, he heard his name being called.

"Yo, Julian!"

Julian leaned over the staircase railing and looked down. On the bottom landing, Hendrick Curry, a sophomore who had returned from boot camp a few months ago, stood smiling.

"Drick, is that you?" Julian called.

"Yez, sir!"

Julian flew down the stairs, and when he reached the bottom landing, both teens pounded their fists together.

Just then Renee's bladder sent her a warning that if she didn't get to a restroom, she would pee on herself right there. "Julian, I gotta go!" she called over the railing.

As if he had forgotten all about nature calling, he looked up at Renee and waved her off. "Go. I'll be right behind you."

Renee had no time to give him an attitude. All her attention was placed on making it to the bathroom while she still had control of herself. She turned the corner and was relieved to see that summer school wasn't run like the regular school session. If it were, no classrooms on this floor would be empty and the school would have a woman stationed at the girls' bathroom door, collecting IDs and assuring that the girls were in and out of the stalls in an orderly fashion. Renee ran inside the bathroom and breathed a sigh of relief when she finally got to go.

"I didn't think I was going to make it," she said aloud to herself.

In the middle of relieving herself, she heard the bathroom door open, then close. Soft footsteps walked past

*her stall. After ripping off pieces of tissue, Renee cleaned
herself up, left the stall, and headed for the sink. She
jumped a little when she saw the boy they all called
Psych leaning on the windowsill.*

"What are you doing in here?"

"What are you talking about? What are you *doing in
here?" Psych shot back.*

"I'm using the girls' *bathroom," Renee answered,
emphasizing the word* girls.

"No, you must be mistaken. This is the boys' bathroom."

*There were dozens of rumors about how Psych had
got his nickname. According to one, he had once been
committed to a mental institution. Others said that he
was bipolar and would change moods on you in a second,
and that this had earned him the nickname. However, the
most popular assumption was that he was a hotheaded
eighteen-year-old who had been accused of rape and
found guilty, and for this crime, someone had dubbed him
Psych. No one knew which rumor was true. Psych had no
friends and kept to himself. However, when you were six
feet tall and close to three hundred pounds, it was hard
for people to ignore you.*

*"Wait a minute. I know what you want." He stepped
closer to Renee. Only a small space remained between
them now, and when he smiled, Renee could clearly see
his chipped tooth.*

*Renee backed up, but he quickly closed in on her.
Renee flung open one of the stall doors. The door knocked
Psych in the forehead, and Renee took off. Her hand was
reaching for the doorknob when she felt a hand grab her
by the back of the neck. Psych threw her down on the
floor.*

*As she crashed against the floor, Renee screamed.
Psych straddled her and held her down the by neck. With*

his free hand, he pushed Renee's skirt up and snatched her underwear off. He tossed the cotton material to the side.

"I know why you're here," he growled. "I know exactly why you're here."

"Get off of me! Get off of me!" Renee kicked Psych and clawed at his arm, all to no avail, because he never flinched. The blood that oozed from his arm had no effect on him. He was enraged, like a battered soul high off drugs. There was just so much moving Renee could do under his solid frame, but that didn't stop her from trying. And when she tired herself out, she clamped her legs shut.

Not again. This can't be happening, *she thought.*

Without warning, Psych stood up and pulled Renee onto her knees. He wrapped her hair one time around his hand, and with the other hand, he dropped his pants, followed by his boxers. He shoved Renee's face in his crotch.

"Suck it, bitch."

Renee clasped her mouth shut. Her jaw was tight, and her lips were sealed.

Psych put his face close to hers. "I said suck it!" Psych pushed himself farther into Renee's face.

She opened her mouth and threw up on him, spraying him with a mixture of liquid and clumps of that morning's breakfast.

"What the fuck!" He shoved Renee away. His first reaction was to get the vomit off of him.

"Help! Help me!" Renee shouted.

She scurried past Psych as he was cleaning off his shirt with a paper towel. He attempted to run after her, but he became wrapped up in the pants around his ankles and lost his footing. He fell forward. Renee's body was halfway out the bathroom door, but Psych was able to grab her foot and pull her back inside. Again, she cried out in pain when she hit the floor. The loud thump resembled a low-level earthquake. He dragged her farther inside the bathroom.

"The last one didn't get away. There's no way you are," Psych snarled as he climbed back on top of her.

Psych was tugging at the bottom of her shirt at the very moment Julian barged into the bathroom. He took in the sight of a half-naked Psych pressed against Renee and caught a glimpse of her panties on the floor. Julian pulled his right leg back, and with all the power he could muster, he brought it forward and kicked Psych under his chin. Psych's head cocked back, and he flew backward. He hit his head when he landed a few feet away, and was knocked unconscious. Julian stepped in front of Psych, his hands balled into fists.

Seconds later Mr. Banks stepped inside the bathroom. "What the hell is taking y'all so long?"

Julian was towering over Psych, and Renee was sitting in the same spot, her arms wrapped around her bent legs.

"What the fuck happened in here?" Mr. Banks scratched his head, his mouth open.

"This bitch ass—" Julian began, but Renee cut him short.

Renee knew what it looked like, knew what Julian thought. And she had to correct him. She had to let him know that she hadn't been violated again. "He tried. He tried to rape me, but Julian stopped him."

Mr. Banks examined an unconscious Psych. "I knew that piece of shit was a rapist." He shook his head after noticing the underwear on the floor and the tears glistening on Renee's cheeks. "Get out of here, you two."

"Nope. You get out of here, and take Renee. I'm not done with him."

"Leave, Julian! I got this!"

Julian got in Mr. Banks's face. "What the fuck are you going to do?"

Mr. Banks pulled a partially smoked blunt out of his pocket and tossed it a few feet from Psych, then took a baggie with half a pound of weed out of his pocket and placed it inside one the pockets of Psych's pants, which were around his feet.

"I seen Mr. Phillips on the cameras walk inside the girls' bathroom. By the time I made it up here, I found him smoking weed. Once caught, he became irate and attacked me, so I knocked him on his ass. It was self-defense."

"What about cameras in here?" Julian questioned.

"There are no cameras in the bathrooms, and the rest of the cameras in this school are shitty. For the past week, they've been erasing footage simultaneously. By the time you're out of this building, I'm sure there will be nothing to show for the past hour. Now leave."

Julian ran over their alibi once in his head. "I owe you."

The memory of this event was as detailed as if it had transpired yesterday. Renee had repressed this nightmare for so long, she had forgotten that years after her almost rape, Psych was murdered, and Mr. Banks retired early and moved to LA, where he bought his own beach house. She had asked no questions about their fate. She had just buried their existence deep inside. Renee left the terrace doors open, got back in an empty bed, wrapped herself in her blanket, and forced herself to think of anything but her life.

Chapter 12

Jared was at war with his emotions. Sex with Renee had given him a high he had never before experienced, and he wanted it to go on forever, but witnessing her nearly being sexually assaulted had ruined any inkling of happiness they had enjoyed just moments before. Once back in her bedroom, Jared had tried to initiate a hug and a kiss, the only way, other than murder, he could come up with to show his support. However, Renee had gone back into her shell and had denied him of any sort of skin-to-skin contact. The minute she was back inside her bedroom, she had rattled off strict instructions on how she wanted Slice's body handled, then had retreated to her terrace.

Jared had wanted to cover Renee with his body and make her forget all that transpired and tugged on her soul. Yet he had pushed away the urge to lose himself inside her once more, and instead he'd made the necessary calls, one of which to Lyfe. Jared's desire in life was to stay at Renee's side all day and then spend the night with her in her bed, with her in his arms. But Lyfe appeared at the house like a bat out of hell, his aggression and protective nature on ten, so Jared crowding Renee didn't seem like the answer, no matter how much he wanted to pin her against the terrace railing and have round two.

An early morning drink was not ideal. However, it was the perfect way for Jared to celebrate the accomplishment of bedding the woman his heart belonged, while also giving her some space. Around ten o'clock, Jared headed out to a bar he backed financially. In preparation for opening, the bar's floor was being mopped, tables were being wiped down, and chairs were being taken down off the tables. Strolling over to his favorite table, located at the far end of the bar, Jared received constant greetings from the workers. He took a seat and basked in the solitude. Nobody gave him a menu. Instead, one of the employees immediately came over with a tray holding two shots and one beer and placed the drinks in front of him. Jared took a shot, then moved on to a take sip of his beer. When the drinks were finished, the bar's new bartender cleared the table and then placed more drinks on it.

"Take a break and have a drink with me." Jared gestured to the chair across from him. Jared was a loner, but that morning he was feeling social.

"Thanks, boss man, but I'm on the clock. Roy would have my ass."

"If you want to get technical, I'm Roy's boss, and I run this shit, so sit your ass down, Gomez."

Hesitant but appreciative of a break after coming to the bar straight after his second job, Gomez took a load off and welcomed the relief given to his feet. Jared slid a shot over to him and held his in the air. The older gentleman followed suit.

"To great sex!" Jared's voice danced from the bar to the dance floor, a hard chuckle not far behind.

"Oh, so that's what this is." Gomez kicked back the brown liquid. "I remember those days, but I don't miss those days."

"What are you talking about?" Jared moved on to his beer.

At that moment the bar manager began doing a walk-through, the loud sound of kitten heels announcing her arrival before she physically made her presence known to Jared. When she did appear at the end of the bar, her Botox-filled face strained to smile at Jared.

"Dena, bring over some shots and join us!"

"This early?" Dena meant for her eyebrows to rise, but nothing happened. Dena might have been unable to move her face, but she was sure it was just about to happen after she saw the look Jared gave her.

Changing her tune, she rushed to fetch the drinks. "You got it!"

Before all the shots were placed on the table, Jared scooped one up and emptied the glass. He had a dire need to celebrate, and to forget what Slice could have done to Renee.

Gomez and Dena, who sat down at the table, did not touch a shot.

"Gomez, what, are you gay or something?" Tipsy, Jared slid another shot over to Gomez. Then he slammed one down in front of Dena, his eyes telling her, "Drink."

Both employees did what was expected of them.

Gomez shook his head. "Nope. It's just that the best sex I ever had was with the woman who screwed me over. After a while, not even the sex could keep me around."

Jared glided another shot over to his manager. "What she do?"

"She didn't love me. I loved her, but she didn't love me. Turned out the reason she even dealt with me was for the sex. Eventually, she stopped dealing with me altogether and got back with this dude she was on and off with."

Reliving the events responsible for leaving him a lonely old man, with no woman or kids, Gomez took another shot.

"You, my friend, are what we call a booty call." Dena laughed behind her comment and took the last shot. She rubbed the back of her neck and batted her false eyelashes at Jared.

You have to be kidding me. This uptight broad is a lightweight? Jared thought.

"That's exactly what I was. I loved that girl with everything I had. Never had a relationship sense."

Jared observed the graying man and saw in his eyes when he spoke about his ex the same type of love he felt for Renee. "I'm sorry to hear that."

"Yeah, me too," Gomez replied. "I just hope your woman is in it for the right reasons, young blood."

"Without a doubt."

"You sure about that?" Dena asked. Neither man noticed she had left the table and had returned with three more shots of vodka. She hadn't bother to sit back down. She stood there and downed one of the shots.

"I'm positive," Jared slurred.

Gomez held his glass high for a solo toast. "Then, to great sex!" The older man got up and swayed to the right a little.

"You okay, old man?" Jared said, still slurring.

"I'm better than okay, young blood!" Gomez said. He had a little pep in his step as he left the table.

Once she was alone with Jared, Dena leaned her elbows on the table, placing her cleavage in Jared's face. "Let's go in the back real quick. I bet I can make you forget all about her." Dena tried smiling, but it looked more like a frown.

Jared's phone went off a second later, interrupting the conversation, and he looked down and saw a picture of Janae on the screen. He pressed IGNORE.

"That's her?" Dena licked her lips.

"No." Jared finished his beer and his last shot. He got up, and as he walked by Dena, he told her, "Get back to work."

Jared wasn't heading home just yet. He now had the need to celebrate elsewhere, but he just didn't know where.

Jared opened his eyes, and Janae was staring right at him. Seeing her eyeballs so close to his face made Jared jump back, and he almost fell off the bed.

"What the hell? What are you doing?" he muttered.

"Where were you last night? Coming home after the sun rises isn't cool. Who is she, Jared?"

Jared sat up while shaking his head. Every day that passed reminded him how much this relationship wasn't working. If he came home ten minutes late, he was cheating. If he had to go into work on his day off or had to work longer than usual, he was cheating. Janae wasn't the woman he'd met. She had transformed into this needy, overprotective monster. She was suffocating him. When he met her, he'd thought she was the one, but now he saw that she wasn't. After spending the night before with Renee, he'd realized that *she* was the one.

"Don't start, Janae. You know where I was."

"Yeah, that's what you always say, but I know there's more to it than you're letting on. Just be honest, Jared. Be a man about it."

With his back turned to her, Jared got out of bed and started laughing. When he stood up, Janae saw her sister, Leslie, standing behind him, with her arms crossed, shaking her head at her. Jared couldn't control his laughter. Janae truly thought that by telling him to be a man, he would oblige and tell her anything she wanted to know, just to prove that he was an adult. He knew better than that. He stared at her and thought of all the mean things he could say to her, just to hurt her feelings.

He thought about coming clean and telling her everything. *I don't do maintenance at an office building, and I don't have parents who feed me with a silver spoon. The truth is, I work for a rich, powerful woman who pushes coke, and guess what? I'm madly in love with her, and last night I slept with her, and it was the best sex I've ever had.* Jared laughed harder, picturing the look on Janae's face if he actually said that to her. Once he turned around to face her, he thought against it. *She's not even worth it.* Jared shook his head one last time and walked to the bathroom.

As soon as he turned to walk away, Leslie suddenly vanished. Janae placed her hands on her face for a brief second. She shook her head and quickly bounced up off the bed. She knew Jared was preparing for one of his disappearing acts, and this time she wasn't having it.

"Oh, no, no, no. Don't leave."

Jared turned to see what nonsense Janae was talking now. She was out of bed, completely dressed, and was now bending down and putting her sneakers on. After she finished, she walked over to the closet and pulled out her oversize Puma duffel bag.

"I'm the one who's leaving," she announced. She started packing, stuffing her bag with shirts, pants, bras, and panties. She didn't bother folding anything. She was a woman on a mission.

Jared shook his head, a faint smile across his face. "What are you doing?"

"I'm leaving. There's some things I have to take care of. I'll be back soon, and when I do get back, I expect the ho you have on the side to be gone."

After placing one more outfit in her bag, she looked at Jared and saw Leslie standing behind him, clapping her hands. Her ever so memorable smile decorated her face. Ever since Janae had gotten involved with Jared, she'd completely ignored a major responsibility, which was to avenge her sister's death. She had told herself that moving with Jared to Brooklyn was a great move, because that was where Renee had taken Leslie's life and where Renee's family still resided. She knew it was only a matter of time until Renee returned home, and if she didn't, her family would pay for her absence.

The more Janae had fallen for Jared, the more she'd forgotten about finding Renee. Eventually, the hunt for Renee had come to a complete halt, and she'd started concentrating on Jared's whereabouts. She had become obsessed with why he was always coming home late, and she wanted to know why his infatuation with her had decreased drastically. Jared was a distraction. Janae truly believed that if the relationship had been going fine, she would have continued to ignore her mission to find Renee, just because she would have remained on cloud nine. That was a major problem.

After putting off her hunt for Renee, Janae had started to see Leslie. Every time she appeared, Leslie was not happy. She'd show up when Janae least expected it. The first time she saw her, Janae was in the shower, crying over Jared. When she stepped out, Leslie was standing there, with her arms tightly folded across her chest, eyes lowered. Janae screamed and immediately stepped back, then fell back into the tub. Then there was the time Janae stayed up waiting for Jared to come home, juggling ideas on how she could find and get rid of his mistress. While she was lost in thought, she looked up at the bedroom doorway and saw Leslie standing there, giving her an icy look while shaking her head in disappointment.

After constantly seeing her sister, Janae realized the cause of her appearances. Whenever she was preoccupied with Jared, and thus neglecting the search for Leslie's killer, her sister would appear to remind Janae what she had to do. Finally, Janae got the hint and stopped being scared whenever she saw her sister. The previous night, it hit her how she had been neglecting her sister for Jared, and it broke her heart. She lay there for hours on end, deciding that the best thing to do would be to leave for a while and find Renee. Afterward, she'd come back to Jared and give him 100 percent of herself, since she would not have to devote any more time and energy to her sister.

All Janae had was Jared. She had no one else. And she'd be damned if some girl took him away from her. That was why she had come to the conclusion that after she got rid of Renee, she'd find Jared's mistress and get rid of her too. When she told Jared she was leaving to take care of business, it was the first time she'd seen Leslie smile. Janae had a feeling it'd be the last time she saw Leslie. Seeing her sister smile made Janae smile, something she hadn't really done in months.

"Do me a favor. Come back by midnight," Jared told her.

Janae didn't look up at Jared. She just continued to pack, throwing additional items in the bag. "No can do. I'll be back as soon as I take care of things."

"No, I don't mean that," Jared said in a cold tone. "Is that bag all you're taking?"

Janae still didn't look up. "Yes. I don't need to take every little thing when I'll be back."

"Come back by midnight," he repeated.

Janae's face tightened, her top lip twitched, and then she rolled both lips into her mouth so Jared wouldn't see. "I told you, Jared, I can't. I'll be back when I can." She heaved the large duffel bag over her shoulder and walked toward the door.

"If you want your stuff, you'll come back tonight."

Janae stopped, her back facing him. "What are you talking about?"

Jared walked over to her. She could feel his breath on her neck. "I want you out," he whispered in her ear. His breath was cold, and his voice chilling. "Your things will be on their way to Goodwill if you're not back by midnight. Your choice."

Janae's blood boiled. *This girl really has turned him against me.*

She nodded. "Okay," she said. "I'll return for my things, but know this isn't over. After I take care of what I need to, I'll take care of your slut. Then, once that's over with, I'm coming back here, and we will be together." Janae never faced Jared the entire time she spoke.

She would never admit it, but having Jared break up with her would destroy her. She refused to accept that they were over.

Just like I'll take care of Renee, I'll take care of her.

When all was said and done, Janae left, and the hunt began.

Chapter 13

Last night the liquor had got the best of Waves. He'd got so drunk that one of Renee's street soldiers had had to drive him to his mother's house in Brooklyn. He lived in Staten Island, but at the time, he hadn't been able to remember his address and had been able to recite only his mother's, so Mommy's house was where he'd gone.

The next morning, he woke up and plopped himself down on the floor in front of his mother's sixty-inch flat-screen, which he had bought for her living room, and played his sister's PlayStation 4. Even though he was suffering from nausea and a headache, he was still in a good mood because of the money he knew he would be coming into. Jared had told him that if he did everything he was told correctly, there would be a bonus in it for him.

He smiled while pressing various buttons to release a fireball in the *Street Fighter* game. As soon as You Win! flashed on the screen, a high yellow, red-haired female who was younger than Waves walked into the room and sat on the couch. Her eyes were puffy, and her skin appeared to be clammy.

Waves glanced at her, then quickly turned his attention back to the game and laughed. "I got the same sickness," he told her.

She looked at him, confused, with one eyebrow raised.

"You know what I'm talking about. The bug going around that causes you to throw up, have headaches, and that makes the whole room spin."

"What are you talking about?" the girl asked, her frustration apparent in her voice. She now had a hand on her forehead. "What bug?"

"You know, the one people get after they're unable to say no to their third, fourth, and fifth drink."

He took his attention off the television and turned to smile at her. She gave him a nasty look, picked a small jar of Vaseline up off the coffee table, and threw it at him. He blocked the jar, then turned his attention back to the game and pressed a combination of buttons so loudly that it was hard to ignore.

"Where's Mommy?" Waves had been looking forward to seeing his mother, so when he woke up and noticed she wasn't there, he was a little disappointed.

"At work."

"On a Saturday?"

"Yeah. She's taking next week off. She wanted to take care of her workload, so that when she returns, she'll be ahead and not behind."

"Mommy is always thinking ahead."

Waves started to think about his mother, Tina. He remembered when she and his father divorced and the day she moved to New York, leaving him with his father down South. It had torn her apart to have to leave her son, but she'd known that it would be better for him if he grew up with his father.

Tina had had to find herself; she hadn't been ready to settle down and be a mother and wife. Sadly, like many women, she had realized this after the fact. Being tied down hadn't been for her; she hadn't wanted to resent her child or husband. That was something she couldn't bear, so she'd filed for divorce and handed over custody of Waves. She'd left as soon as possible, hoping that one day she'd return.

Years later, things started to improve. She landed an advertising job in New York and quickly rose to the top. She then fell in love, got remarried, and was soon pregnant with Waves's sister, Tina, whom she named after herself. Tina Sr. had made a huge change. She'd gone from being a free-spirited woman whom no one could tame to a well-established businesswoman. There were days when Tina felt guilty about never returning to Waves and his father. She truly loved both of them and hadn't expected to fall in love and start a whole new life, but things happened.

She had made sure when she left that she let Waves know he still had a mother. Once she created a whole new family, she worked ten times harder to show him he had not been forgotten or replaced. Because of her hard work, Waves had never felt like he sat in coach. He knew he was in first class with the rest of her loved ones.

The only thing wrong with this picture-perfect family was Tina Jr. She partied a lot, gossiped to no end, and was 100 percent selfish. She was the black sheep of the family, the black sheep that no one knew existed. Dying her hair red should have been a sign, but people shrugged it off as being the new trend.

Holding her stomach now, Tina wished she hadn't drunk so much at the bar she went to the night before. She remembered having her head in the toilet, promising herself to never drink like that again. A smile crept across her face. While they had a hangover, everyone said they'd never get drunk again.

"When did you get here?" Tina asked her brother. "You weren't here when I got in, and I got in around five thirty in the morning. So you must have stumbled in after six."

Waves turned off *Street Fighter* and put in a racing game. "I got in at around four. You must not have noticed me. Speaking of getting in late, you need to calm down. I can look past you dyeing your hair, but you partying so much is getting out of hand."

Tina rolled her eyes. "I don't party a lot. You and Mommy act like I do it every night."

"You do. Listen, I know dudes who frequent bars and clubs. Every time I see them, they mention seeing you. I'm not Mommy, so don't try to front."

Tina smiled. Her brother's back was facing her when he spoke, so she took advantage of it and smiled like a kid on Christmas morning. She knew that she partied almost every night and that it was out of hand, but she liked it. As long as she liked it, she was going to continue. She remained quiet. There was no way she'd be able to beat her brother in an argument, so she immediately threw up the white flag.

"That's what I thought," Waves commented.

"Anyway, what brings you here?"

Waves took a minute to respond. His sister's partying really bothered him. He loved her more than he loved himself, and he was afraid of the life she was leading. Waves didn't believe that a respectable woman stayed out all night partying. He wanted her to calm down and live a decent life.

He took a deep breath and erased his thoughts. "I got drunk last night and forgot my address, so a friend of mine dropped me off here. It's funny, I couldn't remember the place I go to every day, but I could remember the address to the place I come to almost every other week."

"You know what they say. Home is where the heart is."

Tina propped her feet on the couch, closed her eyes, and stretched her body out. When she opened her eyes, they immediately landed on Waves's diamond Rolex, which he had bought right after he got his promotion.

"Warren, that photography job must be really treating you well," Tina said to Waves, referring to him by his government name.

Waves quickly glanced over at Tina and saw her looking down. He followed her gaze to his Rolex. Nervously, he fiddled with it in an attempt to hide it. Realizing he was caught, he stopped fiddling. Waves didn't like lying to family, but working for Renee required him to do exactly that.

Since childhood, photography had been his passion. When he moved to New York to work for Renee, he'd told his family it was because he had landed a job as a photographer for *Vibe* magazine. The more his family mentioned the job and expressed their happiness for him, the more depressed he felt. Hearing his sister ask once again about "the job" was like the straw that broke the camel's back.

She won't tell, he thought.

"I'm not a photographer." Waves never took his eyes off the game. Instead, he constantly crashed his sports car into trees and other cars. It was unbelievable that he hadn't died already.

Tina's right eyebrow rose. "So, what? You got fired or something?"

"You have to work in order to get fired."

Tina sat up and leaned forward. She didn't know what her brother was talking about, but she wanted to find out. "What are you saying?"

Waves sighed and turned off the game. He stretched out his arms and leaned back against the glass coffee table without looking at his sister. "I was never in the photography game. I work, but it's not what you think. I work for someone very wealthy and powerful." As soon as the sentences left his mouth, Waves regretted them, but it made no sense to shut up now. "I know you've heard of Jordan."

"Of course. Dude runs New York."

"Jordan's not who you think. Everyone thinks he's a dude, but it's all a lie just to hide her identity. Why, I have no idea. If I was wiping my ass with hundred-dollar bills and had everyone's heart full of fear in the streets, I would want everyone to know my name."

Tina's mind was blown. Right before her eyes, she saw dollar signs appear. She knew people who would pay top dollar for this information. So much dough would rain down on her that she would be able to get a Rolex, just like her brother. Tina was on the edge of the couch, Waves's back still facing her. She had a feeling that the information wouldn't stop there, that it would only got better.

Waves knew that if it ever got back to Renee that he'd revealed her identity, she'd kill him. But he trusted his sister and thought, If he couldn't tell her, who could he tell?

"So who is he, I mean, she?"

"Tina." Waves stood up and faced her. "Before I tell you, you have to understand that by me telling you as much as I already have, I'm putting my life on the line. If she finds out that I told you anything, she'll kill me."

Tina searched her brother's eyes to see if what he was telling her was the truth. Sure enough, the truth filled every part of his eyeballs.

"Tina, do you understand? What is said here stays here." Waves gave his sister a stern look.

"I understand."

He took a deep breath and sat back down on the floor. "She's this chick by the name of Renee. This woman is untouchable."

Tina's eyes bugged, out and her mouth nearly dropped. *It can't be.* Tina scrambled for words. "Renee?"

"Yeah. Chick's a monster. Her heart beats venom. What makes it worse is that she got a partner by the name of Julian, who's just as deadly. Both of them motherfuckers residing in Manhattan has to be a curse. Their asses shouldn't even be in New York."

"Where in Manhattan?" The question just rolled off her tongue, and she quickly bit down on it, hoping Waves wouldn't notice her anxiety.

"Over on Fifth Avenue, near Central Park."

Tina smiled, happiness taking her over. "Damn. She living like that?"

"Yup, her ass is literally living in the sky."

"Wow," Tina mouthed.

Ain't that a bitch? Her ass has been right under everyone's nose this entire time, running shit like it's nothing, she thought. Today was the first time that Tina was happy her brother hadn't grown up with her. He was completely unaware of Renee's past. He knew nothing about Renee being a suspect in Leslie's murder and disappearing some time later. It was incredible how everything had worked itself out.

Tina sat back and thought about all the things she could do with the money Page would give her. She knew this would be her ultimate payoff. For years, Page had asked her if she'd heard anything pertaining to her sister's whereabouts, and Tina finally had.

While she was deep in thought, Waves told her he was on his way out.

"Remember, Tina, tell no one."

She nodded and watched as her brother walked out of the living room and out of her sight. For an instant, she felt bad, but that feeling quickly subsided.

Sorry, bro, but little sister gotta eat too.

Chapter 14

Julian dropped his luggage in the foyer of his home and looked around. Everything was exactly how he had left it—quiet, pristine, and without a trace of a living being. He couldn't help but feel disappointed. He had hoped that when he opened the front door, he would discover that his house had been trashed and rendered unrecognizable. Hoped that Renee had gone all out and had had a search party tear up New York in search of him. Julian wanted no rock to have been left unturned and for her to have moved mountains, all so they could be reunited. As usual, there was no evidence of the type of love Julian was seeking. Julian had disappeared for the well-being of Renee, but in the back of his mind, he had secretly wished his absence would make her heart grow fonder and would turn their love into a priority.

Expecting Renee to express love the healthy, normal way was like asking a hard apple to transform itself into a soft-centered orange. Julian had wished to find Renee curled up on his couch, raccoon eyed, snot running down her nose, worried to death over his disappearance. What Julian wanted was for Renee to give her all for him. The person Julian fell in love with had vanished a long time ago. Her fucked-up, soul-crushing family had demolished all the positivity and love Renee once offered, leaving him to love the ice queen herself.

He needed Renee to move past the pain and enter into an official relationship with him. The "friends with benefits" bullshit had got old. He needed back the person he knew she could be; he needed a partner. He wanted Renee to step out of her darkness. Revisiting all that Renee was denying him made the veins in his neck bulge and his jaw lock. The ache within his heart was radiating throughout his body, and he felt out of his control. Loving Renee was destructive, but he couldn't let her go. He couldn't give up hope that she'd see the light and step out of her selfishness.

Julian stuffed his hands in his pockets and started to laugh so loud, the sound traveled throughout the house.

"Welcome back, Julian," he said aloud to himself. "I've missed you."

Lyfe jumped out of bed with his latest one-night stand when got he the call from Jared telling him that he needed to get to Renee's ASAP. His heart damn near beat out of his chest, and his eye twitched. The constant eye movement was a distraction as he drove. He wanted to bang his head against the dashboard, frustrated yet again that he hadn't been there for Renee. It was funny, the more things changed, the more they stayed the same.

Lyfe had been furious when Jared told him what had happened between Renee and Slice. Slice had got what he deserved, but it didn't stop Lyfe from wishing he'd been there to seek justice for Renee himself. But he was happy Jared had been there to save Renee's life. It was a comfort to know Renee had others there to pick up his slack, no matter how many times he dropped the ball. Jared had spoken with such passion and anger, Lyfe was sure that as long as Jared was on their team, no one would come within a foot of Renee. The O.G. knew a man with lovesickness when he saw one, and Jared had it bad. Lyfe didn't believe in mixing business with pleasure, but if it ensured Renee's protection, he'd allow it.

The following day Jared and Lyfe were back at Renee's home. Jared had returned earlier than usual, and Lyfe had never left. The two would have attached themselves to her in order to guarantee she never left their sight, had they been able to. The incident was still a topic of conversation, and Jared and Lyfe were still consumed by the same anger and disgust they'd felt yesterday.

"I'd kill that son of a bitch five times over if I could!" Jared yelled as he and Lyfe sat on the couch in the living room. "And that punk-ass Julian is gone with the wind. Fuck kinda partner is that?"

Jared must have conjured Julian up, because as soon as those last two sentences left his mouth, the front door opened and Julian stepped in. He walked through the door just as he had hundreds of times before. Jared flew off the couch, raced toward Julian, and stopped once they were nose to nose.

"I should body your bitch ass! You got motherfuckers on this team about to rape Renee. What kind of shit is that?" Jared snarled.

The confidence Julian had walked in with evaporated. The welcome back he'd envisioned had gone out the door.

He pushed Jared out of the way and ran toward Renee's bedroom. He had no time to argue with Jared. This was bigger than their egos; this was about Renee.

Julian wasn't a fool. He had seen the way Jared looked at Renee and tried to cater to her every need during every moment of every hour of the day. Jared wanted her, and what his behavior revealed to everyone who was paying attention was that he would do whatever it took to get her. Because of that, and that alone, Jared had to go.

Julian flung the bedroom door open and saw Renee standing out on the terrace. Her hair and her silk robe blew in the wind. Her complexion was a richer hue than he remembered. She looked like a character in a fairy tale, a princess stuck in her very own mental prison, waiting to be saved and sat on the horse that would carry her and her prince off to their happily ever after. However, when she turned around and saw Julian, the softness in her stance evaporated against the peaceful backdrop of the city, and she lost her princess status and turned into the ice queen, icicles and all.

"What happened?" Julian grabbed Renee, ushered her into the bedroom, and looked over her body.

He searched for bruises and scratches, any signs of injury. He was desperate to know whether Renee was psychologically the same woman he knew. Renee snatched herself away from Julian's grasp, and with all her might, she smacked him. There was no doubt that all of New York heard her hand connect with Julian's face. He breathed heavily and suppressed the urge to choke the life out of her. Then he just stood there and, by regulating his breathing, calmed himself down.

"I deserved that," he said quietly when a minute or two had passed.

"Where the fuck were you?"

"I can't—"

Whap!

Renee smacked Julian again. The words trying to find their way out of her lover's mouth weren't the words needed to mend their relationship. She couldn't hear anything other than the truth. Julian needed to say the right things quickly, as things had already gotten ugly, and they didn't need to get worse.

With a burning red cheek, Julian took additional deep breaths. "Are you done?"

"Not even close." When she spoke, her voice cracked a little.

She tried her best to hide her emotions and keep them at bay, and although her heart was in shambles, she never showed it or acknowledged it to herself. Recognizing how she felt would result in recognizing she loved Julian more than she loved herself. This was a selfless act no one could foresee. He was her better half, her best friend, her everything. For him not to be there in her time of need crushed Renee and ruined her in ways she couldn't comprehend. Being in love caused her to lash out when he hurt her. The lines creasing the sides of Renee's mouth and the story her eyes told screamed pain and abandonment. A small change between soul mates was evident, whether spoken or not, and Julian couldn't take it, so he turned away, withholding eye contact.

"Look at me. You had a month of running. Now face me like a man," Renee told him.

Look, she thought.

Julian looked at her.

"You broke your promise. You promised me you would always be there for me, and like a fool, I believed you! Where were you when that piece of shit's dick was in my face? What kept you away for so long that it made Jared step into your shoes?" Renee scanned Julian's eyes, searching for an answer before his tongue and lips gave one. "Where were you?"

Right then, he wanted to die. Reality was standing in front of him, and what it showed him was crippling. Julian struggled with the various emotions he felt, the questions that being with Renee conjured. In every direction Julian looked, Renee's past was close to repeating itself. He wanted to punch a hole in the wall and relieve the tension exploding inside him, because he knew that whenever Renee thought back to this moment, she would remember that Jared had been her knight in shining armor. Slowly, past events started to come forward in his mind, and he thought back to when he had promised Renee he would always protect her.

Julian's home was Renee's place of refuge. She found comfort there, and if she could have, she would have moved in and started her life over from scratch. Every night, while she was in her bed, fearing that Curtis would walk in, she would tell herself, Only a couple more hours and you'll be back at Julian's.

And hours later, curled up in fifteen-year-old Julian's arms, Renee eyed the Notorious B.I.G. poster on his bedroom wall.

"We have to tell someone, Renee. If not, I'll kill him. I promise. I'll wipe him off this earth in the blink of an

eye." *Julian's head lay on top of Renee's, and all he could imagine was Curtis taking his last breath.*

For as long as Julian had known Renee, Curtis had been raping her, and she had refused to tell a soul. He had begged her to tell someone, or at least allow him to tell someone, but she wouldn't have it. She wouldn't even talk about it. She had always told him that he was her getaway, and while she was away from her nightmare, she wanted to enjoy her paradise. But Julian pushed her now to tell someone, no longer able to accept her abuse.

"No. Soon I'll be off to college, and this will all be nothing but a dream." Renee buried her face in Julian's chest and took in his scent, allowing herself to drift off into a faraway land.

"You think I'm playing? You think I won't kill for you?" Julian said a few minutes later, breaking the silence.

Renee sat up. Her black hair flowed past her shoulders. "You're not built for that," she told him, smiling. "You're the good guy." She tried to lighten the mood and be done with this depressing conversation, but by the look on Julian's face, she knew that he was not letting it go.

"I'm serious, Renee. Open your mouth, or your mama will be picking out that black dress." Julian's eyes were chilling.

Renee had never seen this side of him and honestly didn't know how to take it. She placed her head back on his chest. "Promise me something, Julian."

"What?"

"Promise me that you'll never leave me, that you'll always protect me. And promise me you will never allow anyone else to hurt me. My daddy is gone, so you're all I got."

A tear dropped from Julian's eye and landed under Renee's, giving the illusion that she, too, was crying. "I put that on my life."

A year later, at 2:00 a.m. one morning, Renee wound up on Julian's doorstep, soaking wet. Her hair clung to her face, and the moonlight revealed her busted lip and black eye. The thunder made her jump as she stood and waited for someone to answer the door.

Life had just gotten worse. That night Curtis had not been gentle and calm when he raped her. He'd been rough and angry, to the point of nearly choking her to death. She rubbed her neck and tried to will the pain away. His handprint from when he'd choked her was still visible. While fighting for her life, all Renee had been able to think of was Julian telling her countless times before that she needed to tell someone, and that if she didn't, he would kill Curtis himself. When she'd been on the verge of death tonight, it had hit her. If she didn't tell someone, Curtis may actually kill her. Battered and broken, Renee had dragged herself next door to Julian's house. Her mind was made up. She was going to break her silence.

Julian's mother, Veronica, opened the door, wearing a housecoat and a headful of rollers. She gasped when she saw Renee.

"Renee! What happened to you?" Veronica pulled Renee into the house and took her in her arms.

She didn't know what had happened to Renee, but her heart told her it was rape, every woman's and every mother's worst nightmare. Renee melted in her arms. Her mother never hugged her, so to be in the arms of a mother figure broke her down. Hundreds of tears dropped from her eyes and onto Veronica's floor. They cried in each other's arms for what felt like an eternity. No words were spoken, just pain.

Julian watched from the stairs as his mother and Renee embraced. He knew what had happened and why Renee was there. He walked over to them. When Renee opened her eyes and saw him looking at her, she knew what she had to do. She pulled away from Veronica and opened her mouth. The words fell out like skeletons from a closet.

"My stepfather, he rapes me."

After Veronica called the police and a rape kit was done on Renee, Curtis was arrested and found guilty of raping a minor. He was sentenced to ten years in prison. Renee didn't know why she did it, but when the lawyers and the police asked her if her mother knew about the rapes, she lied and told them no. Renee would never forget the look in her mother's eyes when she told the fib.

Sheila was sure that after she had walked in on Curtis raping Renee and had left the room while her child cried out for her help, Renee would sell her down the river. To hear Renee tell everyone in a very believable tone that her mother had been completely unaware of the abuse shocked Sheila.

After Curtis was sentenced, Sheila's appreciation of Renee not telling on her quickly faded. She put Renee through hell and treated her twice as badly as she had when Curtis was home. Renee had taken her husband away from her, and Sheila wanted revenge. Every day Sheila verbally abused Renee, and when she wasn't doing that, she acted like her daughter didn't exist. Renee was her personal whipping boy, the object of her verbal abuse, and the one she forced to provide maid service.

"I hate you. I wish I had never had you."

"You act like you didn't want it, didn't like it, but we all know you did. You fuckin' slut."

"Your father must be rolling over in his grave, watching over your slut ass."

"Why don't you do us all a favor and just die!"

Those were only a few of the things Renee would hear from her mother, her look-alike, on a daily basis.

"Where were you?" Renee repeated.

Julian snapped backed to the present and looked into Renee's eyes. It killed him that he hadn't been there for her, but in his mind, he had been protecting her, like when he was younger. He had set out to exterminate the evildoer, Curtis. With him still breathing, Renee would never live happily or be anything other than a shell of her former self.

"Protecting you," he whispered.

Like a deer in headlights, Renee stood still and her eyes grew wide. Then what remainder of control she had left, she let go of. Julian did not see where she was coming from, did not understand what she was saying. In her mind, he was lying to her, saying whatever he could to place himself in a better light. With lightning speed, she grabbed the lamp on the nearest nightstand and threw it at him. The crystal and gold lamp flew in Julian's direction, and he ducked and watched it shatter against the floor.

"You liar!" Renee screamed. Her veins bulged on her forehead and neck, and her eye twitched. Her caramel skin had turned beet red. "You were out fucking some bitch, when you should have been here!"

Renee searched for something else to throw. Her eyes landed on the two Chinese stress-relief metal balls that Julian kept at her house, and a sly smile touched her lips.

She swiftly scooped up the balls, and then, one by one, she threw them at his head with the accuracy and force of a major league baseball player. Julian dodged the pitches and listened to the loud sound of the balls bashing holes in the wall behind him.

"I hate you!" Renee's arms shook, and her body jumped slightly. The tough image of herself she had built over the years was unraveling.

Julian stood there, watching layers of the protective shell Renee had created around herself peel away, leaving her raw and vulnerable. He had never meant to hurt her. He had left to better her life, not complicate it. The answer to giving her peace and getting rid of her past was in Jamaica, so that was where he'd gone. Looking at her deconstruct now, he wondered if he had simply added to the problem instead of working toward eliminating it.

Julian slowly walked over to Renee, who continued to rant and rave, scream, punch, and kick the air. She was so involved in her tantrum that she never noticed Julian approaching her. Finally, when it was too late for her to dodge him, she saw him standing in front of her, his arms outstretched.

"Don't touch me!" Somehow, she managed to jump out of his reach, but Julian closed in and tried again to hug her.

Renee became so angry, she couldn't speak and couldn't move. She was frozen, stuck in a time when they were teens and he had undeniable control over her— control she craved, appreciated, and valued. He wrapped his arms around her. Embarrassed and exhausted from all the yelling, she fell into him, her fist weakly punching at his chest.

"You promised me," she whimpered. "You promised."

There wasn't much in life that Renee was proud of, but she was proud of Julian. So if he failed her, she had nothing, nothing to look forward to, and nothing to call her own. Renee wrapped her arms around him and held on tight, vowing to never let him go. Love wasn't easy, and neither was life. Life was too harsh, too cold, and too lonely for her to let go of her best friend and her one and only love. Life had already taken away her father. She couldn't lose Julian too.

He rubbed her back, his hand making soft circles, causing her body to relax and release all its tension. She placed her face on his shoulder and, as she had done when they were kids, inhaled his scent. He still smelled the same, like cocoa and shea butter. She had missed his scent this past month, and now she took it all in, trying to make up for lost time.

Wrapped so tightly in one another, they both felt Julian's phone vibrate in his pocket. Neither of them moved. They let it ring and go to voicemail. This was their time.

"I'm sorry," he told her. "You may not understand, but you soon will. Trust me. Just trust me." He held her tighter and kissed the top of her head, and Renee stared into space. She had no choice but to trust him. He was all she had. Their love was what pumped through her veins into her heart.

Julian lowered his head and kissed Renee. The fullness and moisture of his lips on hers moved the earth and rattled everything back into place. He grabbed her by her chin and looked in her eyes. No words were necessary.

Their kiss had said it all. Renee pushed her lips against his and savored another kiss. She had missed him and didn't want to fight anymore.

After what felt like hours of kissing, they stood in each other's arms and rocked back and forth, the motion as soothing as a summer day after months of winter. Renee closed her eyes and inhaled his scent again. When she opened them, she saw Jared staring at them from the doorway. Just hours ago, she had been in Jared's arms, caressing his skin. She looked at Jared for what felt like an eternity and then turned away and buried her face in Julian's shoulder. She stood like that until Jared went away.

Chapter 15

Lincoln was beginning to lose his mind. It was day two, and he still couldn't get in contact with Julian. All he had was his cell phone number. No address, no home number, no nothing. Just a cell phone number, which was looking just about useless. The very first time he dialed Julian, the called had been ignored, and ever since then, his calls had gone straight to voicemail. Lincoln threw the phone on his bed in frustration and placed his face in his hands.

This can't be happening. Page wants to kill Renee, and there's no way I can warn her!

Lincoln picked up his phone and dialed again, but just like the last time, his call went straight to voicemail.

"Leave a message," Julian's voice said on the other end of the line.

Lincoln was becoming frantic. His legs shook, and he was sweating profusely. After his recent conversation with Page, Lincoln had become suspicious about Page's feelings toward her sister. One night a week later, he had overheard her talking as he passed her bedroom on his way to the bathroom. He'd figured she was on the phone, and he'd been curious as to what she was saying and to whom she was saying it, so he'd stood by her bedroom door.

"That dumb motherfucker talking about I got nothing on my sister. Motherfucker must not know about me! She ain't got nothing on me. That whore! I hate the bitch. I hope her ass is rotting away somewhere. Putting my daddy in jail! Do she know how lucky she is to have slept with him? I'd give my right arm to sleep with him, but *no*, she had to have him. So much for me being Daddy's little girl," Page said.

Lincoln tiptoed to the house phone and slowly picked up the receiver. All he heard was a dial tone. As he went to place the receiver back on the cradle, he saw Page's cell phone lying on the living-room couch. She definitely wasn't on the phone.

It's only nine p.m. There's still time for a nineteen-year-old to have company, he thought as he made his way up to Sheila's bedroom.

"Baby, does Page have company?" he asked when he'd closed the bedroom door behind him.

Sheila took her eyes off the TV and placed them on Lincoln. Every time she looked at him, it amazed him how much she looked like Renee.

"No."

"You sure?"

"Yeah. I just came from downstairs a few minutes ago. Before I came to bed, I went in her room to say good night. She was already in bed. Why?"

"I thought I heard her talking to someone."

"Probably on the phone." Sheila directed her attention back to the television.

Lincoln headed back downstairs and stood next to Page's bedroom door. At first, he heard nothing and figured she had fallen asleep, but when he turned to walk away, she started to talk again.

"She just couldn't leave him alone. Had to have the one man I want. The one man I need. Why does it have to be so difficult? Why can't I just have my cake and eat it too?"

Suddenly, there was a long pause. Without warning, Page's cat Phoebe walked between Lincoln's legs, pushed the door open, and walked into her bedroom. The door stood open a crack.

"Hey, Phoebe. How's my girl?" Page asked.

Lincoln peeked through the crack and saw just what he expected: Page was alone.

The next night, when no one was around, Lincoln was ready to give Julian a call and tell him everything he'd heard. He made his way down to the finished basement and was about to press the last numeral of Julian's phone number when he heard someone descending the stairs.

"I'm telling you, it's not only worth your time, but your money too," an unfamiliar voice said.

"That's good to know, but refrain from talking until we get to the basement," Page replied.

Lincoln hid in the closet and prayed that Page wasn't so paranoid that she'd check every inch of the room before she spoke. He cracked the door open just enough to see Page walk in and sit on the couch. A female followed behind. He couldn't see her face. All that was clearly visible was her fire-red hair. The young woman sat down, her back to the closet. Page crossed her legs.

"So what's so important that you had to come to my house at eleven at night?" Page asked.

"I found your sister." Lincoln could tell the young woman was smiling when she said it.

Page quickly sat up. The look on her face was priceless.

"What do you mean, you found my sister?"

"I mean, your search is over. I not only know where she is, but who she is."

"I'm listening."

"Little Miss Renee also goes by the name of Jordan, and in case you're wondering if I'm talking about the drug dealer Jordan, who has the streets of New York on smash, then you're oh, so correct."

At first Page was shocked; then she slowly became angry.

Lincoln was surprised. He knew little about Renee's situation. All he knew was that she didn't get along with her family and had moved away without them knowing.

"You have to be shittin' me." Page dropped her head and looked back up at the redhead. "So you're telling me she's here in New York?"

The young woman nodded, and Lincoln saw her body shift a little to the side. "Here's where she rests her head."

Lincoln pressed his face against the closet door, afraid he would be seen. It was obvious that she had given Page a piece of paper with Renee's address on it. He stood in silence, anxious and holding his breath, waiting to see if one of them would say the address. He needed to know it.

"She's at—" the redhead began, but Page cut her short.

Page lifted her hand, her eyes on the paper. "I can read."

After a second of staring at the paper, Page slipped it in her pocket. She placed a hand under her chin and sat there, deep in thought. By the look on Page's face, it was apparent that she wasn't happy.

Finally, she faced the redhead and opened her mouth. "You'll get your money."

The redhead nodded and then got up and walked toward the stairs.

After Lincoln heard the young woman walk up the stairs and the front door close, he watched as Page continued to sit on the couch in the basement. She sat so still that Lincoln wondered if she was still alive. She didn't move, seemingly not even to breathe. After ten minutes of no movement, she took the piece of paper out of her pocket and looked at it.

"Right under my damn nose all this time. Damn, bitch. You're good, but not *that* good. Because when I see you, you're dead."

She folded the paper up into little squares, tucked it back in her pocket, and left the room.

Later Lincoln searched the house from top to bottom, looking for that piece of paper, but came up empty.

Sitting on Sheila's bed now and constantly getting Julian's voicemail was stressing him out. He had left so many messages that Julian's mailbox became full. Lincoln clutched his phone in his hand and held it against his head. Slowly, he lowered it and dialed Julian again.

"Leave a message."

Lincoln lowered his head in defeat.

"I have to get him. If I don't, Renee is dead."

Chapter 16

Renee knew she was acting bipolar. One second she was all lovey-dovey with Julian, and the next she couldn't stand his guts. It was an emotional game of tennis. Back and forth, the mood swings went. She had yet to get over the fact that Julian had abandoned her, but she couldn't deny that she was happy he was back where she could see and touch him. Now Renee felt a lot more balanced. Julian was the man she wanted to spend the rest of her life with, but she didn't know how to express that she was in love with him without experiencing pain. Her past was her roadblock. It had forced her to drive down misery lane and isolate herself from the big, happy world, which she considered foreign and out of reach. The more she thought about it, the more she knew she would never be happy, because she wasn't open to it. And if she did find happiness, keeping it would be a battle she wouldn't easily win.

After what had taken place with Slice, she didn't want to show it or admit it, but she had fallen into a deeper depression. It had happened a little over a week ago, and every night, she had dreamed about it, smelled it, and relived it. Except parts of what she dreamed hadn't happened. She'd dreamed that Slice was raping her, and while he held her down, she'd look at him and discover he was Curtis. Each time she looked at him, he'd smile and reach out to rub her face. Renee would wake up in a cold sweat, her heart beating a mile a minute and her mind in shambles.

She didn't like leaving the comfort of her home, but she needed a release. She needed to pound the pavement and go jogging in order to deal with her rage. She threw on a pair of black sweatpants and a matching sports bra, and strapped her gun to her ankle. It was 10:00 p.m., and hardly anyone was strolling in one of the largest parks in New York City. As she stepped into the park, she jammed the earbuds connected to her smartphone in her ears and started running.

By leaving her home, Renee risked being spotted by enemies. Julian and her crew, whose job it was to protect her and contribute to the growth of the business, would be none too pleased if they found out she had slipped out without them noticing. But her own safety had to take a backseat right now. She needed to breathe. When jogging, she had nothing to do but think about her life. As she jogged now, for a brief second she thought of Jared. It was funny how sex changed everything. Like a light switch, it turned on and off certain behaviors, and it added heartache to the mix. Whenever she looked at Jared, his eyes were flooded with emotion.

Eminem's song "Cleanin' Out My Closet" blasted through the earbuds. She knew every word and sang along, like she'd written the song herself. Every other time she listened to the song, she would flash back to the time Curtis raped her and her mother poked her head in the room. When Renee called out to her, Sheila closed the door and never intervene. Renee had always viewed her mother as an accomplice, a dog without a muzzle. As she listened the song, her mind would then drift to the verbal abuse and the horrific beatings her mother used to give her for little things she had forgotten to do, such as washing the last dish in the sink or cleaning spilled milk on the counter. Page had walked around, making a mess, and had never been confronted. Had never been held to the same standard as Renee. She'd been the house's princess, and Renee had been nothing but a stepchild who was used and abused beyond repair. Renee had been an enemy in her own home, and not a day had gone by when her mother hadn't reminded her of that.

Renee balled her fists up as she jogged, and bit down on her bottom lip. She was past the crying and the constant pity parties she had thrown and attended. Once upon a time, she'd cry for hours over her past. She'd sit there and play again and again what used to be, what had broken her. There had been times when Renee didn't think she would survive the abuse, times when she didn't know how she'd grow up and transcend the horror of her household. The only person she had had was Julian. He'd been her sanity and her hope, but down the road she'd started to sabotage that relationship. She was already tarnished and knew that she could never be what Julian wanted and needed, which was a normal, caring, loving girlfriend without baggage, one on whom a trilogy could be based. He needed a girlfriend who could one day be his wife and the mother of his children. His dreams surpassed the life they were living.

Renee was everything Julian didn't deserve; she was miserable and coldhearted, far from the definition of a wife and light years away from being mother material. Deep down inside, she wondered how it would feel to allow herself to be loved and to live a life of peace. Renee hadn't noticed it, but she was running fast now, the kind

of fast that people thought of when they heard the name
Flo-Jo. She could barely hear Eminem now, and her legs
seemed to have a mind of their own. Sometimes, all she
wanted to do was run and never stop.

Then it happened, what always happened. Her legs got
weak, and she started to slow down. Renee pushed and
struggled to keep the speed going, but her body wouldn't
allow it. It functioned or didn't function regardless of
her wants. Finally, Renee gave up. She stopped and bent
over to catch her breath. When she caught her breath, she
stood up straight and snatched the earbuds from her ears.
Her phone continued to play loudly.

As she stood there, lost in her thoughts, it finally hit
her that all her life, all she'd been doing was running. Yes,
she had got Curtis locked up, but she had run away from
her problems by going off to college without anyone
knowing but Julian, only to come back to New York and
hide out. She hadn't even shown her face in the very
streets she ran. And she'd run away from love and even
herself. She had tried to physically outrun everything, but
she couldn't. The only way to stop running, she decided,
was to put the whole situation with Curtis behind her and
out of her mind, heart, and soul. And it finally penetrated
her thick skull that the only way out . . . was through.

Raindrops started to fall on the concrete jungle. Her
phone was nicely tucked away in the inner pocket of
her sweats, so she had no reason to worry about it being
ruined and abandoning her during her time of need. She
didn't move. Instead, she stood there, with her fingers
running through her hair, trying to figure out a way out of
her personal prison. A loud crack followed by the roar of
thunder sounded before lightning flashed. It lit up the sky
and caused the few people about to run for shelter. Renee

felt as if one of the lightning bolts had struck her, because a thought came to mind that would end all her problems and allow her to bury all her pain and misery for good.

She stood erect, a grin across her face. She'd been fighting this plan for years, or maybe just avoiding it, and now she was actually ready to carry it out and put to use her hard-heartedness. There would be no more running. She was tired of it, and of the misery she had grown comfortable with. Sheila's and Curtis's luck had run its course, their years of being let off the hook for their sins were over, and Renee was now ready to make her dream a reality. She was going to kill them and free herself from this prison she called life. It was time she moved on.

Chapter 17

Lying next to her in bed, Julian watched as Renee's chest rose and fell. He found comfort in her breathing pattern and could stare at her like this forever. His eyes traveled up her face, and he got lost in her beauty. She was a breathing work of art, a masterpiece he imagined God took time in creating. Renee looked so peaceful. However, behind those eyelids and those angelic looks, Julian knew the inner turmoil that was taking place. He wanted so badly for Renee's past to release its hold on her and allow her to live.

For the past three days, he had been battling her mood swings. Like a faucet, one second she ran hot, and the next cold. One minute she was tangled in his arms, unable to get enough of him, and the next she was unforgiving and was spewing obscenities about his disappearance. Every day was a whirlwind he endured for the love of a woman. He knew she was battling the demons Slice had brought back, and even some that he had possibly created, but Julian still couldn't help but wonder how much more of her behavior he could take. However, whenever he looked at her face, the question turned into a distant memory.

He stroked her hair and kissed her lips, the softness of hair strands and skin a blessing. "Soon your past will be erased, and it will be just us," he whispered.

It was an unspoken fact that Renee and Julian belonged to each other, but he needed it to be official and out in the open, for strangers and all to know and not assume. They were no longer in high school; they were grown-ups and needed to act as such. With her parents gone, Julian hoped that it would open the door for Renee to be an emotionally stable, loving person who understood her worth and set out to better herself. He hoped she'd accomplish what she had always desired and had once spoken about many moons ago—letting go of the past, eliminating all the anguish her family had caused her, and living a life of peace and happiness, which she hoped would one day include Julian as her husband and the father of her children.

The hit on Curtis was due to go down in two weeks, but after what had gone down with Slice, Julian was wondering if it should happen sooner. What Slice pulled had affected Renee, whether she wanted to admit it or not. She was twice as angry and unpredictable. She had ordered her crew not to dispose of Slice's body right away, but to throw it in an abandoned warehouse in Brooklyn for the time being. She had plans for it and needed it to be as close as possible to where everything would unfold, so that when the time came, she could show everyone that turning on her was never an option. A thought maybe, but an actual option never.

Renee started to twist and turn in her sleep, but she didn't settle until her naked legs fell on Julian's and her head landed on his chest. He squeezed her in his arms and thought about his unborn child. Life hurt, but that would all end soon. Disturbing the peace, Julian's phone danced across the nightstand. Ever since he'd returned to New York, his phone had been ringing off the hook each and every day, but he had ignored it and had sent every call to voicemail. Renee was his main priority; nothing else mattered when trying to repair what was broken with her.

Julian looked at Renee and knew there was no waking her. She was snoring lightly, and based on his experience, Julian knew her snores would soon grow louder, signaling that she was deep asleep. So he slithered out from underneath her, grabbed his phone, and stepped out onto the terrace in nothing but his boxers. The cold air that hit him felt good. He punched in the code to his phone and listened to his messages.

"You have fifteen unheard messages," the recording said.

Fifteen messages? Julian wondered what was so important that he had fifteen unheard messages.

"Jay, this is Lincoln. Hit me back. I have some urgent news for you."

"Yo, Jay, hit me back as soon as you get this. It's important."

"Jay, you haven't returned any of my calls. Man, this is life or death."

"Jay . . ."

After the third message, Julian stopped listening. He remembered Lincoln. He was the nerdy kid whom Renee was cool with in high school. He had kept in contact with him, and they talked occasionally, because Julian understood the importance of having alliances, and not enemies, and of fostering relationships with those who knew him before he became the man he was.

Julian dialed Lincoln's number, and on the first ring, he picked up.

"It's about time you called!" Lincoln exclaimed. "I can't talk on the phone. Meet me at that diner over in Brooklyn, on Flatlands, Monday, at ten. There's something you should know." Lincoln constantly looked around the room, hoping Sheila couldn't hear him on the phone. They were in Atlantic City for the weekend, and she was in the hotel bathroom, getting dolled up to hit a club that would filled with people half her age.

"Monday? Shit. Must not be serious if you can't talk until three days from now."

"I'm in AC right now, and this shit has to be spoken about in person. I don't trust these phones and, son, if you know where Renee is, stay with her until you meet with me."

Julian scrunched his face up and looked at the phone. "What the fuck are you talking about, L? Don't fuck with me."

"Baby, tell me what you think about this dress!" Sheila yelled from the bathroom.

Lincoln heard the doorknob turning.

"I'm not bullshitting you. Meet me at the diner on Monday and watch over Renee," Lincoln whispered into the phone.

Julian opened his mouth to speak, but Lincoln had already hung up. He contemplated calling back, but something told him that if Lincoln had been able to talk, he would have. Lincoln wasn't a street dude, and although he had got clowned in high school, there wasn't a time when Lincoln hadn't used his best judgment. Julian had no choice but to sit back and wait until Monday. He sucked his teeth and went back into Renee's bedroom.

The sight of the sheets cascading down her body and exposing her skin put a smile on his face. Julian had no patience and needed a release, so he walked over to Renee and slid his hand up her thigh. She was the perfect distraction.

Chapter 18

Julian couldn't believe what he was hearing. For weeks, he had wondered if putting a hit out on Curtis and Sheila without Renee's knowledge was smart on his part. He'd been sure that killing them would free Renee of her demons, but he'd wondered if he was wrong for hiding his plan from her, because Renee had to have her hand in every pot that concerned her and she despised secrets. But now that Renee sat across from him, with her arms planted on the bedroom table and her eyes staring into his, having just finished telling him that she had decided to put a hit out on her mother and stepfather herself, he knew he'd made the right decision.

"Is this what you want? Do you truly believe you can live with yourself after the fact?" Julian waited for an answer, hoping she had thought everything through. It was one thing for him to make such a decision for her, but it was an entirely different thing for her to plan it on her own.

"It has to be done. After all these years, as embarrassed as I am to admit it, I finally figured out what I have to do." She laughed, even though nothing was funny. "The only way I can get over my past is to let it go, literally." Renee stared in his eyes. "I'm just hoping to find myself when it is all said and done." Renee tapped her fingers on the tabletop.

She went on. "I'm a miserable woman, Julian. In order to deal with pain, I inflict it on others. I push coke and murder whoever stands in my way. I ruin lives and will probably go down in history as New York's most notorious drug dealer," she smirked. "Yet I can't even show my face or let my government name ring through the streets, because I'm too busy hiding from my past. I'm too busy running from my mommy." She shook her head. "I'm tired of hiding. I want to live a normal life and be happy. When people think of me, I want to be associated with something positive, and this isn't it."

Renee looked around at her expensive surroundings. So many of the things people gawked at behind the glass windows of high-end stores now disgusted Renee. She'd come to realize that money and material objects meant nothing if your heart was in turmoil. Though he hadn't grasped this, Julian could see that living a queenpin lifestyle had quickly becoming old and boring for Renee. Long ago she had stop spending money and purchasing what many couldn't afford. Her bank account had grown, and so had the dust in her closet and on her furniture.

She looked at him, and a lone tear ran down her cheek. "And when you look at me, I don't want you to see the monster that killed our baby."

Chills ran through Julian. It felt like a hand had torn through his chest and held his heart in a vise grip. Was this a dream? If so, he didn't want to wake up. He wanted to see it through and find out how it ended. Renee having brought up the topic of their unborn child was no easy pill to swallow, but the direction the conversation was going had piqued his interest.

"I want to be happy, Julian, like when my father was alive and I first met you. I was living in hell, yet somehow meeting you brought me to heaven."

Julian didn't know if it was the words she spoke that took his breath away or the fact that she was staring in his eyes while saying them. He swallowed, trying to remove the knot in his throat. He didn't know how to react. Renee had never been so calm, so . . . human.

She went on. "You made my life bearable, you made it a lot easier to live, and you gave me something that I hadn't had since my father died . . . love. And let's not forget your mother was more of a mother to me than my own, may God rest her soul."

Renee's eyes fell down to the table, and she played with a soda cap, pretending it was a dreidel. She spun it and spun it. Both her and Julian's eyes followed it. For a long time, the two just stared at the cap while lost in thought. Then it spun off the table. Julian's mother, who had died three years ago, was a touchy subject for both Renee and Julian. No matter how many years passed, her death was a wound that would never heal. The thought of his mother now made Julian emotional. Her passing had been one of the hardest things he'd had to endure. She was his best friend, and in the blink of an eye, she'd been taken away from him. This loss had ripped Julian to shreds, but at the same time it had brought Renee and him closer together. Losing his mother had enabled Julian to understand fully the pain Renee endured daily since losing her father.

Renee had taken the death of Mrs. Black hard, almost as hard as she had taken her father's passing. She had locked herself in her room for days after her funeral and had allowed a dark cloud to hover over her. Not only had she lost her friend, but she'd lost the only person who was a real mother to her. The death of Mrs. Black had made Renee sink deeper into the black hole she was already in, and it had made the effort of getting herself out of her funk harder.

Julian turned his head away from the cap and wiped the fallen tear from his face. Renee reached across the table and placed her hand on top of his. Her touch paralyzed him. Sure, he felt her whenever they had sex, but this was different. This was actually the feelings that he had for her being returned to him after all these years. This was their partnership and love.

He told himself to grab her, to cover her with his arms and torso, and never let her go, but his body wouldn't comply. He was frozen, a sculpture ready to be placed in front of an ancient building in some foreign place that tourists would pay to see. After finding the strength to take his eyes off their clasped hands, he looked up at her.

"If you're sure about this, if this is what you want, then it's a go. Just know there's no turning back. Once you lose your mother, there's no going back."

Renee's eyebrows caved in, and her eyes darkened. The cold, emotionally deprived woman whom Julian wished away every night had returned.

"I have never been more sure about anything in my entire life. In order to lose a mother, you must have once had one."

She stroked his hand, and he felt at ease. He had always thought the ultimate revenge was offing Curtis and leaving Sheila alone. But after revisiting the situation, he now realized that a mother who kept quiet and did nothing about abuse was just as guilty as the man who committed the crime. Both evils were equal, and now that he saw that, he understood what Renee needed to do, and he felt justified about putting a hit out on them both, without Renee's knowledge. It was the right thing.

Everyone and anyone who had hurt Renee deserved to die, and no one would get a "get out of jail free" card. Even though Julian despised Sheila and couldn't wait for the day she was wiped off this earth, he craved seeking revenge against Curtis. It motivated him when bad days showed their face.

Curtis had took Renee's innocence away, and Julian believed he was one of the reasons she'd aborted their child. Julian didn't care if he was in prison. That wasn't enough, because as long as Curtis was still breathing, eating, and having an hour of recreation a day, he still had it good, according to Julian. The thought of Dane taking Curtis's life in the place where Curtis had spent many years made a smile creep across Julian's face. His trip to Jamaica to meet with her and plan his hit was the best thing he could have ever done, and he couldn't wait until it was carried out.

As if in deep thought, Renee bowed her head. When she finally looked up and didn't say a word, Julian knew she was asking for his approval and support when it came to killing her mother. He knew she needed him now more than ever.

He squeezed her hand, then kissed it. "I'll get Dane on the phone."

Renee smiled. "She's my favorite. Not to mention, she and her husband remind me of Bonnie and Clyde. Kinda like us, only assassins." She entwined her fingers with his.

Julian returned the smile. Hearing the word *us* in the same sentence in which couples were mentioned made him believe they were a couple too. He knew that before he assumed anything, he had to hear her say it.

Julian stood up and pulled Renee up with him, then pressed her body to his. Renee didn't put up a fight. She was tired of running away from love, and she knew that in order to start over and become a better person, she had to express her love to Julian. She had to make this relationship official and stop playing this "friends with benefits" game. Renee had to tell him she loved him and only him, that is, if she wanted happiness as much as she claimed to.

Julian placed his lips to her ear. "I love you," he whispered.

Maybe he shouldn't have said it first, maybe he should have let her open up on her own, but he couldn't help it. He had to give her a little push.

Renee opened her mouth, but no words came out.

All I have to do is say it back. Everything will make sense and will become a little better if I say it back. Besides, isn't that how I feel? she thought.

Renee closed her eyes and shook her head. The words *I love you* were foreign to her. She rarely, if ever, said those words. And now that Julian needed her to utter them, she found it difficult to do.

She looked up at Julian, who was staring back at her. He showed no emotion, but she knew he wanted her love. And, damn it, he deserved it. Renee smiled a radiant smile and told him, "I love you."

Julian couldn't hide his happiness. For years, he'd waited to hear those words escape her mouth, and now that he had, he wanted to sing and dance. But then his smile quickly disappeared, and seriousness took hold of him.

"You love me, but what exactly does that mean?" As much as he loved her, he honestly couldn't be her fool for much longer. He needed to know exactly where their relationship was heading.

Renee rubbed his face, and Julian felt himself melting into her palm. Her touch was the smoothest thing ever.

"What does it mean? It means that it's you and me against the world, baby. It means that we're the new Bonnie and Clyde, and the last time I checked, Bonnie and Clyde were a couple."

That was all Julian needed to hear. He picked her up and laid her down on the bed. Then they consummated their relationship.

Chapter 19

"Poison . . . poison is my favorite way of murdering my victims." Dane took a sip of her red wine, and her bloodred lipstick left her lip prints on the wineglass. "I've always been fascinated by the fact that with poison, I can literally sit back and watch the victim commit suicide from start to end, without any interruptions."

Metro, Dane's husband, slowly shook his head and grinned. "It's not suicide if you're poisoning them, Dane."

"I know, but them eating or drinking whatever I've put poison in always makes me believe that they're committing suicide. For example, I truly believe that if they didn't want to die, they wouldn't consume whatever I've put the poison in. I believe they'd suddenly remember that they have an engagement to attend, their clothes to pick up from the cleaners, or a telephone call to make. Their subconscious or survival instincts would kick in. But if they don't hesitate for that brief moment, if they don't think twice about what they're about to devour or drink, I believe subconsciously, they want to die and therefore are committing suicide."

A smirk came across her face, making even her eyes smile. Metro looked at her with loving eyes. From her seat at the head of the long table, Renee watched the couple interact. There was no denying that the two were madly in love. No one would have ever imagined that these two people, who were such a dangerous combination, could be so kind and loving toward each other.

Dane, a ruthless assassin, and Metro, a retired kingpin who had supplied hundreds of dealers, were an unlikely duo, but one that worked well. They had met through Dane's aunt Laura. At the time, Laura was running Staten Island's drug supply and was in need of a new connect, so she sought out Metro's services. Metro had a background check run on Laura, as did with every person he was considering doing business with, and this included having her followed to learn whom she socialized with. Metro was supplied with pictures of Dane, and he instantly fell in love. He courted her, and within two years, they were married and inseparable.

For years Renee had admired their love. Sitting across from them now, she became more hopeful that living a life of love and happiness was possible. And it gave her additional confirmation that putting a hit out on her parents was long overdue and a necessity if she wanted peace.

Ten years Renee's senior, Dane was like a big sister to her. She had shown Renee the love Renee's own family had withheld, and Dane had made her feel a part of something. Renee had never revealed her full life story, but Dane could see that she was a hurt young woman in need of guidance. Because of that, she had introduced Renee and Julian to the game and had made them her and Metro's protégés.

Renee had met Dane at Barnes & Noble while she was away at school. The two women had lived in the bookstore, and after seeing each other for the millionth time, they'd finally decided to have a conversation.

They'd hit it off while conversing about literature and the hardships of life. After some time passed, during which Dane found no faults in her new friend, she took Renee under her wing and introduced her to Metro. Instantly, Renee became the couple's favorite person, and when the time came for Metro to retire, he handed her his crown and schooled her on the game. Metro supplied her with his knowledge and contacts, while Dane provided protection. In time Renee took over new territory, territory that Metro hadn't owned, and made a name for herself.

As they sat around the long table now, everyone leaned back in their chair. They had just devoured the marvelous dinner Renee had prepared. Lobster, steak, shrimp, baked chicken, rice, potatoes, spinach, corn, devil's food cake encased in white frosting, and parfaits with whipped cream had once graced the table. There was now nothing more than crumbs atop the plates, and while everyone desired to finish even those, they just couldn't.

One of Renee's pleasures was cooking. She enjoyed it because it took her mind off her miserable life for the few hours that she allowed herself to indulge in it. Renee had learned how to cook from her mother. She used to watch her sashay around the kitchen and cook like her life depended on it. Her mother had tried to teach Page, who couldn't have cared less about the ins and outs of preparing a meal. Renee would pretend she was doing something like mopping the kitchen floor, when really she was listening and learning how to prepare a five-star dish. Julian loved when she cooked. For the few hours she devoted to cooking each time, she shed her ice queen persona and became a normal woman and his dream come true.

"I have to tell you, Renee, I don't know how you managed to cook such a feast. Are you sure you didn't hire a chef or something?" Metro's right eyebrow rose.

"You know you taught me better than to have someone cook for me if I don't have to. I'm not out of the game like you. I can't have chefs and shit like that yet," Renee replied.

Renee ate a piece of shrimp that was left on her plate, and Metro smiled. Years ago, when he schooled her, he'd taught her always to be overly cautious in the business they were in. Sometimes the smallest things, things people never viewed as a threat, such as someone preparing their food, could lead to their demise. Enemies came in many forms. Anyone could pose a threat. He was proud she remembered everything he'd taught her.

"Then you have to come out to Jamaica and cook for us sometime, especially when we have guests. You will put our chefs to shame." Metro took a sip of his wine and glanced over at Dane, remembering the chef that had no clue how to make collard greens two weeks ago.

Renee shook her head. "No thanks. I lost a night's sleep over making this spread. I'm not trying to lose weeks of sleep by making food for hundreds of your friends. You're too popular, Metro."

Dane finished her red wine, poured herself another glass, and looked over at Renee, her eyes piercing through her soul. Sometimes Renee wondered if Dane was one of the reasons that she was so cold. Granted, when she left home and headed to college, her heart had already been broken and her anger full blown, but Renee couldn't help but wonder if Dane had shattered her heart and made her into a beast.

Dane and Metro had molded Renee into the most ruthless queenpin New York had ever seen. They had taught her that feelings would get you killed. Therefore, she must not show any. They had made her more angry and had rationalized this by telling her that her anger would come in handy when she was running the streets. They had created a monster. But the one thing they had failed to teach her was how to turn the coldness off and become human again. Renee sat there looking at Dane, her mentor, her sister, and she wondered whether she should thank Dane for the riches and the power she had bestowed or curse her for the additional pain this lifestyle had brought her.

"Okay. We ate, drank, talked, and laughed. Now we do business," Dane announced.

Renee had been dreading this moment. She wanted the hit on her mother and her stepfather to go through with all her might, but she didn't want to have the conversation with Dane that was about to take place. She eyed the Pinnacle bottle, lifted it, and poured the vodka into her glass until it almost ran over the rim.

"Let's do business," Renee responded.

"Are you sure this is what you want?" Dane held her glass so tight, it almost burst.

"Yes."

"She's your mother."

"I know."

"Why?" Dane leaned over the table, and her brown skin glistened under the ceiling lamp. Her long hair was slicked back into a tight ponytail, and it dangled over her shoulder, nearly landing in her plate. Dane wanted answers, and her tone was anything but polite.

Renee didn't answer. All she did was sip her drink.

Dane knew Renee was stubborn. She never cared to talk about her life. Whenever the topic of her family was brought up, Renee simply shut down. They were nothing but people she had lived with once upon a time.

"You do know I ask every client of mine who puts a hit out on their mother why. If I don't believe the reason is good enough, I don't do it," Dane explained. "And don't think about getting another assassin, because I'm the best."

"I don't want another assassin. I want you."

Killing a client's mother was a touchy issue for Dane. Before she turned into a contract killer, she had actually been normal and had lived a life only people on TV, like the Cosbys, had. She was the oldest of three kids, the daughter of an architect and a lawyer who had turned into a stay-at-home mom. Her childhood had been great. She and her mother had been best friends, and they'd done everything together. Her mother had always had cookies or brownies waiting for her after school. She had been there for Dane during her first heartbreak, had helped her pick out her prom dress, and had visited her almost every week during her first year of college so she wouldn't be so homesick. Their relationship had been so special that Dane had thought everyone's mother was like hers.

Of course she'd known there were mothers out there that were horrible, but not to the extent that their children wanted them dead. She didn't find out how horrible some women could be until she became an assassin and people put hits out on the women who had birthed them. When she asked them why they wanted their mother dead, she heard lots of horrid reasons.

"She molested me."

"By the time I was ten, she had broken ten of my bones, one every year."

"My mother used to test her products on me. What better way to prove her drugs were better than her competitors' than to show it."

In those moments, she knew that she was lucky to have had the mother she had, whom she missed terribly. Both Dane's mother and father were murdered when their restaurant was broken into and robbed. That was the event that had led Dane to drop out of her last year of medical school, slaughter her parents' murderers, and become addicted to killing. Timid, harmless Dane had fallen into a dark hole and had dedicated her life to protecting her two younger siblings, who were in the custody of her drug-dealing aunt and uncle, and killing for pay. Dane was a shattered woman with a knowledge of medicine and an addiction to killing: two things that had earned her a great amount of money. But she always had to know why she a client wanted someone killed.

"Then tell me why," Dane ordered, staring at Renee. Her glass was now on the table, and her nails dug into the cherry-colored tablecloth.

Renee wouldn't answer. She merely stared back. The tension was so thick, you could cut it with a knife.

Metro tossed a piece of chicken left over on his plate into his mouth and chased it down with wine, knowing Dane would not give up.

Julian finished his drink and poured himself another, knowing Renee wouldn't give in.

It was like a scene from an old Western, except both *men* were on the sidelines, looking on while the women walked in circles, never taking their eyes off one another, with their hands on their guns. All that was left to be do was for someone to yell, "Draw!" and whoever got to their gun fast enough and shot would win.

The only difference was, Dane was not going to win. She had found happiness in Metro, and she had eventually found the three people who murdered her parents and had killed them. She had had some sort of closure; Renee hadn't. The people who had hurt her were still walking. She couldn't give herself to Julian 100 percent until they were dead. For Dane to expect her to give her what she wanted was unrealistic. Renee was like no other.

The two women continued staring at each other. Renee remained in her same position, her expression never changing and her lips never moving. After ten minutes, Dane sat completely back and took a deep breath. She was close to Renee and viewed the young woman as her sister. So she let her have this one. She'd do this one favor for her, without knowing why, but only this one time.

"You're a stubborn woman, Renee, but I'll let your reasons remain just that, your reasons. But are you willing to tell me why your stepfather?"

When Dane asked that question, Renee wanted to tell her everything, from top to bottom. She wanted to tell her that he was the devil and that he had ruined her, that he had robbed her of her innocence and zest for life, but she couldn't tell it, couldn't get the words out of her mouth.

"Let's just say he's a thief," was all Renee told her. "I want this done as soon as possible, and I want them to die slowly. The worst death is a slow death. I want them to know why they're dying. All you have to tell them is that they know what they did to me. They'll know. You'll see it in their eyes."

Dane nodded. She would take this hit very seriously. Whatever these individuals had done, it was enough for Renee's anger to lead her to the top.

Metro loudly let out his breath. He had been holding it the whole time. He said, "Now that that's over, like I was saying earlier, that was a good-ass meal."

He sat back comfortably and rubbed his stomach. Everyone sat in silence as they drank the wine. No one at this table was normal. They had all been hurt, and their souls cried out for one reason or another, but they were good at what they did. They would work the streets until the wheels fell off.

Chapter 20

After discovering that Page wanted Renee dead and gone, Lincoln had found himself watching his back wherever he went. Anyone who was willing to kill their own flesh and blood was a certified psycho, and Lincoln didn't trust them. All he could think about was Page coming after him if she found out he knew her secret. For days, he had been on edge and had wanted to relay the information to Julian so he'd take care of things and leave Lincoln in the clear. The fact was Lincoln wasn't built for this. All he wanted was to have a good time with an older woman. He'd also reached out to Julian because he felt he owed it to Renee to inform her of the danger she was in. He was grateful that he and Julian had finally exchanged words and that Julian had agreed to meet up.

At the back of the Arch Diner, Lincoln sat in a booth, watching every car that pulled into the lot. As if he were a spy, he watched closely and waited for people to exit their vehicles, hoping each person was Julian, and not Page coming after him. He was paranoid, and for good reason. When he finally saw Julian exit his Maybach, he was so relieved that he finally glanced away the parking lot and kicked back his rum and Coke.

Damn. Homey getting money like that? Lincoln watched in awe as Julian, decked out in Armani, stepped out of his car and activated the car's alarm. His appearance screamed money, and Lincoln was listening.

Julian entered the restaurant and automatically spotted Lincoln. Heading to the back of the diner, he turned his cell off. When he reached the booth, he slid in opposite Lincoln.

"L, long time no see." Julian gave Lincoln a pound and flashed back to high school, when Renee befriended the nerdy kid and had Julian scratching his head as to why.

"You don't speak to many people, Renee. Why him? He's like a real-life Urkel." Julian looked at a teenage Lincoln sitting at their lunch table with Slice.

He wore Coke bottle glasses and clothes that were way too small for him, and the look on his face said that begged to fit in.

Renee bought a soda from the vending machine and looked Julian in his eyes before answering. "Urkel or not, everyone deserves a friend."

Now, almost twelve years later, Julian sat across from the man he'd befriended only because of Renee. His glasses had been replaced with contacts, and his once small clothes were now oversize and the colors of the rainbow. Julian suppressed his laughter and reminded himself that this fashion-challenged man was saving the love his life.

Thank God Renee saw more than what meets the eye, he thought.

"Damn, man, you must be living it up. Rolling up in here in a Maybach." Lincoln couldn't take his eyes off the car.

"I'm doing all right. So what's good?"

Even though Julian appeared to be at ease, he was scared to hear what Lincoln had to say. All he knew was it concerned Renee and her sister, and anything dealing with her family couldn't be good. He watched as Lincoln looked every way except his, and saw how sweat threatened to fall from his forehead. This only made Julian panic more, but he hid it well, never allowing anyone to see him sweat.

Lincoln took a deep breath and looked around one more time before speaking. "Renee's sister, Page, is a nut, Jay. She's going to try to kill Renee."

"What? They haven't seen each other in years. What beef could they possibly have?" Julian was all ears.

Lincoln swallowed the knot in his throat. How could he answer Julian's question without sounding crazy himself? he wondered.

"I think Page is in love with her father."

He looked at Julian. When he saw his eyes blow up and a question mark appear on his face, this confirmed that Julian was taking the news just as Lincoln had expected.

"Page is what? What the hell are you talking about? And what does that have to do with Renee?" Fury filled Julian's eyes. He wasn't in the mood for games, and Lincoln was surely playing them.

"Listen, man, this chick is straight loony tunes." He turned away from Julian, gathered his thoughts, then looked back at him. "I know this isn't any of my business, but why is their pops locked up?"

Julian thought he was going to choke the life out of Lincoln. He was sticking his nose where it didn't belong, and Julian was two seconds away from ripping it off his face.

Lincoln saw the look Julian was giving him and quickly continued speaking. "I heard Page talking to herself. She was saying something about Renee landing their father in jail, and how . . ."

Through clenched teeth, Julian growled, "Spit it out."

"She said that Renee was lucky to have slept with their father. She wanted it to be her. She's in love with him, and because of that, she's jealous of Renee. That has to be why she wants Renee dead."

Julian sat in silence. Renee's past had come back to haunt her.

"She wants her dead, man. I heard it out of her mouth. She had some chick with red hair looking for Renee, and when the chick found out where Renee lives, she gave Page the address. Page said that when she sees her, Renee will be dead. Page is out for blood. This girl ain't playing with a full deck of cards, Jay. I did some research, and there are females out there who are in love with their pops. It's called the Electra complex. Something's not right with her, man, and I had to tell you. I couldn't look the other way when Renee's life is in danger."

"I assume it's true, then, that you're fucking Sheila. If you wasn't, you wouldn't know shit. When will this go down?" Julian knew about Lincoln's relationship with Sheila. He always kept his ears to the street.

Lincoln shrugged his shoulders. "That's the only thing I don't know."

Julian blew out air and tried to calm himself down. It wasn't Lincoln's fault that shit was hitting the fan. He was just the messenger.

"Good looking out. You didn't have to let me know shit, but you did, and because of that, I'll inform you about a few things. Renee had a fucked-up life. That dude you're talking about is Page's father, not Renee's. He's in prison because he raped Renee. As for this whole Electra complex shit, I don't know anything about that. All I know is Renee went off to college after high school.

She wanted to get away from her moms, who abused her every chance she got."

Lincoln wasn't prepared for anything he'd just heard. He was speechless. This entire time, he had been in the presence of a bunch of wolves in skirts.

As if he could read his mind, Julian said, "Yeah, homie, you sleeping with the enemy. Because you're here in one piece, I know Page doesn't know you're hip to her. Keep it that way, and take my advice. Stop fucking with their moms. No good can come of it."

Julian got up from the table and prepared to leave. He paused and bent down toward Lincoln so only he could hear him and asked, "Is there anything else I should know?"

Lincoln was now sweating bullets and wished this were all just a bad dream. "Page knows Renee's Jordan."

Julian's heart dropped. Things kept getting worse by the minute. "You tell no one nothing, you hear me? Nothing. If you hear anything, you call me. And get out of that house ASAP."

Julian dug in his pocket, looked around the diner, and threw ten stacks at Lincoln. He believed in rewarding people for valuable information.

Lincoln looked at the money like it had two heads, scrunched up his face, and said, "Nah. I ain't doing this for no money. I owe this to Renee." Lincoln pushed the money back over to Julian like it was on fire.

"I hear you." Julian stuffed the money back in his pocket. "But take my advice, bro, and leave that witch alone," he told Lincoln once more before leaving.

Chapter 21

The next morning, Julian sat at his huge oak desk, with Dane across from him. Julian had his face in his hands and felt like he was losing his mind. He wanted a drink, but he had drunk all night, and his migraine forbade him from taking another sip of alcohol, forcing him to face reality and suffer.

"We have to kill her," Dane said in a dry tone.

Julian slid his hands from his face to look at Dane, exposing his bloodshot eyes. "Are you crazy? That will kill Renee. Her sister is the only family member she has love for."

"What will kill Renee is her sister, if we don't get to her first."

"Fuck! Why can't she have a normal family!" Julian shook his head and placed his face right back in his hands. Dane was right. However, that didn't make matters any easier.

"It can be done as early as tomorrow—today if I didn't already have a job to do. Trust me, Julian, she'll never know that her sister wanted her head or the fact that we got to her first," Dane remarked.

Julian dropped his hands. It was déjà vu all over again. He and Dane plotting the death of one of Renee's family members in order to protect her, telling themselves that she'd never know they were the ones behind it. The only difference was they were in Julian's office in the States, instead of Dane's in Jamaica.

"Her sister's death will crush her. She has a heart of gold when it comes to Page. And what if she finds out we're the ones behind it? Are you prepared to lose her? Because that's exactly what's going to happen." Julian's eyes begged Dane to rethink her idea and come up with another solution. The situation had to be looked at from every angle.

Dane curled her lips and shrugged her shoulders. She wasn't budging. "I'd rather lose her and know she's still breathing than lose her to death, but all of that shouldn't worry you, because she'll never find out."

Julian sat quietly, stuck between a rock and a hard place, and thirsty for a drink. He pictured the look on Renee's face when she got wind of the fact that her sister was dead. That horrific pained look of hers would resurface and eat away at her beauty. Renee was already broken because of the cards life had dealt her. The death of her sister would only annihilate her, Julian feared.

Dane got up and headed toward the door. Before turning the knob, she looked back at Julian.

"Think about it, but don't be long. The longer you wait, the more danger Renee's in."

Chapter 22

After meeting with Dane, Julian made his was way over to Renee's. His stress level was a little high since he'd just learned that yet again a family issue had arisen. He walked into the house and found Renee in the home theater, where she was watching childhood videos of herself and her father playing. He took a seat next to Renee, his heart breaking. Renee was hurting and knew that before anything got better, it would only get worse. For five minutes, the two sat in silence while watching the home video. Renee's and her father's faces were plastered all over the screen. They were all smiles while he tickled Renee, and her laughter danced throughout the room.

"I'm gonna get you! I'm gonna get you! Tickle monster attack!"

Five-year-old Renee laughed so hard, you couldn't see her sparkling hazel eyes. They were closed. "Daddyyy, stop it!" Renee chuckled.

"Daddy? Who's Daddy? I'm the tickle monster!" Her father sat her down, and the two looked directly into the camera. Their smiles tugged at both Renee's and Julian's hearts.

"Renee, say, 'I love you, Daddy.'"

"I love you, Daddy. Now you say, 'I love you,' Daddy," Renee squealed.

"I love you, Daddy."

"No, Daddy! Say you love me! Not 'I love you, Daddy.'"

"You love me."

"No, Daddy! Say, 'I love you!'" Renee fell back into her father's arms, laughing all over again. Her father smiled and looked at his daughter.

"I love you," he told her.

Julian looked at Renee and saw her eyes watering. He watched, hoping and praying a tear would drop, but like always, it never did. He continued to look at her. He noticed her bright, shimmery eyes were now dull and hard. The video cut off, and the screen went black. Julian saw that there were bags under her eyes, that her hair was in disarray, and that her once glowing skin was now pale and ashy looking. She was going through hell and obviously hadn't slept a wink. Lately, she had been constantly thinking about what took place with Slice. She was feeling betrayed and hurt all over again.

Julian went to grab her hand, but Renee pulled away. She was withdrawing again. Julian took a deep breath. He didn't know what to do, so he just sat there.

"You wanna talk?" he finally asked.

Renee turned and looked at him like he had lost his mind.

Julian turned away from her, wondering why he would ever ask such a thing. He was crazy to think Renee would want to talk. She *never* wanted to talk.

"I'm out. There's money people owe us that I have to get." Julian got up and walked out of the theater. There was no money he needed to retrieve; he just needed to get away from Renee. There was no helping her when she got this way.

Julian walked past Lyfe. He was standing in the doorway, and Julian was sure he had watched the home video. His eyes were as soft as night, and his legs as weak as a newborn's neck.

"Come sit with me, Lyfe."

Lyfe jumped when he heard Renee speak to him. He had no idea she knew he was there. He took a deep breath and walked toward her, his eyes never leaving the empty screen. He sat beside her and tried not to look so uncomfortable.

Renee cut the video on and watched it all over again. There were moments when her father's face filled the screen, and Lyfe felt like the wind had been knocked out of him. He'd died many years ago, but Lyfe still found it hard to look at pictures, videos, or anything pertaining to him, including Renee. Lyfe turned to look at Renee, and for the first time since he could remember, he felt scared.

"I don't know how you do it," she said. "After all these years, how are you so loyal to a game that loves no one?"

Relieved by her question, Lyfe stopped holding his breath. He knew it was sad to admit, but he'd been a gangster for most of his life, and he loved it. He loved every aspect of being a criminal and his boss's muscle. Lyfe would live a life of crime until the wheels fell off. What could he say? He was built that way.

He sat back and refrained from answering Renee's question. He knew she had more to say. No one knew this, not even Julian, but Renee had confided in Lyfe on many occasions. He was the perfect ear: He never voiced his opinions; therefore, she didn't feel judge. And Renee felt a sense of comfort with him that she didn't feel with anyone else. She didn't know what it was, but she felt connected to him, so she took advantage of this connection from time to time and confided in him about her past and current feelings.

"I'm tired, Lyfe. I'm tired of living a life where every day I have be more ruthless than the last, just to secure my position on this throne. This shit has turned me so cold. I no longer have any regard for humankind, and I am nothing but a parasite. Yes, I was fucked up before I became Jordan, but now I'm just a monster." Renee paused and looked at the screen. Her father was waving at her.

"I miss him to death," she said, looking at her father. "I would give my last dime just to see him again. I have no family, no nothing, and that shit is eating me alive. I would love to have my baby sister in my life, but I don't see that happening without my mother getting wind of it. So that's just one more person I have to say goodbye to. All I have is Julian, and I'm putting him through more hell than you know." For a moment, Renee stared into space and thought about the life she'd never had, the family, the friends, the happiness. "Tell me about your family, Lyfe. Tell me what I'm missing out on."

Renee knew she was asking for a lot. Lyfe spoke to no one, yet she was sitting here, asking him to open up to her. Lyfe looked into her eyes and saw the desperation they held. She wanted a family so badly that she was willing to live through someone else's.

Lyfe tensed up. Family was a touchy subject for him, and he didn't know what to do, let alone say. He did the only thing he could: he told the truth. Lyfe cleared his throat, preparing his voice box for conversation.

"My parents are retired in Miami, Florida, where I grew up. We don't talk much. I'm the black sheep of the family. I've been doing this shit for most of my life, and no one in my bloodline would have anything to do with me except for my brother. My brother was the good kid. Me and him were like night and day, so my parents didn't feel like total failures."

"You said your brother *was* the good kid. What's up with the past tense?"

Lyfe looked up at the screen, tears threatening to fall.

"He's dead."

Renee saw the pain etched on his face and told him, "I know how you feel." For a few seconds she was quiet. Then she continued with her questions. "No kids, no woman at home?"

Lyfe shook his head. "No kid deserves to have a father with my lifestyle. As for a woman, many have come and gone, but none have captured my heart."

"Is there anyone in your family you're close to? Don't tell me you're an orphan like me."

The two laughed, and Renee had to admit it felt good.

"I have two nieces I'm close to."

His eyes met Renee's, and instantly she became uncomfortable. Something inside her told her not to continue with this conversation, but she did, anyway. Hearing about a family outside of hers was a distraction from her life.

"Tell me about them," she said.

Lyfe didn't want to have this conversation, but he couldn't avoid it any longer. It was now or never.

"There's not much to say. I done right by the youngest. I gave her everything she ever needed and wanted, and even acted as a father figure to her. The other one, the oldest, I failed miserably. I fucked up. Before my brother died, he begged me to look after his girls and allow them to have a relationship. But like I said, I'm the black sheep of the family, so my relationship with everyone except my brother was nonexistent. The girls have different mothers, but his wife, the mother of the oldest, hated me and called me a thug every chance she got. Sometime after his death, she got up and moved without telling anyone where she was going. I searched for my niece for years but came up empty. Then, around five years ago, I found her. She's all grown up now, and she's the most powerful woman I've ever known." A lone tear cascaded down Lyfe's cheek.

Finally, he had released years of pain.

Renee saw the tear, and her chest got tight. Instantly, she became more uncomfortable and didn't want to hear any more. This was not the type of story she wanted to hear. But for some reason, she still fixed her mouth to ask, "What happened next?"

Lyfe swallowed. He'd got this far, and there was no turning back.

He looked Renee in the eyes, his heart beating a mile a minute, and said, "I started working for her."

Chapter 23

Ever since Dane had brought it to Julian's attention that Renee could possibly die if they didn't kill Page, Julian had been in a bad mood. He didn't think he could take away the only family Renee had left, but he knew for a fact that he couldn't live with himself if something happened to her. However, after seeing what he'd just seen, he temporarily forgot about it all and allowed happiness to wash over him.

Julian stepped out of the shower and threw on a white button-down shirt, a pair of blue jeans, and white uptowns. He flashed his award-winning smile and his fresh haircut, which was only a couple of days old, all the way to his car. He looked at all his cars parked in his building's garage. His smile grew, and he nodded his head, thinking, *Yeah, I'll go with the Jag.*

Julian got into his Jaguar and jumped when he looked up and saw Dane in the passenger's seat, reading Tolstoy's *The Death of Ivan Ilyich*. She knew that she'd startled him, but she didn't take her eyes off the book. Just as Julian suspected, there sat Metro in the backseat, with his head back, eyes closed, and hands folded on his lap. Immediately, Julian started to look around his car.

How did they get in? Everything looks intact. Julian shook his head and pushed the question to the back of his mind.

"Judging by the smile you had on your face while you were approaching the car, I assume you saw the news." Dane's eyes were still glued to the pages of the book.

Julian smiled again. If he kept this up, his face may permanently be stuck like that. "Sure did. You do some good work. They have no idea who's behind the murder, and magically, the prison's video footage of that night disappeared."

"It pays to have lowlifes in high places. The wardens and everyone on that prison's payroll are dirty as shit. Not to mention I've done business with more than half of them." Dane laughed.

"What about the prisoners?" Julian asked.

"The prison's top dog is a loyal client of mine and is serving life. He put the word out for everyone to turn a blind eye."

Julian's smile grew.

"You should have seen it. Once I infected him with the poison and mentioned how you took joy in putting this hit out on him, his eyes got big. They got even bigger once I said Renee's name."

Curtis sat in his cell, with only minutes left to live. His body was paralyzed from the eyes down. Dane lay next to him.

"Normally, I just watch my victims die, right down to their last breath, without speaking a word. But you, you, my dear, are a very, very special case. I was called on by some close friends of mine to take care of you."

Curtis looked at Dane. His eyes were pleading with her to save him. He felt his body quickly shutting down, organ by organ, with every second that passed.

"You remember my friends Renee and Julian?" Dane said.

Curtis eyes widened, and Dane smiled.

"See, I told you, you'd remember them. Well, anyway, back to what I was saying, because I'm sure by what you're feeling, you know you don't have long. This visit is courtesy of Julian *and* Renee. They couldn't wait for us to meet, and I'm sure once they get wind of your death, it'll just make their day."

Dane was now antagonizing Curtis, rubbing his death in his face. She might as well have put her hands on both sides of her head and said, "Na-na-na-na-na-na." And it didn't escape Dane that the sound of Renee's name for a second time had almost made Curtis's eyes pop out of their sockets.

"Oh, I see. Since *Renee* disappeared without a trace, you thought no one knew her whereabouts or if she was alive. She's alive, all right. Better yet, she's right in Manhattan," Dane told him.

Tears dropped from Curtis's eyes and hit the prison floor. All these years he had wondered where Renee was. Now that he had finally got the answer he'd longed for, he was on his deathbed, unable to move or speak.

"I hope you have sunscreen, because it's hot where you're going."

As soon as that comment left her mouth, Curtis closed his eyes and died.

Julian smiled. He was pleased with Dane's account of how she'd murdered Curtis. It only made his day better.

"Since y'all broke into my car, I assume you're heading to Renee's too?" Julian asked.

"You damn right," Metro said out of nowhere. He surprised Julian. For a second, he had forgotten the other man was there. "I ain't spend weeks in a shitty-ass prison not to see her reaction."

Julian and Dane laughed. And then the three of them made their way to Renee's.

Chapter 24

The next morning in Brooklyn . . .

Page didn't notice her legs give out as she dropped to her knees. She didn't notice the waterfall of tears cascading down her gorgeous face, and she didn't even hear the blood-chilling scream her mother let out or see Sheila collapse and Lincoln catch her seconds before she hit the floor. She noticed nothing except the news reporter on the television, who was delivering breaking news.

"Fifty-five-year-old Curtis Bookend, an inmate in an upstate New York prison, was found dead in his cell by a guard hours ago. The apparent cause is poisoning. Police do not have any leads at the moment, but they are questioning the prison guards and inmates as we speak."

Page repeated what the reporter had said over and over again in her head.

After laying Sheila down on a couch, Lincoln focused his attention on the television. The dark-skinned reporter with long black locks was now summarizing the criminal charges that had landed Curtis behind bars. She told the public how Curtis's stepdaughter had spoken out about being molested by him and had chronicled the physical abuse she'd endured. Hearing the reporter give a rundown of Curtis's charges made Lincoln flash back to his conversation with Julian at the diner. He understood why Renee had disappeared. She had no one, and she was probably trying to run away from the pain and into the arms of happiness.

He shook his head and looked at Page, who was now situated in front of the television, on her knees, giving the screen her undivided attention. He then looked at Sheila, lying on the couch, crying her heart out while screaming, "Why! Why!" The scene disgusted Lincoln. These two women were crying their hearts out over a man who had raped their family member, yet they hadn't uttered a word of concern over Renee being missing and never heard from again. All he had heard pertaining to Renee was Page's desire to find her and kill her, because of the jealousy she possessed. Sheila had never, not once, even spoken about Renee to him. It was as if she didn't exist.

These women were nothing but vultures, and looking at Sheila, Lincoln had no idea what he had seen in her. Granted she was a good lay, but sex was no match for coldheartedness. Lincoln had to get away. These women were bad news, and he wanted no part of it.

Finally, Page sat back on her behind, but she didn't take her eyes off the television, which was now showing pictures of Curtis. Once his face appeared on the screen, Sheila cried louder and harder. Page was in shock. Curtis was gone; her love was gone; her dream was gone. As she looked at nothing but prison pictures plastered across the TV screen, Page had the scary realization that life for her was now over.

They didn't even call us. Those motherfuckers didn't even have the decency to contact his family before making it public, she thought.

Page was frozen. She couldn't and didn't want to

move. All she wanted was for Channel 11 to scroll the words *April Fools!* across the TV screen. When her eyes darted over to the calendar and she saw that it read July, her heart broke all over again. She struggled to breathe. She couldn't believe her father was gone. Countless tears dropped, making a small puddle at her feet.

It was Renee's fault. None of this would have come to be if she'd kept her mouth shut or, better yet, if she'd never been born, Page thought. She took someone who belonged to me, threw him in prison, and ultimately ended his life. It wasn't enough to have him. She had to take him away from me, literally.

Page willed away the tears that threatened to fall.

No more planning, she thought. *No more waiting. She's dead. End of story.*

Chapter 25

Over in the Village, Club Midnight was in overdrive. Liquor was flowing, music was blasting, and the people on the dance floor were moving so fast while battling each other, they were sweating bullets. The women were half naked, hoping to snag a baller, and the men were on the sidelines, admiring the women like fine pieces of art, trying to decide who they were going to kick it to.

The club was crowded and hot. Overwhelmed by the number of people, Lincoln decided to step out into the parking lot and get some air. The night air slapped him in the face and gave him a boost of energy. Sheila was taking a lot out of Lincoln. She had noticed him pulling away and wasn't having it. If she couldn't have Curtis, she would settle for Lincoln, and she wouldn't let go until she was ready.

The thought of Sheila stressed Lincoln out. In order to hold on to his sanity and avoid her craziness, which obviously ran in the family, he had limited the time he spent at her house and had not been visiting nearly as much as he used to. He planned to slowly get away from her. He was going to take Julian's advice and leave her.

In the parking lot Lincoln kicked back the last of his Pinnacle and orange juice, then leaned against a white Mercury with tinted windows. He closed his eyes and took a moment to enjoy the fresh air and quiet.

His moment of peace was interrupted when he heard
someone stumbling out of the club. A redhead in a
miniskirt and tank top struggled to keep her balance as
she began wandering around the parking lot, in search of
her car. When she finally caught her balance and stood
up straight, she looked around the lot and saw her car
parked next to the Mercury. Staggering, she made her
way to her car and then fumbled in her purse for her keys.

Coming up empty, she slapped her forehead with
her right hand and screamed out, "Damn it! Leana, you
drove. Get your ass out here!"

Watching the drunken female, Lincoln shook his head.

"What are you shaking your head at?" she snapped.

"You."

The redhead rolled her eyes. "Listen, I don't give a
damn what you think, because in a matter of hours, I
am going to be ten thousand dollars richer." She looked
Lincoln up and down before continuing. "And by the
looks of it, you could use it." She laughed at her own joke
while slapping her knees. "Yup. So be nice, and maybe
I'll give you a few dollars." She proceeded to walk away,
but Lincoln wasn't going to let her off the hook that easy.

"Ten Gs? Is that what you charge for a blow job?"

The redhead stopped in her tracks, turned around, and
rushed toward Lincoln, her high heels and drunkenness
making her wobble.

"Fuck you! For your information, I know something
worth millions. Something anyone would pay me that
amount of money for!" she yelled.

Lincoln couldn't get enough of this young woman's
meaningless ranting. Her face was now turning as red as
her hair, and he was loving it. He continued to taunt her.

"Really? And what might that be?" With a smirk on his face, he straightened up and crossed his arms over his chest, ready to hear this important information.

"Not only do I know who Jordan is, but I know where she lives."

Lincoln felt like the wind had been knocked out of him. Did he hear what he thought he heard? Did he just hear this drunken fool say she knew who Jordan was and where she lived? Lincoln's eyes darted to the club. He was now in great need of a drink. When he looked back at the female, he had a flash of the basement closet he'd hidden in at Sheila's house.

That hair, that red hair, he thought. Lincoln stared at her for what seemed like eternity. *She's the one who told Page about Renee.*

"It's not nice to tell lies." Lincoln's eyes were cold.

"Who said I'm lying? I speak the truth. Jordan is a woman, and her behind is laid up in a penthouse over on Fifth Avenue. That information right there just earned me ten thousand dollars."

"Who'd you tell? Who's giving you the money?" Lincoln was still in shock. He couldn't believe he was face-to-face with the person who had basically signed Renee's death certificate. He wanted to make sure she was the culprit.

Tina looked at Lincoln with glossy eyes. She had run her mouth one time too many while in her drunken state, and she couldn't stop. "Her sister. Jordan is really Renee. She's been MIA, and by me telling her sister her whereabouts, I hit the jackpot." Tina smiled a crooked smile.

"How did you find out?"

"Damn, you ask a lot of questions. My brother works for her. He goes by the tag name Waves. Why? You know him?"

Lincoln shook his head. "Nah, I don't know him. But what's your name?"

"Tina. Listen, I would love to talk more, but I have to be out." Tina turned around and started to make her way back to the club.

Lincoln stood there and had the sensation of smoke coming out of his head. He couldn't believe he had just spoken with the person who gave Page the ammo she needed to kill Renee. He watched her stumble into the club and nearly fall face-first on the threshold. He thought about dragging her back to the parking lot and taking her life. No one would know. The club was in full swing, and not a soul was in the lot. But the longer he mulled over the idea, the more he knew he couldn't. Lincoln didn't have it in him to take a life, but he did have it in him to tell a person who did.

Lincoln leaned against his car again, pulled out his cell, and once again dialed Julian.

Chapter 26

Janae sat in a bubble bath at the Hilton Hotel, sipping on bubbly. Things couldn't get any better for her. Renee had fallen right into her lap, and it hadn't even been a full two weeks since she'd left Jared's place and the hunt had begun. She had thought the streets would talk, but their lips were sealed. People still had no information on Renee's whereabouts. The chick had literally fallen off the face of the earth. That was until Janae had attended an old friend's funeral. Janae poured herself another glass of champagne and thought back to when she had finally caught her prey, just hours prior.

Almost all of New York had come out for Slice's funeral. Everyone in attendance was dressed in black, and they all had low faces and eyes concealed with shades. They were all there to pay respects, but whether it was intentional or not, they all talked about how Slice's body had been discovered. Slice had been found sprawled out on the sidewalk of Jordan's most profitable street. Most of Jordan's crew had been hugging the block when Slice's body was thrown from an unmarked midnight-black minivan that had come creeping down the street in broad daylight. His body was badly decomposed, his tongue had been cut out, and half of his head was gone. Everyone knew that Jordan was sending a message.

*Word on the street was that Slice had crossed Jordan,
and Jordan had got wind of his betrayal. After witnessing
Slice's body laid out on the concrete, everyone knew
it was no coincidence that they had all received a text
telling them all to meet on that very street at the exact
time the van made its presence. Although no one knew the
real reason why Slice was killed, Jordan had decided to
make it known that anyone could get it. Before they even
thought about pulling a fast one, they would be dealt with
just like Slice.*

*No one had thought this would happen to Slice.
Unbeknownst to Renee, many had heard that he was plotting against her, but honestly, they had thought he would
get away with it. Slice had been what the crew called "an
insider." He had worked directly with Jordan and had
known the operation inside and out. Many had thought
he had the chance, the knowledge, the tools, and the trust
to take what he wanted, but right along with Slice, they'd
all been wrong.*

*In the church, the streets mourned the death of Slice.
People described Slice as the realest dude they had ever
known. Although he'd been hard to the core and his
mouth had been disrespectful, many respected him. He
had told it how it was and hadn't apologized for who he
was. He'd been comfortable with himself, and because of
that, he'd drawn people to him. His was a closed casket;
however, in their minds, the mourners saw Slice's half-
missing head and his wide-open mouth, which afforded
a front-row seat to his missing tongue. His mouth had
finally got him in trouble, and now that he'd been made
an example of, he was pitied.*

*The church was packed. Slice's father sat in the front
pew, with his wife and children by his side. His color*

had faded, his face was sunken in, and his eyes were surrounded by dark circles. He was seconds away from resembling a zombie. He blamed himself for not having more control over Slice and for allowing him to go down this road. He was supposed to teach his son how to be a man, and he believed he had failed, and now his heart was broken.

In back of Slice's father and his family, scattered among the churchgoers, were various women Slice had dealt with, including Janae. Every woman except for Janae was crying her eyes out while giving the others dirty looks. Out of respect, none of them acted out or tried to state their claim during the service, but the looks they gave each other said, "I'll see you when I see you."

Janae was decked out in an all-black, knee-length dress and black stilettos and had her hair pulled back in a tight ponytail. She wanted to cry but couldn't. She had used all her tears on all the other funerals she'd been to in the past, funerals that had broken her down. She looked around and could point out every hustler, gold digger, stick-up kid, and law-abiding citizen in attendance. Although she still had a pinch of feelings left for Slice, she didn't understand how everyone known to man could be so heartbroken over his death. The two of them had been together right before she met Jared, and he used to beat her each and every time he got the chance. If she looked at him wrong, she got slapped. If she wore tight pants, she got pushed down a flight of stairs. And if she stayed out too late without his knowledge, she got punched in the face. There was no chance of her having her own identity while she was in a relationship with Slice. He owned her.

Slice was a lot of things when it came to the streets, but no one knew he was a woman beater. Surprisingly, the memories of her ER visits and of her neighbors calling the police during the wee hours of the morning couldn't stop Janae from hurting over his death. A piece of her missed the man he had pretended to be during the first two months of their relationship. However, she wondered whether everyone would they still love him if they knew this side of him.

As she sat in the last row of the church, Janae listened to the pastor talk about life and death. Her eyes were dancing across the sea of tear-drenched, sorrowful faces when Janae saw her. Janae thought her eyes were play-ing tricks on her, but the more she looked and focused on the woman, the more she knew her eyes were far from deceiving her. Renee sat in a formfitting, sheer-sleeved black dress and had a pair of wedged heels on her feet. A veil graced her face, but Janae could see right through it. Next to her sat Lyfe. The two were emotionless.

Did she return to pay her last respects to an old friend? Janae asked herself. She remembered Slice running with Renee when they were in high school. She bit down on the inside of her lip and shook her head. All it took was death to bring her ass back, Janae thought. I should have killed her family when I threatened to do it.

Janae's leg began to bounce, and the hand that held on to the obituary started to sweat. If she had killed Sheila and Page when she first returned to Brooklyn, she would have forced Renee out of her hiding spot a long time ago. However, looking at the face of her sister's killer now, Janae knew it was too late for shoulda, coulda, woulda's. Renee was right there, right in front of her. She'd finally found her, and that was all that mattered.

During the remainder of the service, Janae watched Renee's every move. She was so mesmerized by Renee, she nearly forgot the reason she had attended the funeral. When it was time for the mourners to make their way to the burial site, Renee and four men, including Lyfe, were the first ones up and out the door. Janae hugged the sidelines and watched as Renee gracefully exited the church. As she walked out, she stood between the men, as if surrounded by armor.

Keeping a safe distance, Janae followed Renee out of the church. She was grateful she had got a parking spot right in front of the church, because she was right behind Renee when they pulled off. This was Janae's lucky day. After the burial, she followed Renee all the way home and smiled throughout the ride.

Reliving Slice's funeral and how it led her directly to Renee caused Janae to smile as she enjoyed her bubble bath. She hadn't been this happy and at peace in God knows how long. Yes, Jared had brought happiness to her life for a certain period of time, but deep down inside, she had known this happiness was temporary. She would never live life to the fullest if Leslie was unable to rest in peace. Janae needed her to cross over.

Finding comfort in the hot bathwater, Janae closed her eyes. When she opened them minutes later, she saw Leslie sitting on the edge of the tub. Leslie didn't look angry, but she wasn't ecstatic either. Janae sat up, the water rocking back and forth and racing down the side of the tub. She gave her sister her full attention. A small smile formed on her lips.

"Don't worry. I found her. It'll all be over soon, I promise," she told Leslie.

Leslie looked at Janae for a second, then reached her hand out.

Janae followed suit, but right when their fingers were about to touch, Leslie disappeared. And just like that, Janae was no longer as happy and at peace as she'd been just a couple of minutes ago. Reality had set in, and Janae needed just a few minutes to herself, so she sank to the bottom of the bathtub and lay underwater for as long as her lungs would allow.

Chapter 27

Just hours ago, Renee had walked up to Slice's closed casket and kissed it. Those aware of her identity kept their shock hidden. Incapable of taking their eyes off her, they exchanged whispers.

"Is that Jordan?"

"What the fuck is she doing here? She never shows her face."

"She's sending a message."

Renee bypassed the whispers and caught their stares. The corner of her mouth rose, her half smile confirming their conclusion: things were changing, and it started with Renee stepping out in the open. This moment was liberating and gave her the confidence and push needed to promise herself she'd never hold herself back again.

However, Renee's exhilaration over this achievement dissolved when an uninvited guest visited her home after the funeral. Renee sat across from her lookalike, her face tight, lips in a frown, and eyes cold. It disgusted her how much they looked alike. Those looks she'd received from her father, she saw in this woman. Renee wanted so badly to be able to go back in time and erase finding out that her father had had another child. Had she been given the opportunity, she would have chosen to remain in the dark a little longer. Finding out about this sibling had brought her no comfort or delight, and she wanted this woman to disappear.

"What the fuck is this supposed to do?" Renee spit at Lyfe, who sat next to her at the table. "There's no need for us to meet."

Renee was angry beyond words. Her skin was hot, and every word that left her mouth dripped with venom. Ever since Lyfe had told her their family secrets, she had disrespected him every chance she got. Now that he had brought her father's illegitimate child to her home, she despised him even more. Renee didn't want to meet the young woman and accept the fact that she wasn't Daddy's only little girl. All she wanted to do was go back in time and cut out the part when Lyfe came clean.

Never in Lyfe's existence had he felt so helpless and weak. Ever since he told Renee the truth, she had been giving him hell. He had been around her for years and knew the coldness she had in her heart, but looking at her now, he saw that her cold heart was about to burst and leave her with no heart at all.

"She's your sister, Renee. Don't you want family you can see and talk to?"

Renee knew he was referring to the fact that she did not communicate with her sister Page and her mother. "She's *not* my family. Her ass is a mistake, a product of my father's infidelity."

"Fuck you!" Carmen screamed.

Renee smiled, happy to have gotten under the young woman's skin.

Lyfe raised his hand, signaling for Carmen to be quiet. He took a deep breath and focused on Renee. "Your father didn't have an affair. He was separated from your mother when he got with Raquel."

"If they weren't *legally* separated or divorced when he fucked that woman, then he had an affair, and no one can tell me different." Renee had fire in her eyes as she stared at Lyfe. She dared him to challenge her. He may have been her uncle, but she was still his boss. "You bring this bitch to my house, expecting me to welcome her with open arms. You must be out your damn mind. I suggest you take her raggedy ass back home."

"I'm not about to let you keep disrespecting me, so I suggest you watch your damn mouth!" Carmen yelled. Carmen had had enough. She hadn't asked to be born into this situation, yet Renee insisted on treating her like dirt. Renee didn't even know her to speak so rudely about her.

Renee whipped her head in Carmen's direction. "And what the fuck you gonna do?"

Carmen opened her mouth to respond but quickly shut it. There was nothing that she could do. This wasn't Miami, and she was no longer the head bitch in charge. Once upon a time, Carmen was the woman of a wealthy hustler in Miami, Florida, where she grew up. Carmen was the biggest gold digger you could stumble upon, so when she snagged Benz, she milked him for all he was worth. Materialistic, greedy, and self-centered, Carmen loved what he could give her.

After two years of living the life of the rich and famous, it all came crashing down. Benz met someone else, a good girl, and she talked him into leaving the game alone. Before Carmen knew it, Benz kicked her out of his home and deserted the game. Carmen was devastated. She had no money and no place to go, so Lyfe flew in and saved the day. He moved her to New York, where he got her a brownstone, and he had been taking care of her ever since, financing her shopping sprees and all.

Carmen wished she still had Benz's goons, so that she could set Renee straight, but she didn't. It was obvious from the magnificent home and the way Renee spoke that she was the boss. So Carmen sat there and bit her tongue.

Lyfe looked at Carmen. It pained him to see the look on his baby niece's face. He knew the life she had once lived, and he knew she wasn't used to such disrespect. Renee had the life Carmen used to have, and Renee probably would always have it.

"Renee, give this a chance. Family is all you have. You're gonna need her one day," Lyfe pleaded.

"Need her for what? There's nothing this . . ." Renee pointed at Carmen. "Thing can do for me. You know better than to bring random motherfuckers into my circle. Now get her the fuck out of here!" Renee stood up and headed toward the dining-room door.

Carmen admired her outfit and the diamonds that graced her wrist.

That has to be custom made, she thought to herself.

When Renee was gone, Carmen looked at her uncle, who looked like he had aged overnight. "What do we do now, Unc?"

"I don't know." Lyfe leaned over the table with his hands folded. "Carmen, I know you wanted to meet your sister and even hoped to have a relationship with her. But I'm going to be honest with you. I don't see her ever accepting you. Are you sure you want to keep trying?"

Carmen looked Lyfe dead in his eyes. She hadn't been surer about anything in her whole life. When Lyfe had sat her down and had told her she had a half sister, he'd held nothing back. He'd mentioned how she was older, tough and, most importantly, rich. When Carmen heard that Renee was wealthy and was the person responsible for paying Lyfe his shitload of money, she wanted in. Carmen planned to kill her sister with kindness and mooch off her. Now that she had seen that her sister was indeed a millionaire and in command, she no longer wanted to be taken care of by others. She wanted to be the boss.

Renee had shown Carmen the light and had proved that compared to what she was doing, being a gold digger got you pennies. Renee was a boss, and seeing a woman in power like that made Carmen want to be a boss herself. She'd never have to worry about anyone taking care of her or kicking her to the curb again. The only thing wrong with this picture was that Carmen didn't want to work for it. She didn't want to start at the bottom and build her way up. She wanted to take it. She knew that if she was going to take Renee's spot on the throne, she had to get close to her and gain her trust. She needed to know things, such as who Renee's connect was, and she had to pull Renee's soldiers over to her side. Carmen didn't care how hard Renee was. She was going to get into her circle and snatch her crown.

Carmen smiled her winning smile. "I'm not giving up, Unc. I'll do whatever it takes to win her over."

Chapter 28

Sheila sat her purse on the passenger's seat of her two-week-old Jeep and rolled down all four windows. The loss of her second husband had left her spending huge amounts of money uncontrollably in an attempt to build a wall between herself and her emotions. But what was worse was that ever since Curtis's death, she had been suffering from nightmares on a nightly basis. One recurring nightmare was of her standing in the middle of a giant circle. Strangers of every sex, race, and size surrounded her, each person's arm stretched out, fingers pointed at her while chanting, "Black widow! Kill her before she kills again!"

This was not the first time death had brought an unhealthy number of nightmares to steal Sheila's sleep. Vicious dreams had plagued her every night after the death of her first husband, and these recurring night terrors had resulted in her driving around the city night after night. Sheila had driven faster than the law permitted on the empty road, and with her windows down, she had relished the wind whipping through the car. The breeze and the absence of large numbers of people out on the street had helped ease her mind and had enabled her to forget the nightmares that had forced her awake.

Tonight's dream had been of both her late husbands. They'd stood in front of her, and she'd felt a sense of peace that was so soothing when their smiles found their way to their eyes. Neither of them had spoken, however, when she reached out to rub each of their cheeks. Then they disappeared. Sheila sat at the foot of the bed, crying, when Daniel, her first husband, returned in a new form. His face was filled with black vines that hung below his neck, and his mouth was stitched shut. Sheila tried moving away, then sprinted for the door, but he pulled her backward and stabbed her in the back. She could feel the knife penetrating her skin, shredding her flesh, and destroying any organ in its way.

This was the first time she had ever conjured up her own death in a dream. The experience had caused her breathing to increase, her chest to tighten, and her eyes to shoot open. There were plenty of things worth being frightened of after Sheila closed her eyes, but this terror had felt more like a punishment than her subconscious talking to her. Now as she pulled off in the Jeep, Sheila turned the volume of the radio up to the highest notch and got lost in the memories the music brought to her, all in an effort to rid herself of the imagery of death. She caught the tail end of a popular R & B song that had played in the background when Curtis proposed to her. The tune then turned into the slow jam she and Daniel had danced to on their wedding day. Then came the one song that broke her heart three times over every time she heard it. It was an oldie but goody, a heartbreaker, and she had played it over and over again the night she discovered Daniel was having an affair.

Sheila forbade herself from singing along and becoming emotional about the best and the worst times of her life that she recalled, but as with everything else she set out to do, she failed. When the singer of the heartbreaker hit her final high note, her musical goodbye released Sheila's pent-up tears. The torrent of tears clouded her vision, and her breathing became labored. With one hand she drove, while forcefully drying her face with the other. The outpouring of tears relieved the pressure on her heart; however, the amount of heartache her past relationships had left her with kept her tears on repeat. As she drove, she looked in the rearview mirror, and looking back at her was her bloated, dry face.

When she felt another round of tears gathering, she kept it at bay by holding air in her mouth and giving herself bubble cheeks. She sped down the street and then turned into a neighborhood covered in darkness owing to the large number of trees and the limited streetlights. After screeching to a halt in a parking space on the street, she slapped on the dome light above her head, balled her hands into fists, bent her knees, then freed her tears and wails.

"Ahhh!" Her screams leaked out of the car and seemed to disturb the darkness. Sinking her head into the headrest, she caught her breath, pushed out more tears, and went for a second round of screams.

"Ahhh!" she screamed, letting go of the negative energy eating away at her.

"Let it out. Let it out," Sheila told herself out loud. Then she gathered as much air into her lungs as possible, steeled herself in her seat by holding on to the car, and screamed bloody murder. "Ahhh!"

Keep going. You're almost there. You're almost there.

Sheila screamed some more and pushed her head harder against the headrest. Then her screams seemed to get stuck inside her mouth, and what did come out was muffled. Sheila grabbed at the hand that was now covering her mouth, and dug her nails into the leather glove shielding that hand. She swung one fist behind her while still trying to tear the hand off her mouth. The longer she fought, the more her fear intensified and the more the hand tightened its grip on her mouth.

Sheila pushed her body upward and managed to loosen slightly the hand that covered her mouth. She reached for the door and was unlocking it when she was stabbed in the side of the neck. Overwhelmed and in shock from the unknown poison that had been injected in her, Sheila froze in her seat. Venom traveled through her bloodstream, immobilizing her and then rendering her unconscious.

Sitting near the water in New Jersey, there was a run-down, raggedy house long overdue to be torn down. The family that once occupied it had left over five years ago, and ever since it had stood empty, an eyesore for the city. Anyone who walked by cringed at the sight of it. The outside was hideous, so folks could only imagine how the inside looked. Most thought it was probably cold, dark, and damp, the result of no life inhabiting it. Only a crazy person would walk into that house and dare to stay in there for more than five minutes without fear of the floor collapsing or rats running across their feet. That crazy person was Dane. She wore a dark brown wig in the style of a bob cut, and she was dressed in all black. Beside her stood Metro, who wore a bald cap, a fake mustache and goatee, and was also dressed in all black.

They stood in a room in the basement, where heavy plastic covered the floor. There was nothing but three metal chairs, a bathtub in the middle of the room, and one lightbulb hanging from the middle of the ceiling, giving the room all the light it needed. For a summer day that had nearly hit ninety-five degrees, the room was fairly cold.

Dane and Metro wore black hoodies to keep warm. They had been in that room for over an hour, waiting for Sheila, who was tied to one of the chairs, to wake up. The two were tucked away in the darkness when Sheila started to move. Her head slowly moved from left to right, and her eyelids began to flutter. Finally, Sheila's eyes opened, she blinked a few times, and she tried to focus on what was in front of her. When her vision was where it needed to be, she looked around the room.

Where the hell am I? Confused and lost, Sheila felt her heart rate increase and her body start to tremble. Then intense pain kicked in and forced her to be still. Once the pain subsided enough to bear, Sheila looked down and discovered that not only was she naked and tied to a metal chair, but her body was also covered in countless tiny cuts.

"No! No! No! Help me! Somebody help me!" she yelled.

Sheila pulled against the ropes binding her and frantically rattled the metal chair. The chair slid just a little on top of the plastic-covered floor. The more she moved, the more the ropes rubbed against her skin and dug into her cuts. Sheila whimpered and tried to will away the pain.

"You're not getting out," Dane informed her.

Sheila's head shot up. "Who said that? Where are you?"

Husband and wife walked out of the corner that cloaked their identity. Sheila laid eyes on the two of them just as the events of the night came back to her—the late-night drive, her pulling over, then being attacked. Blood trickled down her face and fell on the plastic floor, which her toenails scraped against.

"Please! Why are you doing this?" Sheila sobbed. She twisted around as best she could, trying to loosen the ropes around her legs and arms, as she ground her teeth and took on the pain.

"I'm going to be honest with you, Sheila. *I* want to know why I'm doing this too." Dane folded her arms.

"I don't understand." Sheila wished her tears would stop falling. The more she cried, the more the tears burned her cuts.

"I was sent by Renee. You remember Renee, don't you?"

Sheila's eyes grew wide, and her mouth opened slightly. "Renee . . . ," she whispered.

"Yes, your daughter. Now that we can all agree that we know her, I think you have some explaining to do. Why would your daughter send me to torture you?"

Sheila fell silent. She thought she would die from the pain; however, her mind still focused on her daughter while she gazed up at what was left of the basement ceiling.

She's alive?

Even though Sheila was trying to gather her thoughts, Dane didn't like being ignored. Dane looked over at Metro and nodded her head. He pulled out a jar filled with rubbing alcohol and threw half of it on Sheila. A high-pitched noise arose from Sheila, and her big toes banged against the floor.

"Now that I've got your attention, I'm only going to repeat this once more. Why would your daughter send me to torture you and then kill you?"

Sheila's head whipped in Dane's direction. Her blood and tears mixed together. "You're going to kill me?"

"If you don't tell me what I want to know," Dane lied.

Sheila fidgeted in her seat, using the remainder of her strength to try to break free of her restraints, but to no avail. She took a deep breath, cut out the crying, and nodded. "I bet it's about what it's always about. My husband." Sheila clenched her teeth. It hurt to blink.

Sheila went on. "When Renee was young, her father died in a car crash. We moved from Miami to New York, where I met my second husband, Curtis. We got married and had a daughter together soon after. I was blessed with a second love after losing my first." She gave a small smile that didn't last long. "Things were great. Then Renee started to flirt with Curtis. At first, I took it as an innocent crush, but then she seduced him and started sleeping with him." A tear slid down Sheila's face, and she shivered.

"How old was Renee when your husband first slept with her?" Metro asked.

"I don't know, but I know it had to be before the little slut was a teenager."

Metro smirked. "There's a kid and a grown-ass man, and in your eyes, your daughter was the one doing the seducing and she forced herself on him?"

Sheila gave a small nod. "What else could it be?"

Dane pushed out her breath. Her hands formed into fists. "So your husband has no part in this at all, huh?"

Sheila looked over to Dane. "Of course not. If you're insinuating that he raped her, then you're wrong. All he was doing was being a man and taking what was flaunted in his face."

Dane's head was spinning. She couldn't believe what she was hearing. Everything was making sense now. She now understood why Renee hated her mother and didn't want to tell her why. Dane knew nothing about this, but she knew Renee had not thrown herself at Curtis. She'd been raped.

Dane looked at Sheila. She had Renee written all over her. She looked like an older version of her daughter, older thanks to the wrinkles and the bags underneath her eyes, products of years of being angry, in pain, and stressed out. She had been making herself age faster than God intended.

"You're sick if you actually believe your husband had no hand in any of this. Your husband raped your daughter, and you did nothing? What did you do? Listen while he raped her? Does that get you off or something?" Dane snarled.

Right when Dane was finished speaking, Sheila tried with all her might to get out of the chair. It started to wiggle, and she nearly tipped it over. Her cuts were so deep that she screamed while trying to move.

"She's the sick one!" Sheila shouted. "She knew how devastated I was when her father died. She knew that if I could, I would have died right along with him. It didn't matter to her. She still had to take Curtis from me when she saw I had found happiness again! She was Daddy's little girl, got all her father's attention, and that's exactly what she was trying to do with Curtis. Have all his attention, leaving nothing for me."

Her words bothered Metro so much, he walked toward her to give her one good back slap, but Dane held out her hand and stopped him. Sheila sat in her chair, crying uncontrollably now. She had never actually sat down and told someone exactly how she felt concerning her husband and her daughter. Her tears burned her cuts so bad, but she couldn't stop crying.

"Do you know how it feels to have to compete with your daughter every day? To always be reminded that no matter what you do, you can never compare? She had her father's heart under lock and key. There wasn't a day that went by that Daniel could forget about Renee for just one second. Just one second, so that it could be about me and him. It was always about what schools we should start looking into for Renee once high school and college rolled around. What career we believed best fit her, and what activities we should get her into. It was the Renee show twenty-four hours a day, seven days a week. When he died, that show went off the air. Because of that, she looked to Curtis to give her what she wanted." Sheila finally calmed down, and her tears started to let up.

She went on. "I miss Daniel. I know he was only being a good father. He didn't have sex with Renee or even put one finger on her, not even to discipline her. And I'll admit, from time to time, he showed me a lot of affection, unlike Curtis. It's just that I wanted more. I wanted more of his time, without Renee around to interrupt. I wanted it to be the way it was before she was born." Sheila's head hung low. She knew she was wrong to feel this way about Renee, and she refused to look anyone in the eye.

"I don't feel bad for you. You're a monster. Because of your selfish tendencies, you allowed your daughter to be raped under your own roof. I should kill you now." With every word Dane spoke, she spit venom.

Her hair covering her face, her eyes barely visible, Sheila looked at Dane. Her face was so cut up, she looked like an evil villain. "She just wouldn't learn. I did everything in my power to try to keep her away from Curtis. I beat her, treated her like a stepchild by making her do any and everything. I even made it my business to tell her daily how she disgusted me and how I couldn't stand her. But every time I turned around, she was with him again. Screaming and crying like she didn't want it, like she didn't ask for it. She seduced him to the point where he started putting her first. He stopped sleeping with me. He even killed for her."

Dane and Metro looked at each other after she made her last statement.

"What do you mean, he killed for her?" Metro walked closer to Sheila.

Sheila bit down on her lips, and when she did, she was surprised that her lips weren't cut too. "When Renee was a teenager, there was a girl her age that lived in our neighborhood and went to school with her. The two didn't get along. Every other day I was getting calls from school, telling me how the girl was harassing Renee. It was never Renee's fault. The girl started with Renee every chance she got. Teachers and students said the girl did it because she believed Renee took her boyfriend. In actuality, Renee didn't take the girl's boyfriend. The boy left her because he liked Renee, but Renee wouldn't give him the time of day. One day the girl got suspended for opening the door to the classroom Renee was in and throwing a textbook at her. Later that day, when Renee was walking home, the girl and a bunch of her friends jumped her. She came home with a busted lip and a broken nose. I will never forget that day." Sheila stopped talking and looked up in the air, as if she was reliving every moment.

She continued. "I'll never forget how it creeped me out when she didn't cry. She walked into the house and headed straight for the bathroom to clean herself up. Boy, was her face messed up. I watched her apply alcohol and bandages to her face, and she didn't even flinch from the sting I knew the alcohol was giving her. She just cleaned herself up, as if she was cleaning a paper cut on her finger. When she was finished, I asked her if she was okay, and she gave me this look . . . this look that shook me down to my soul. The look in her eye, I had never seen before. It scared the hell out of me. She looked like she was in a trance. Finally, I couldn't take it anymore, so I left the room.

"That night Curtis went out and didn't come home till after three in the morning. I waited up for him. I was worried. When he finally came home, he was dressed in clothes he didn't have on when he left the house. I asked him where the clothes he'd had on earlier were, and why he'd changed. He didn't answer me until we got to our bedroom, and when we did, he went to the window and glanced out of it and smiled." Tears dropped from Sheila's eyes. "As he held the curtain open, he looked at me and said, 'I did it. I killed the little bitch. Now she'll never mess with my girl again. Never.'"

Sheila paused to catch her breath. "The next day the girl's body was found in a Dumpster miles from our home. She had been raped, and her throat was slit. The little girl's name was Leslie. It was at that moment that I knew he was in love with Renee, knew I could never capture his heart as she had. I ended all communication with Renee after that. I pretended she didn't exist. It was incredible how everyone loved Renee except for me and that girl who died. She had it all, little boys running after her, gorgeous looks, and brains to match. She was the belle of the ball, a princess. I gave birth to her, so why couldn't that be me? Why couldn't I possess the same qualities as her?" Sheila looked into Dane's eyes, truly asking these questions and awaiting answers. When she didn't get any, she took a deep breath.

"Renee wound up going to the police and got Curtis locked up," Sheila continued. "Then, around a year later, she disappeared. I never seen or heard from her again. It's been so long, I thought she was dead. Her leaving crushed Curtis. He went into a deep depression for months while in prison. He always asked if we had heard anything about her. He always held on to the thought that one day she'd come back. And I always held on to the hope that she wouldn't. When I saw that she was never coming back, I was happy, and I thought Curtis would be too, since she's the reason he's in prison. Charging him with rape, that little bitch!" Sheila stopped for a second, slowly shaking her head. "After that, it was just me and my baby, Page. Just me and my baby."

Dane just stared at Sheila. "So tell me, are you jealous of Page, like you are Renee?"

"Of course not. She's my baby girl. Yes, she's gorgeous and smart, but she's nothing compared to Renee. Renee is the type of woman you have to look out for, the type of woman who's the total package and can be dangerous if she discovers it and uses it. Why do you think I always put her down? Of course, it's because she took my husband, but it's also because she is who I always wanted to be. A woman like that can never reach her full potential if she doesn't know what she has, and if I didn't have it, I'd be damned if she would. Anyone, anyone, I tell you, but her should be so lucky."

Sheila paused for a second. "Page is no threat. I hated Renee for Page just as much as I hated her for myself. I never treated them the same or loved them the same, because if I had, Page would forever be living in her sister's shadow and would have only tried to be, if not better, just as good as Renee. And that is something I know Page can never accomplish. She just doesn't have what it takes."

For two minutes, the basement was quiet. No one had a word left to say. Everything Sheila had just said blew Dane's and Metro's minds. To hear such hate aimed at a daughter coming from a mother's mouth was unreal.

"Well, at least I know why your daughter wants you dead. And I can't say that I blame her," Dane noted.

"Is there anything that I can say to make you change your mind?" Sheila gasped.

Metro laughed. "Don't you think you said enough?"

Sheila put her head down and bit down on her lip, holding back her tears. When she wasn't looking, Dane nodded in her direction.

Metro took out an X-Acto knife used for artwork and cutting. He walked over to Sheila and began cutting into the cuts she already had. He made many of the cuts deeper than they were. Sheila thought she would pass out from the pain. It hurt so much, she could no longer scream, let alone open her eyes. When he was done, Metro untied her arms and legs. She was so weak from the pain, she could not even sit up straight. She just let her body fall forward. Metro grabbed her and picked her up. Then he carried her over to a bathtub filled with liquid and dropped her in it. Immediately, Sheila found her voice and started to scream. The tub was filled with nothing but alcohol and peroxide. Dane and Metro just stood there and watched her scream, all emotion absent from their faces.

When Sheila's screams turned into whimpers, Dane said to her, "You're not feeling even half the pain you've caused your daughter over the years."

Dane then slipped a needle filled with the same poison used to kill Curtis out of a pocket of her hoodie. She walked over to Sheila. When Dane got close enough for Sheila to see what she was carrying, Sheila opened her mouth, but nothing came out. Fear consumed her. Dane bent down so that she was at eye level with Sheila, whose body was bloody and weak.

"There's something I want you to know. There's poison in this needle here." Dane shook the needle in Sheila's face. "The same poison I used to kill Curtis."

Sheila seemed to stop breathing when she heard those words. She didn't know what to think, say, or do. Hearing Dane had killed Curtis hurt more than sitting in a bathtub filled with alcohol and peroxide when her body was covered in open wounds.

Dane leaned in closer and whispered something to Sheila. She spoke so low that only Sheila could hear. "And when I'm done with you, maybe I'll use the same remedy to kill your precious daughter Page."

A second later, Dane plunged the needle into Sheila's neck. She just lay there and took it. What else could she do? She had no energy whatsoever to even try to push Dane away. She closed her eyes as more tears dripped down her mutilated cheeks. She actually found comfort in knowing she was dying the same death as her husband. That made things a lot easier. The only thing that tugged at her soul was the knowledge that her daughter would also die this death.

Unexpectedly, Sheila's body became paralyzed. Even though she had been weak before, at least she could move her fingers and toes. Now she could not even do that. Dane stood to her feet and placed the needle back in her pocket.

"Normally, I watch my victims take their last breath, but after I got to know you tonight, you don't even deserve to die with someone around. You'll die the worst death, a lonely death," Dane told her.

There was not one body part that Sheila could move. All she could do was watch Dane and Metro leave the basement room and close the door behind them.

Chapter 29

Sheila felt her organs shutting down. She knew she couldn't scream or move her mouth, but she tried, anyway. She knew she was dying, so she thought about her life, starting with when she was a little girl and going up until now. Sheila was a very angry, negative person, and she now understood why she was in the position she was currently in. All those years she had hated Renee, when she really should have showered her with unconditional love, like a real mother, and formed a bond with her. Besides, if it wasn't for Renee, Daniel would have left her long before he died.

Before Renee was born, their relationship had been going downhill. The only reason he stayed with her was that she got pregnant with Renee. After she gave birth, he fell in love with little Renee and completely forgot about leaving, but their happily ever after didn't last long. When Renee was two, they separated and were on the road to divorce, but once again, because of Renee, he stayed with Sheila and eventually came back home.

Staring at the ceiling, which was sure to collapse at any second, Sheila thought about when she and Daniel separated. She could still smell the perfume on his clothes and could still see the red lipstick on his shirts. He claimed to have stayed at a hotel while away, but Sheila knew better. She just never said anything, glad to have him home. The memories broke Sheila's heart all over again, and she cursed Dane and Metro for making her relive this again.

I'm so glad I didn't tell them about the separation, about the countless times I cheated on Daniel, which led to me almost losing him not once, but twice. They would have really thought I was a monster then.

While deep in thought, Page appeared right before Sheila's eyes. Sheila thought she was hallucinating, but she soon realized that the person before her was indeed Page. A wave of relief came over Sheila, and she promised herself that since she was now getting a second chance at life, she would change.

Page hovered over her mother and didn't say a word. But when she did open her mouth, Sheila wished she had done what Dane intended for her to do, die alone.

"I'm nothing compared to Renee?" Page screeched.

Sheila couldn't speak. All she could do was let one last tear drop from her eyes.

"I'm no threat? I don't have what it takes to be better than Renee?" Page growled.

Page felt her body temperature rise. Her hands balled into fists, and she felt herself get dizzy. All her life, she had fought to be better than Renee, had fought to achieve all that came easily to Renee. Deep down inside, she had known she wasn't better, had known she could never compete. This had been confirmed when she learned Renee's status. But to hear it come from someone else's mouth made Page not responsible for her actions.

Page didn't hesitate to open her mouth and slowly remove the razor blade. She held it in front of her and stared her mother in the eyes. "It's okay. I know that I can never compare, but I also know that you chose to love the wrong daughter."

The poison was taking its toll, and Sheila was dying. Her eyes rolled to the back of her head, but before the poison could do its job, Page placed the blade up to Sheila's neck and cut.

Chapter 30

The fresh air that hit Renee's face did enough to place her at ease. Walking toward the front door of the bar, she took a deep breath, a small but beneficial attempt at shaking off the stress plaguing her insides. As she reached for the rusted gold doorknob, the door flew open, causing Renee to step back and watch as a man and woman walked out of the bar, their fingers intertwined. Their uproarious laughter and energetic steps brought the word *tipsy* to the forefront of Renee's mind.

Once she was inside, Renee's eyes automatically adjusted to the dimly lit, smoke-filled bar. The music was loud, forcing patrons to repeat themselves when speaking. There was a decent crowd. Enough bodies maneuvered around and sat around that newcomers just blended in. Behind the bar, the face of a young woman with a shaved head, a crop top, and pants two sizes too big glistened with sweat. In a hurry, she handed beers to three loud men embroiled in a debate, then immediately started making drinks for two women captivated by the sight of the men who had just been served.

Focused on the drinking making, the bartender addressed Renee. "What would you like?" Her voice was raspy, as rough as sandpaper.

"A Long Island," Renee announced.

The bartender nodded, carried the drinks over to the women who were thirsty in more than one way, and then began working on Renee's drink. Briefly, Renee closed her eyes and took a deep breath. The cigarette smoke she inhaled distracted her from the stress that had led her here, and she drew in more air in hopes that the more smoke she took in, the greater the chance that she'd totally forget the past few hours.

It was taking a lot for Renee to process the fact that Lyfe was her uncle. She had yet to decide how she felt about the situation, so when Lyfe had brought Carmen into her home today without her permission and had caught her off guard, she'd become consumed by rage. Renee had been given no time for her own history to sink in before Lyfe pushed Carmen into her life. Two hours ago she had lain beside Julian, but her thoughts had prevented her from entering into the deep slumber he was in. Held captive by her anger, she had roamed her home in search of liquor therapy. But then she'd decided she needed to be in a different environment, around people she didn't know, who couldn't surprise her with long-lost relatives. She'd headed to the bar.

Renee's phone vibrated now. She reached inside her back pocket, pulled out her phone, and read the text on the bright screen.

You left while I was in the bathroom. Where are you?

Raspy was on her way with Renee's order, her canvas shoes poking out beneath her pants, when Renee answered the text.

Out.

Renee stuck the device back in her pocket and ignored the vibrations from new text messages coming in just as

Raspy placed her Long Island down on a paper coaster. She couldn't deal with Jared now; she couldn't deal with anyone now.

"Want me to start a tab?" Raspy asked.

Renee removed the straw from the glass, detached the lemon slice from the rim, and automatically placed the drink to her lips. Head back, Raspy watched the drink, which she'd added a lot of kick to, race down her customer's throat.

Without extending the courtesy of hiding their gaze, the women Raspy had served right before Renee also watched her down her drink, for the first time taking their attention off the three great debaters.

"*Okay*. I'll take that as a yes," Raspy said.

Renee slammed the empty glass down. "Another one."

"Coming right up."

Page pulled a fifth of vodka out from under her driver's seat, removed the top, and guzzled nearly half the bottle before she could no longer ignore the burning sensation in her throat. A group of people dressed down in jeans and T-shirts waited patiently at the door for an older gentleman full of gray to exit the bar, his feet dragging and chest heaving in and out with every step he took. Halfway out the door, Page took one last swig of her drink, slapped on a pair of oversize dark shades, hopped out of her car, and stepped behind the waiting group.

Eventually, each person in the group strolled inside the bar, and their leisurely pace gave Page the opportunity to look around. Just as the group suddenly stopped walking, in an attempt to scout out a place to sit, three men stepped away from the bar, giving Page a clear view of her sister. Now in close proximity to Renee, Page realized that she hadn't changed. Page would have guessed, or at least she hoped, that Renee would appear battered and lifeless, her skin sunken in and her flesh clinging to her bones, for which the only logical explanation would have been drugs. However, Page's bad wish had not been answered. Renee had held on to her teenage looks, though she now had a mature, womanly aura about her.

Page took in Renee's slouched posture and the glass she was holding up to her mouth and tapping on, determined to extract every drop of liquor. The group Page was hiding behind walked away, having found a place to sit, and Page was now visible for all to see. She pulled the rim of her baseball cap down lower and sat at the bar, opposite Renee. An expansive collection of liquor bottles and drinking glasses separated the siblings and blocked their view of one another. Through a small opening between two bottles of rum, Page had a glimpse of Renee and was able to follow her actions. The tall glass she'd been tapping now sat in front of her, empty.

As Page watched her prey, someone bumped into her stool, stealing Page's attention away from Renee. An overly skinny, blond-haired girl plopped down on the seat next to her. She moved her head back and forth, and strands of blond fell on Page's shoulder. Disgusted, Page shrugged the hair off her and watched the blonde lean into the man she sat beside and indulge in a make-out session.

"You taste good," her date told her in between kisses.

The blond giggled. "Mango lip gloss."

Raspy walked over just then, repeatedly drying her hands off on her jeans. "What can I get you two lovebirds?" she said, interrupting the two.

He pulled away, but the blonde playfully attempted to smother his face with kisses. "I'll have a Bud," he said. Laughing, he dodged Blondie's kisses. "We have all night for that. Place your order," he told her.

Blondie blew him a kiss, then tapped his nose with her finger. Without looking at Raspy, she placed her order. "I'll have a rum and Coke. More rum, less Coke."

Raspy hit the bar with her palm. "Coming right up."

Between the liquor bottles, Page watched Renee look down into her vacant glass, her facial expressions changing minute after minute.

"Enjoy." Raspy sat the drinks down in front of the couple and took off.

"I'll be back. I have to go to the little girls' room." Blondie snickered and stole a kiss right before she took off.

The guy dragged his date's drink over to him. After two swigs of his beer, he leaned over and tapped Page's shoulder. "I'm sorry to bother you, but would you mind getting the bartender's attention? You're a little closer to her than me." He gave Page a bright, "good guy" smile, his ivory cheeks filling with red.

Page blew air out of her mouth and looked down at the end of the bar, where Raspy stood drinking a glass of water. She threw her arm up, only for Raspy to walk away before she noticed her. Page rolled her eyes and turned back to Blondie's date. "Sorry. I lost h—"

Just then he pulled his hand away from the rum and Coke and stuffed a small plastic baggie inside his pocket. When the bag was out of sight, Page looked at the glass and watched whatever he'd put in it dissolve. She looked at him. He looked around. Then, with flared nostrils and his hands balled into fists on top of the bar, he spewed,

"You saw nothing. Got it?" Quickly, he faced forward and continued to drink his beer. His leg on the stool shook.

"Do you have more?"

"What?" Her question forced him to look at her.

"Do you have another roofie?"

His eyes jumped around the bar before falling on the hall leading to the restrooms. "Yeah."

"I'll give you a hundred dollars for it."

A shaft of bright light indicated that one of the restroom doors had opened. An Asian lady came out of the women's restroom, followed by the blonde. In haste, the guy dug inside his pocket and then handed over the baggie. The hundred-dollar bill Page gave him took the place of the baggie.

A fresh coat of lip gloss on her lips, Blondie sat down on her stool and crossed her legs. "Did you miss me?"

"Tremendously." He pulled her to him and kissed her. "A table opened. Let's head on over." He got up from his seat and helped his date do the same. "Don't forget your drink," he instructed.

Raspy found her back to Page.

"Her in the brown, give me whatever she had," Page said, gesturing to Renee as best she could due to the liquor bottles blocking her view.

New neighbors moved in next to Page shortly after Raspy slid her, her drink. Raspy looked around the bar, then checked in on other customers in need. In one quick movement Page dropped the pill into her drink and watched it dissolve.

Not long after, she mumbled, "Shit! This is a Long Island? I don't fuck with Long Islands!" After getting Raspy's attention, Page pointed at the drink. "The shit she was having was a Long Island, right?"

"Yes. You said you'd take what she had, and she had a Long Island."

Page pushed the drink toward her. "It didn't look like one from over here." Page's face scrunched up. "Give it to her. I don't want it."

Raspy's thin eyebrows fell inward.

"I didn't drink from it. I can obviously tell what it is up close by the smell," Page said.

The bartender took the drink. "I'll toss it and give you something else."

"I used to bartend, and if there's one thing I know, it's how much the boss hates wasting liquor, not to mention how tough it is not to receive a tip after giving such good customer service, even when you're the only bartender serving a packed bar." Page paused and gave her a sad look just before placing a fifty-dollar bill down on the bar.

Raspy eyed the bill.

"Yo, bartender! Over here!" shouted a man wearing a Mohawk.

Raspy's cheek caved in. Page imagined a glob of flesh sucked in between her teeth.

"Bartender!" a different voice yelled.

"I bet they won't even tip," Page noted.

With her free hand, Raspy snatched the bill.

"Tell her it's on the house," Page instructed.

The bartender rushed over to the side of the bar Renee sat on, and placed the drink down in front of her.

"I didn't order this." Renee slurred a little.

"Today's your lucky day. It's on the house." Raspy tucked the fifty-dollar bill inside her bra strap and got back to work.

***

Forty-five minutes later, and not even halfway through her "courtesy" drink, Renee was overwhelmed by feelings of discomfort and dizziness. Her elbows sat on the bar, while her fingers combed strands of her hair out of her face. Suddenly, the bar became hot, and sweat covered her face.

"I need air," she mumbled.

Renee slid off her stool and started walking slowly. Not far from the door, she swayed from side to side. She grabbed ahold of a wall and used that to help her keep her balance as she walked out the door. Once outside, she pressed her back against the building and caught her breath. Her hands repeatedly wiped her face.

"Fuck it," she huffed. "I'm going home."

Her feet carried her in the direction of her building, but they failed her once she got to the dark entrance of a park. She stumbled, feeling as if a boulder were attached to her feet. Trees leaned into one another, their leaves blocking the light of the moon. Renee passed empty benches then stumbled farther into the park, to where the swing sets and basketball courts were. Her vision was blurry now, and she felt sleepy. Renee lowered herself down onto a bench and felt relieved to finally be off her feet.

"Miss, are you okay?" Page stood a few feet away from Renee, the trees her shield.

Renee was trying to focus on Page, whose voice she did not recognize, but her eyes crossed and Page's silhouette became distorted. "Ye—" Before Renee could get the entire word *yes* out, she passed out.

"Miss, are you okay!" Page yelled again. When she got no response and saw no movement, Page reached inside her pocket and took her box cutter in her hand. She walked up to Renee, whose body was limp and lifeless, her hand hanging off the bench. "You fuckin' bitch," Page snarled as she lifted the blade up to Renee's neck.

"What the fuck are you doing!" yelled a male voice.

Not far from Renee and Page stood a tall man. He made his way toward them.

Page quickly put her weapon away. When the man reached her and Renee, she said, "Thank God! I didn't know what to do. I think she's drunk. I saw her in the bar up the block and found her here."

He slid himself between Page and Renee. Then he bumped hard into Page, and she staggered backward. "I got her," he spit.

"Do you know her?"

"She's my girlfriend. You can leave now."

"Oh, okay. Good. I'm glad you found her." Page tried to put on a smile, to convey that she was an innocent citizen who had tried to do right, but really she was seething inside.

Lucky bitch, she thought.

A second later Page rushed out of the park, feeling the need to disappear before she started acting irrationally.

He watched the stranger until she left him and Renee alone. He picked Renee up and headed home.

"I knew putting that tracker on your phone would come in handy one day, but you really have to watch your liquor," Jared said aloud as he carried her. Then he kissed Renee on the forehead.

Once more, he had saved her life.

Chapter 31

Like Laurence Fishburne in the film *Boyz n the Hood*, Julian sat behind his desk in his home office, rotating two Chinese stress-relief balls in his hand. Stress had attached itself to him like a bad rash he couldn't get rid of. His eyes were stuck on the seat Lincoln had occupied only minutes prior, and Julian constantly replayed in his mind what Lincoln had told him. Waves was the one responsible for leaking Jordan's identity. Because Waves had run his mouth to his sister, Tina, Renee was in danger. Her sister was coming for her.

If the balls in his hand weren't made of steel, Julian would have crushed them to dust by now. His anger was at an all-time high. He should have listened to Dane. He should have taken Page out as soon as word got back to him about what she had planned. But he'd hesitated, scared to bring more pain to his woman's life. Now that he had decided to sic Dane on Page, she was nowhere to be found.

Multiple thoughts ran through Julian's mind. *If Waves ran his mouth about who Renee is, what else did he tell?* No words could describe the anger Julian was feeling. He had a blabbermouth on his team, and the reality of it was eating him alive. What made matters worse was that Carmen had had entered their world.

When Julian saw Carmen's face in his mind, he got up and threw the Chinese balls at his office door, and the impact of the balls created a hole in the wood. Everything was falling apart, and it had all started on the day of Slice's funeral. He thought back to that day.

Renee, Lyfe, and a few of their goons attended Slice's funeral. Julian didn't think it was such a good idea to attend, but Renee was adamant. She said that by going, she would be spitting on Slice's grave, and that showing her face would make a statement. Everyone except for Julian went to the funeral and witnessed the streets mourn the death of an old friend. When Slice was put in the ground, Julian was back at Renee's home, furious that she was attending the funeral. Eventually, sleep took him over, and he fell into a deep slumber. Hours later, he woke up to an empty bed and made his way downstairs.

Jared was sitting in the living room, tension written all over his face. When he saw Julian enter the living room, he tried to calm himself down, not wanting to show his displeasure about Julian being in the house.

"Where's Renee? Did she come back yet?" Julian asked. He stood there, dressed only in jeans.

Jared's jaw locked. With an expressionless look on his face, he told him, "She's in her office."

Julian made his way to Renee's office on the lower floor. Jared hadn't told him Renee wasn't in there alone, so when Julian went to open up the door, he heard a several voices coming from the office, so he stopped and pressed his ear against the door to listen. Whomever Renee was talking to, she sure as hell wasn't holding back any punches.

Julian cracked open the door, peeked in, and saw Lyfe sitting beside Renee. Across from them sat a woman in a tank top and jeans. Julian squinted his eyes, trying to get a better look at the woman. He thought he knew her from somewhere. After seconds of searching through his memory bank, it hit him. She was the woman from the plane.

He closed the door quietly. Julian's hands became fists, and he wanted to punch holes in every wall in the hallway, but he controlled himself and leaned against one of the walls instead. The day he was on the plane to Jamaica to meet with Dane, he had met Carmen. She had ordered him a drink, and due to the stress from finding out about the loss of his child, Julian had been rude to her and not very gentlemanlike. The two had instantly disliked each other, but their displeasure with one another had drawn them together. Before Julian knew what was happening, they were in the tight space of the bathroom, having sex.

After they landed, they caught a cab and went straight to Julian's hotel. They had wild animal sex until it was time for him to meet with Dane. After that day, Carmen left, and he never saw her again. It was a fling, a "what happens in Jamaica, stays in Jamaica" sort of thing.

Julian placed his face in his hands as he stood in the hallway outside of Renee's office. He played back the conversation he and Renee had had about Lyfe being her uncle and about her having a sister. After seeing them all in the office and hearing Renee giving them a hard tongue-lashing, it was obvious that Carmen, the woman he had had a one-night stand with, was Renee's sister.

Julian picked the Chinese balls up off the floor now. He didn't understand how things could go from bad to worse with each day that passed. He rotated the stress-relief balls in his hand, waiting for peace to wash over him. What was he going to do? Sooner or later, he was going to have to face Carmen, and Renee would be right there. He was overwhelmed and scared to death at the thought of Renee finding out he had slept with her sister, for he was sure that he would lose Renee. He shook his head and blocked the whole ordeal out of his mind.

I can't worry about that now. I have to deal with Waves.

Julian pulled out his iPhone, dialed Jared, and told him to come to his house ASAP.

Forty-five minutes later, Jared was on Julian's doorstep, knocking on his door. He had no idea what Julian wanted with him. The two didn't like each other, and they spoke only when necessary. Jared found it odd that Julian had told him to come to his place instead of Renee's. He wondered if it was a setup and if Julian had found out about him and Renee sleeping together. As he waited for Julian to answer the door, Jared felt for his gun, which was tucked away in the back of his pants. If Julian wanted him dead, Jared was taking Julian with him.

Seconds later, Julian answered the door in slacks and a white wife beater. Jared had never seen Julian looking so beaten down before. His eyes were red, and he wasn't dressed to impress like the pretty boy he was. Julian stepped back just enough for Jared to enter the apartment. He saw no need to give Jared a tour of his home or allow him to get comfortable. The two just stood in front of the door.

Jared immediately noticed Julian's lack of hospitality and smirked. He couldn't have cared less that he wasn't wanted, because as long as there was air in his lungs, Jared would forever have it in for Julian. Jared took in his surroundings. From his spot in the foyer, he could tell that Julian's apartment, a tri-level penthouse right around the corner from Renee's, was huge. The second floor, the one they were on, was decked out in black and gray. Julian had the best of everything and had pinched pennies on nothing. There were flat-screen TVs, cherrywood furniture imported from France, and an aquarium filled with exotic fish in the foyer alone. The room was dark. The only source of light was the aqua-blue glow emanating from the aquarium, and this created an eerie feeling, which increased the tension between the two men.

When Jared looked at Julian's face, he saw anger and disgust plastered across it. The shadows of fish swam across Julian's face, and it was then that Jared knew no good would come from this meeting. Jared's hand inched closer to his burner. No way would he be caught slipping.

"I didn't ask you here for that. Besides, do you really think I would waste my time killing you? I have people for that," Julian said coldly, his eyes locked on Jared's hand, which sat behind his back. He knew Jared was packing and taking precautions.

"Then what do you want?" Jared growled.

"I want you to kill Waves."

Jared's eyebrows sank in, and he pushed away his confusion. He forced himself to say, "What?"

"You heard me." Julian stood quietly for a second, allowing Jared to digest what he had just said. "Your man talked. He ran his mouth and told everything about Renee."

Jared didn't have to ask exactly what was said. He knew that when Julian said that Waves had spilled the beans about everything, he meant Renee's identity, occupation, and home address. Everything that had been kept secret was now claimed to be out in the open. Jared hoped this wasn't true, so he gave his friend the benefit of the doubt and demanded Julian show proof of his accusations.

"Why would I believe you? What proof do you have?"

Julian walked into the living room, which was visible from the foyer, and grabbed a stack of pictures from his circular coffee table. He walked back into the foyer and handed Jared the pictures and allowed his eyes to tell him the truth.

"She look familiar?" Julian asked.

Jared didn't answer. He just glanced through the pictures of Tina, Waves's sister, his mind discombobulated.

"Your little friend told his sister about Renee. She ran her mouth and officially signed Renee's death certificate."

Jared's eyes flew up from the pictures at the mere mention of Renee being in danger. "What are you talking about?"

Julian didn't miss the concern in Jared's voice once Renee was mentioned. His jaw locked, but he controlled himself, refusing to show Jared his disapproval. "Long story short, Renee's sister Page wants her dead. And because of Waves's sister, Page has all the info she needs to get her wish."

The color drained from Jared's face, leaving him almost pale. He looked back down at the pictures of Tina, which had been taken at different locations without her knowledge. He had always heard that Tina was a blabbermouth and would inform anyone of anything they needed to know for the right price, but never once had he thought she possessed information like this.

"You vouched for Waves, brought him into our circle, so now you kill him," Julian spit, cold as a winter's night.

Julian's words pulled Jared out of his thoughts. He knew that Julian was right. The moment he put Waves on to Renee, she made it known that he was his brother's keeper. He would be held responsible for anything that went wrong. Jared had never thought Waves would do wrong, so he'd never feared the consequences.

Jared was a soldier and had never had problems following orders, but this one was a hard pill to swallow. He was being told to kill his best friend, the very man he had considered his little brother and used to protect when they were growing up. Now he had to exterminate him. He didn't know if he could do it, didn't want to do it, but when he thought of the danger Renee was now in because of Waves, his heart took over. It quashed anything his mind had to say. There was no saving Waves from this one. He knew the rules, and he'd broken them.

"What about Renee's sister Page? And what about Tina?" Jared questioned.

"Don't worry about them. They'll be taken care of. Just worry about making Waves extinct." Julian spoke with such coldness.

Julian was obviously disconnected from all his emotions, but Jared couldn't blame him. His love—*their* love—was in danger, and they couldn't worry about anyone but her. She was their queen, and they had to do whatever it took to protect her.

Jared nodded his head, making it known that he would kill Waves and that he had no objections to doing so.

"Renee doesn't know any of this is going on. I think we both can agree that she has enough on her plate, so say nothing," Julian ordered.

Jared nodded his head again, indicating that he understood. He clutched the pictures in his hand and walked out the door. He didn't bother to give the pictures back, and Julian didn't expect him to. He wanted Jared to keep them, so they would be the motivation he needed to kill Waves.

Chapter 32

Jared didn't know if he was subconsciously postponing Waves's murder again or if he just wanted to enjoy his last moments with his best friend. For days, he had come up with countless excuses as to why he couldn't kill Waves right away. Now Julian was at the end of his rope and was demanding that Waves die today.

It was 11:30 p.m., and Jared and Waves had been inseparable the whole day. Since the previous night, they had partied like rock stars and had drunk like fish. They had spent their day on the basketball court, after a night of strip clubs, sports bars, and a hotel room with some random women. Now they were hanging out together in a bar. In Jared's mind, this was the perfect homecoming for his friend.

Waves didn't know what had gotten into his friend and why he was into the party scene all of a sudden. But he didn't question it. He just went with the flow, happy that Jared was finally coming out of his shell.

Today was the day Waves had to go, and now Jared decided to wait until the very last minute to kill his friend. It was nearing midnight, and Jared's eyes stuck to the clock, watching slowly as the second hand made its rounds. It was a Wednesday night, and the bar was empty. Only Jared, Waves, and the bartender sat around engaging in an idle conversation. Due to the day's events, Waves was drunk out of his mind, but he was happy.

"Yo, son, what are we going to do after this?" Waves slurred. "It's about to be midnight, and I'm ready to get my party on. You know what I'm saying. Ready to bag a couple of broads right quick and take them back to the crib."

Jared laughed. Waves's comical ways never wavered, not even when he was intoxicated. His eyes looked at the clock. It was 11:40 p.m.

"I feel you, son. Let me get one more drink before we bounce. We been partying since last night. I think we're in need of a little peace and quiet." Jared signaled for the bartender to give him another Long Island iced tea.

Waves laughed. "You right about that. Even though it's quiet, I still hear music!"

The bartender handed Jared his drink and proceeded to wipe the bar down with his dingy old rag. Jared sipped on his drink, then looked over at Waves.

"How's Tina?" he asked.

"Still club hopping, still drinking, still Tina."

Jared nodded his head. "She still running her mouth? You know, getting paper in exchange for info?"

It was 11:45 p.m.

"Man, I wouldn't be surprised if she still is. She has a love for money like no other. She probably would throw our own mama under the bus for dead presidents."

"Or her brother," Jared replied while sipping his drink.

Waves looked at Jared, confusion written all over his face. "What?"

"She threw you under the bus, son. We know you confided in her about what you do for a living and who Jordan is."

Instantly, Waves sobered up, and he gave Jared his undivided attention. The bartender stepped away from the bar and headed toward the back room.

"What are you saying, son? You think I ran my mouth?" Waves quizzed.

Jared banged his fist on the bar, causing Waves to jump. "Don't fuck with me, Waves! You opened your fuckin' mouth. You told everything! How fuckin' dumb can you be!"

Fear was drawn on Waves's face. He couldn't believe Tina had run her mouth, couldn't believe his secret was out. He had trusted his sister. No matter how many times he'd heard from various sources that she was beyond greedy, he had always believed they were overexaggerating. He knew she loved money, but he didn't think she loved it more than him.

It was now 11:55 p.m.

Waves shrugged. "What can I say? I'm sorry, son. I made a mistake."

Jared stood up, pulled out his gun, and pointed it at Waves. "Sorry isn't enough."

Shocked that his best friend was pointing a gun at him, Waves fell off his stool. On his butt, he instantly started backing away from the gun.

"Jared, you gonna kill me because I told my sister who Jordan is?"

"You know the rules, Waves. No one talks."..

Anger started to fill Waves. "Who gives a fuck if I talked? Ain't shit gonna happen. Renee will still be untouchable! Who doesn't want people to know they're king?"

"You wrong, homie. Because of you, snakes are after Renee. You brought us beef. Your sister works for the enemy."

Jared never took his gun off his friend, and Waves never tried to get up. He was scared that if he moved, Jared would shoot.

It was 11:58 p.m.

Waves looked Jared in the eye. "So this is how it's gonna end? You're choosing her over me? Your loyalty lies with her? You choosing a bitch who isn't yours and doesn't even want you!"

Waves's words stung, and tears dropped from Jared's eyes. Waves was giving Jared the look of death. Jared had better use his gun, because if he didn't, Waves would end what Jared had started. In all his life, Waves had never felt a pain as strong as this one. His best friend was choosing a woman who didn't want him, didn't belong to him, over him.

"Yes," Jared answered.

His gun exploded, and the bullet ripped through Waves's heart. His body jumped slightly, then fell back onto the floor and became still as night.

Jared stood there for a moment, looking at his best friend's body. He felt a pain that he had never felt before, and wished things didn't have to turn out this way. He would forever be haunted by Waves's last words.

You're choosing her over me? Your loyalty lies with her? You're choosing a bitch who isn't yours and doesn't even want you!

Lost in a trance, Jared didn't notice the bartender standing beside him, staring at Waves's body. Lyfe removed his glasses, his fake mustache, and his goatee. He pointed at the clock under the sign that read LYFE'S BAR AND LOUNGE. It was midnight.

Jared tucked his gun away. Like a good soldier, he had completed his mission. He had sought revenge on the man responsible for the woman he loved being in danger. He'd officially proven he'd do any and everything for her. But now that it was all said and done, Jared couldn't help but wonder, *Why do I still feel so empty*?

Chapter 33

Renee's blood pressure was at an all-time high. She felt her insides about to explode and her killer instincts kicking in. Ever since Lyfe had revealed that he was her uncle and that her father had had a child outside of his marriage, he had been pressuring Renee to give her half sister Carmen a chance, but Renee couldn't. Like a dagger to the heart, it had killed her to find out she wasn't the only apple of her father's eye. He was the only good thing she had from her past, and now Carmen had tainted his memory.

"Get her the fuck out," Renee snarled.

The eyes of everyone in the limo except for Metro were now watching the scene unfold. Metro would never admit this to anyone, but he blamed himself for what was taking place. He couldn't understand how Lyfe had worked as his head goon for ten years, yet Metro had never known this man was related to Renee. Metro prided himself on being one step ahead of everyone else by knowing any and everything, but Lyfe had found a way to keep his family invisible. Metro couldn't shake the feeling that he had been outsmarted. Pissed off, he stared out the window, not once observing the family feud.

"Renee, you need to stop running. This is your sister. She's all you got!" Lyfe's eyes pleaded with Renee to see things his way, but the longer he looked at Renee, the more he knew it wasn't going to happen.

"I don't think you're hearing me. Either she walks out of here with her life, or she gets carried out in a body bag. Your choice, Uncle Lyfe."

Renee's words chilled Lyfe to his bones. He had never thought he'd see the day she called him uncle, even if she was just being sarcastic. After staring into the eyes of his angry, parentless niece, he looked over at Carmen, who was waiting for him to defend her. He then looked over at Dane and Julian, who were waiting for him to pick a side, but Lyfe was torn. Torn between the niece he had protected and showered with love her entire life and the niece he had lost track of, forcing her to find her own way in life.

"Carmen." Lyfe's voice was loud and deep. "Go into the apartment. Wait until we come back."

Just like that, Lyfe had picked a side. His life had revolved around Carmen, but now it was time he became the family Renee had missed out on.

The second the words left Lyfe's mouth, Renee smiled. "You must be crazy if you think she's stepping foot back in my apartment." Renee shifted her attention to Carmen. "You want to be sisters so bad, prove it. Stand your ass outside my building until we return."

Carmen looked at her like she was crazy. "Y'all are going to Atlantic City. Who knows when you'll be back?"

Renee shrugged her shoulders, emotionless about the situation. Although she had told Carmen she had to prove herself, there really was nothing she could do to gain access to Renee's life.

Reluctantly, Carmen got out of the limo, giving her uncle the evil eye in the process. She knew it would be hard to win Renee over, but she had never thought it would be this hard.

I can't wait to take this bitch down, she thought as she stood on the sidewalk.

Carmen had no idea how she was going to gain Renee's trust, but she wouldn't rest until she did. In her mind, Renee's throne had her name written all over it.

I'ma slither in and take her for all she's got.

Twenty minutes passed before the limo finally departed. Carmen stood right there, in front of Renee's building, the entire time. She wasn't dumb; she knew Renee was making her suffer. The moment the limo was out of sight, Carmen turned around and headed up to Renee's apartment.

As she sat in her car, lurking in the shadows, Janae saw someone who looked like Renee walking into Renee's building. Janae couldn't have been any more excited. She would finally exact revenge on the person responsible for killing her sister and tearing her family apart. She reached into her glove compartment and removed her gun. In just a few minutes, it would all be over.

Chapter 34

Renee had sparked something inside of Jared that could never go out, and the small fire she'd ignited demanded her attention. But over a month had passed, and Renee had never mentioned what happened between her and Jared. Her silence and nonchalant behavior had caused Jared to dive deep into a pit of pain, dashing his hope that somehow they'd be together.

Jared sat in the darkness of Renee's downstairs living room, reliving the happiest moment of his life—when he slept with Renee. She had made his dream come true, only to take it away. Determined to get her attention and to show her that he loved her, he had killed his best friend. He had picked Renee over Waves, and when Julian had finally told her that Waves's big mouth had blabbed and that Jared had killed him, she hadn't even said thank you. She'd simply looked at Jared and walked away without saying a word. That was the moment that Jared had broken and his world had crumbled. He now regretted having put first someone who looked right through him and used him. This realization had brought about feelings of confusion and rage, because although the truth was evident and written in ink, he still had to have her.

The doorknob on the front door began to rattle, rousing Jared from his thoughts. Shortly after that, there came a knock at the door. Angry and brokenhearted, Jared grabbed his gun from off the coffee table. Whoever was on the other side of the door had come at the wrong time. He swung the front door open and pointed his gun at Carmen's forehead.

Surprised by the welcome, she froze.

"What do you want?" he snarled.

Carmen didn't recall moving, but her hands were up in the air, her eyes were stationed on the firearm, and her voice box was on vacation.

"What the fuck do you want!" Jared screamed.

The longer Carmen stood there, unresponsive, the angrier he became. It didn't help that he was eye to eye with Renee's look-alike during his time of distress.

Carmen finally found her voice. "I came up here to wait for them to come back from Atlantic City. You know Renee doesn't like me, so she told me to wait in front of the building till they came home. I wasn't doing that." Carmen spoke a mile a minute. Her body shook, and her face was beet red.

Jared inched the gun closer to the center of her face. "Renee would die before she allowed you in her house."

They have the same shaped face and nose, he thought.

"You're right. She told me to wait in front of the building till they came home." Carmen shook her head. "I'm not doing that."

His finger still on the trigger, Jared felt his face contort. He didn't say anything.

"It's obvious I caught you at the wrong time. I'll just go." Her eyes never strayed from the gun while she slowly backed away from the doorway.

"Nah, you ain't got to go." Jared lowered his gun and walked back inside, leaving the door wide open, with Carmen just steps from the doorframe.

Carmen stood still for a second and tried to figure out whether or not Jared was safe to be around while alone. After decided that the threat level was not terribly high, she stepped inside the penthouse and headed straight for the love seat in the living room, which was several yards away from Jared. For an hour, the two sat in complete silence. Carmen pretended to watch TV, when really she was watching Jared kick back shots of cognac nonstop.

"Should you be drinking while on the job?" she asked him.

Jared's glossy red eyes spoke before his mouth. "You think I give a damn? Fuck Renee!" He stuffed his hand inside his pocket and pulled out a small bag of white powder. After emptying the drug out on the coffee table, he used the nail of his middle finger to scoop it up and bring it to his nose. With each sniff he took, his eyes connected with Carmen's, and the mixture of cocaine and alcohol pulled him farther into that pit of pain.

Fuck Renee? Interesting. Something's not right about this guy, Carmen thought.

Jared had sealed himself inside his own world. Occasionally, he mumbled random sentences and words Carmen couldn't decipher. All she understood was one phrase he kept yelling, and that was, "Selfish bitch!" Like a human observing an animal behind glass, Carmen pushed aside her immediate feeling of discomfort in order to witness the monster inside the man.

Jared wiped his nose, took another shot of liquor, and burped. With his mouth wide open, he said, "Fuck that bitch," and Carmen got a whiff of his stale breath.

According to Lyfe, the backbone of Renee's success was her team. Now that she had witnessed Jared's behavior, she wondered if pure madness had overtaken the team and if that madness included disrespecting their queen.

If I really want this life, I need him on my side and for Renee to let him go, she thought.

After an hour and a half of watching mind-numbing reality shows and nearly going deaf from Jared's snoring, Carmen got up off the love seat and took a trip around the house. Since she wasn't welcome in Renee's life, she'd never received a tour of her home, so she thought it best to take advantage of the opportunity that had presented itself. Going from room to room, she discovered two guest rooms and a library. Every room was pristine and looked like it had never been lived in. Bypassing the bathroom, Carmen walked directly toward Renee's bedroom.

Once she opened the bedroom door and slipped inside the room, she knew this was her majesty's chambers. The room was massive and looked as if it had come out of a home-decorating magazine. Jealousy rose to the top of Carmen's chest. Renee lived a better life than she ever had, even when she was with Benz. Renee was on a totally different level. Carmen searched through Renee's closets, and the contents' lack of color instantly depressed her.

Damn! She thinks she's a witch or something? What's up with all the black?

Rummaging through dresser drawers, Carmen looked at the labels sewn into Renee's undergarments. Her face morphed into a scowl, erasing all her beauty, when she discovered that even Renee's underwear was better than hers. Carmen opened another drawer; inside she found mismatched socks and a photo album. She laid the album on the dresser's flat surface, and then she flipped through the pages. She was taken back in time to when Renee was a baby, equipped with fat cheeks and no teeth. Two pages later Renee had moved into her toddler years. Renee in a blue jumper, paired with pigtails and dimples, reminded Carmen of a Cabbage Patch doll, but more importantly, she reminded her of herself.

Pages later Carmen fell into the family zone. In front of her were photos of Renee, their father, and someone she was sure was Renee's mother. Tears dropped from her eyes and landed on her father's face, giving the illusion that he too was crying. Carmen missed her father so much. Although she was young when he died, she remembered the joy and laughter that had filled her home whenever he was around. Everything now made sense in terms of why he had never lived with them. Although he was a great father, Carmen had always felt as though she had a part-time father, since he never stayed with her and her mother for more than a week at a time. Now that Lyfe had told her the truth about him being married and having a family, it all made sense. Lyfe had also made it known that Daniel planned to leave Sheila on many occasions, but he always stayed because of Renee. In her mind, Renee had taken her father away, and she'd never forgive her for that. Carmen's plan to knock Renee off her throne arose not only from a desire to inherit her half-sister's lifestyle but also from a need for payback for what Renee had taken from her years ago.

Carmen slammed the photo album closed. The number of images that portrayed Renee and her parents as the Cosby family sickened her. She snatched up the album, and in the process of putting it back, she dropped it and watched it fall open to the last page. Loose pictures scattered on the floor. These photos were of Renee during her teenage years and her early twenties. Carmen picked up one of the photos and took a closer look. Beside Renee was a dark- skinned, muscular young man. He had his arm wrapped around her. Carmen squinted her eyes, focusing more intently on the image. Shaking her head, she bent down and grabbed a handful of Polaroids. In some of pictures, the two smiled, while in others they made silly faces. Carmen looked through picture after picture, until she found one of the guy up close and alone. Her breath caught in her chest and eyes grew large.

That's him.

"What are you doing in here?"

Carmen jumped at the sound of Jared's voice. As she faced him, her oversize eyes blinked rapidly. "Who is this . . . ? The guy in the picture with Renee? Who is he to her?" She held two images out in front of her; the fingers that held them shook.

Jared walked up to Carmen and snatched the two photos out of her hands. He ignored the picture of a solo Julian and focused on the one with Julian and Renee, which conveyed the closeness and comfort the two enjoyed. Jared's teeth ground moments before he crushed the second photo in his hand. Then he took the photos Carmen was now holding out, picked up the album, and collected all the loose photos scattered on the floor. He threw all the pictures, including the one he'd crumpled, inside the album.

"Where did you get this from?" he growled.

Carmen pointed to the drawer the album lived in, and Jared walked over to the dresser and chucked the album inside the drawer.

"I want to get to know my sister. What the fuck else am I supposed to do?" Carmen squeaked.

Jared got in her face. "You want to get to know your sister, huh? Little girl wants her big sis?" Jared's voice was antagonizing and degrading. He invaded her personal space so much that his body pressed against hers and liquor invaded her nostrils.

Standing firm and keeping her composure, Carmen replied, "Yes." A fib.

Jared took his finger and ran it across her cheek, triggering a sudden urge in Carmen. The last time she had had sex was months ago, with a man who looked a lot like the man in the photos, so whatever Jared had in mind, Carmen was not going to protest. If anything, she was in need of a stress reliever.

"Poor baby. It hurts not getting what you want, doesn't it?" Jared said, treating her with contempt.

Then he grabbed Carmen by the back of her neck with one hand and palmed her breast with the other. He was anything but gentle, owing to the rage and the heartbreak swirling inside him. He needed an immediate release and a target. For years, Jared had done nothing but show Renee respect, and all he had got in return was *nothing*. However, despite his pain, his heart continuously reminded him that he needed her. He needed Renee so much that he'd even go as far as substituting her mirror image, her sister Carmen, for her.

Carmen's lips slid onto Jared's, her lipstick staining his face. He picked her up and laid her on the bed, then tugged at her jeans until Carmen wiggled out of them and kicked them off the bed. After removing the remainder of her clothing, Jared took the opportunity to look over her body. Her perky breasts explained why she hadn't worn a bra, and her cottony softness gained her extra points with him. Satisfied with Carmen's physical appearance,

Jared still could not help but wonder if she felt as good as Renee. Then he stood up and undressed.

Carmen's mind circled around the photographs she'd seen.

"It can't be," she murmured. Wrapped in the bedsheet, she lay on her side and scratched at the palm of her hand until it was red and raw to the touch.

"Jared," she called. Drenched in sweat, she spoke louder when she didn't receive a reply. "Jared!"

Jared lay on his back, his hands folded on his stomach, eyes closed. "What?"

"The guy in the picture, who is he to Renee?"

Jared's fingers fidgeted with the sheet. Carmen rolled over, her hands tucked under her face.

"Please tell me," she said.

"Why?"

She shrugged her shoulders. "Curious. And I—"

"Want to get to know my sister," Jared mocked.

"Yes," she fibbed. Carmen's eyes settled on Jared's pointer finger, which tapped against his knuckles, an uneven rhythm she found difficult to pick up.

"Her boyfriend Julian." His finger tapped faster.

Carmen felt her heart rate slow. Sharp pains hit her stomach. *That's who I slept with on the plane and in the hotel.* Carmen's conversation with Lyfe came to mind.

"How did she become so successful?"

"She has a loyal team, especially Julian and Jared, who's beyond dedicated. When men like them have your back, there's no losing."

"Shit."

"What!" Jared yelled.

"When you say *boyfriend*, do you mean boyfriend as in 'they're in a relationship' boyfriend?"

"No. Boyfriend as in her son. What the fuck else?" Jared ripped his hands apart and slammed his feet on the floor.

Having high, drunken sex with Carmen, his Renee replacement, had done nothing for Jared's rage. Plus, the sex was a flop.

That broad's sex was wack. A fuckin' waste of time, he thought.

There was nothing more disappointing to Jared than bad sex. He stood up, naked, and walked out of the dark bedroom and into the hallway bathroom. He wanted to put as much distance between himself and Carmen as possible. Carmen watched him walk out of the room.

After Jared finished peeing, he flushed the toilet and washed his hands. He looked in the mirror and was surprised at what he saw. He looked so worn out, so stressed. The multiple lines on his face could have told the story of three lives. He splashed water on his face and shook his head. When he grabbed the hanging hand towel and dried his face, he heard something coming from downstairs. Immediately he froze. There was the sound of footsteps slowly moving, then suddenly stopping. Jared knew he had an uninvited guest. No person who belonged in that house would move with such caution.

Slowly, Jared made his way into Renee's bedroom. He moved every time he heard the footsteps move, so the interloper wouldn't suspect that anyone was home. Slowly, he closed the bedroom door and grabbed his gun from out of his pants.

"What are you doing?" Carmen asked.

Jared placed his finger over his lips. "Be quiet and get under the bed," he ordered. Then he moved to the side of the door.

"Get under the bed? Why? What's going on?" Carmen was beginning to panic.

Has this motherfucker lost his mind? she wondered.

Carmen had thrown the covers off her naked body and was getting out of the bed when they heard footsteps just outside the door. Her and Jared's eyes met, and Carmen froze in place. Suddenly, the door was kicked down, and a tall woman stood in the doorway, dressed in black. She looked directly at Carmen and raised her gun.

From the corner of her eye, Carmen saw that Jared's skin blended into the darkness. He was inches away from the intruder, and his gun was pointed directly at her skull.

When the woman saw Carmen look away, her eyes followed Carmen's. As soon as she turned her head, she was looking down the barrel of a gun, with a burst of light heading her way. She didn't have time to react. She was immediately hit and was dead within seconds. Her body fell to the floor, and her gun flew across the room. Her blood seeped into the carpet.

Jared lowered his gun and looked down at the body. The moonlight through the window illuminated half of her face perfectly, making it impossible not to identify her.

Janae, was all Jared thought.

He bent down and looked closer at her body. *What is she doing here?* he wondered. For exactly one minute, Jared regretted what he had done. His heart sank, and he couldn't breathe. However, the longer he looked at Janae, the faster these feelings vanished.

She would have killed Renee if she was here. That's definitely a no-no. Jared stood and continued to stare at the body. He no longer felt remorse, no longer felt pain. It was Renee or Janae, and Jared refused to let it be Renee. He brushed the incident off and treated it like every other murder he'd ever committed.

"I'll take care of this. Why don't you get dressed and head downstairs?" he said.

Carmen obliged. She pretended to be shaken up, when really she was ecstatic. Jared constantly proved himself worthy of being on her future team.

Chapter 35

Jared didn't watch the cleaners take Janae's body away. In fact, he didn't give Janae's death a second thought. He had washed his hands of her a long time ago, so in his mind, she had got what she deserved. Instead, he sat staring into space. His sanity was slipping away, and there was nothing he could do but allow depression to eat him whole. Loving Renee was the worst thing he could have ever done, and now he was paying for it by having the life sucked out of him.

Jared didn't hear the front door slam when the cleaners left. He was too lost in his thoughts about what had taken place between him and Carmen. It was eating him up that he had betrayed Renee. He had just slept with the love of his life's sister as a form of payback, only to wind up regretting it tremendously. He was so angry that Renee couldn't see they belonged together, he was losing it. He had thought revenge would free him of his pain and open Renee's eyes. However, after the deed was done, Jared was left feeling more shattered than ever before. Jared sat there hating himself.

She can never find out. If she does, she'll never be with me. I disrespected her home, her bed, and my love for her.

Carmen sat across from Jared on the living-room couch, curious as to what he was thinking. He hadn't blinked or moved. He looked caught in a trance, lost in a world of pain and anger. Carmen loved it.

*I need him on my team. He's a savage, a no-heart
bastard.*

Jared was winning Carmen over with every minute
that passed. He killed with such precision, and with
such ease. It was nothing for him to do what he did, and
Carmen needed that if she wanted to survive in the drug
game. In her eyes, Jared was a menace to society, but in
reality, he was a broken man led by the demons of his
past and his heartache of the present.

Hours passed, and finally Renee, Julian, Lyfe, Metro,
and Dane waltzed through the door. Jared didn't acknowledge their presence. Still wearing his bloodstained
sneakers, he continued to stare into space, mad at the
world. Carmen had fallen asleep, stretched out on the
couch like a cat.

Renee walked farther into her home, and instantly, her
eyes zoomed in on Jared's sneakers. "What happened?"
she asked.

At first, Jared didn't answer. He just continued to look
into space. It was obvious the lights were on, but no one
was home.

"There was an intruder," he finally said.

Julian's heart skipped a beat. The first person that
came to mind was Page. Had she made her move before
they got a chance to?

"Where's the body?" Julian said, pressing.

"She's been cleaned up." Jared spoke slowly and
almost robotically.

Renee's eyes fell on Carmen. Suddenly, the dead
intruder was no longer important. She hadn't expected
Carmen to wait outside her building; she'd only been

pushing her buttons. What she had expected was for her to go home, not fall asleep in her home.

"Who was it? How did they look?" Dane asked.

Jared opened his mouth to respond but never uttered a word. Renee stormed over to Carmen and dug her hand deep into her hair. The tips of her nails scratched Carmen's scalp as she got a tight hold on her mane. Renee yanked Carmen off the couch and onto the carpet, and Carmen's back slammed against the floor, legs twisted in knots. Carmen screeched as strands of her hair fluttered to the floor. Renee wrapped her hand around her hair one more time and jerked her forward. She was tired of her father's mistake constantly being in her face.

"Get the fuck out!" Renee roared. Her pent-up grief and frustration meshed with her strength as she hurled Carmen away from her. Carmen's 120-pound frame slid across the floor and banged into a wall.

"What the hell is wrong with you!" Lyfe yelled as he ran over to Renee and grabbed her by her arm.

Click! Click!

Lyfe froze. He knew that sound all too well. That was the sound of possible death, known as his one and only warning. He turned around and saw Jared pointing his gun at him. Lyfe closed his eyes and took a deep breath.

This has gone too far.

Lyfe released Renee's arm and walked past Jared. Metro and Dane stood on the sidelines, shaking their heads. Things were spiraling out of control. Lyfe helped Carmen up off the floor. She grabbed her head and tried to ignore her aching back. Carmen's pride wanted her to charge at Renee, but the gun still pointed at Lyfe, and the plan her mind had already set in motion, stopped her from doing so and compelled her to leave without a fight.

***

During the entire ride back to Carmen's place, Lyfe engaged in intense huffing and puffing and ongoing, undecipherable mumbling under his breath.

Feels like I'm right back in the living room with Jared, Carmen thought.

While Renee knew a quiet, almost invisible Lyfe, one who preferred silence over everything, Carmen was familiar with a more talkative, interactive uncle. He was two entirely different men in one body, and now that Lyfe had fallen into a pissed-off state, he was the man Carmen had known since day one.

"Fuckin' disrespectful bullshit," was all Carmen could make out. Lyfe slammed his foot down on the brake abruptly and caused the car to stop just inches behind the car in front of them. "What the fuck are you stopping short for!" Lyfe flung his head out the window and swung his fist around intensely. "You piece of shit!"

Carmen was thrown forward and then back against the seat. As she gawped out the window, she moved around in her seat and tried to rub her lower back.

"You okay?" Lyfe asked her.

Carmen's grimace and tensed-up shoulders made it clear how she felt; however, he still asked.

"I'm good," she moaned. The pain she was experiencing kicked in and out like contractions. Occasionally, she closed her eyes when the pain hit, and tried mentally separating herself from the discomfort, only to fail. "Just forget about it."

Carmen wiped away tears when she thought her uncle wasn't looking. She questioned what it was she felt more, physical pain or fury. Renee was peeling away every layer of Carmen's dignity. Each attack, whether verbal or physical, was a hit on Carmen's psyche and left her to wonder what more she could swallow.

This is too much. Why must she be so difficult?

"I'm sorry." Lyfe's speech was loud and fast, a race among words before he thought against speaking. "I should have went about this . . . introduction more carefully."

"It's not you," she admitted. "It's her. My father created a demon spawn."

"I should have." Seconds passed, with a car honking its horn in the distance, before Lyfe repeated, "I should have." This time he sounded breathless and defeated. Full of regret and longing to change the past, he allowed those three words to punish him each time he said them.

He stopped at a red light and faced Carmen. It was the heaviness of his eyes, the wrinkles on his face, which spread out like tree branches, and the curved corners of his mouth that acted as a reality check for Carmen. Their dysfunctional family was beating on his sanity and on the one thing few had access to, his heart.

"I think you should lay off. Give her some time to take it all in," he said.

There was a moment of peace when Carmen felt no pain and was able to relax. She stayed quiet.

"Think you can do that?"

They pulled off and joined other cars on the road. At that moment a jolt of pain rushed through her and forced her to shut her eyes.

"Do you?" he asked, pressing.

Through the pain, Carmen shouted, "Yes!"

Once the pain eased up a little, she assured herself, *This will not be for nothing. I will get something.*

***

Watching Lyfe sit at the kitchen table with a bottle of vodka stuck to his hand and music from the late sixties and early seventies booming from his phone gave Carmen flashbacks of her childhood. She recalled him doing the exact same thing when her father died and every other time life moved in a direction he hoped it wouldn't. Too intoxicated to get on his feet and dance, he moved around in his seat. Whenever Carmen walked by, he'd tell her, "Now this is music! You hear me? This is talent!" He sang along to the most depressing songs about rolling stone fathers and daughters living in shame until he fell asleep at the table, the liquor bottle empty, his cheek pressed against the tabletop. Had he not insisted on staying the night, he would have become intoxicated from a far cheaper brand of vodka in his liquor cabinet at home.

After Carmen consumed a high dosage of painkillers from her medicine cabinet, her aches dwindled signifi-cantly. She slowly walked into the kitchen, nervous that if she moved too quickly, the pain would return. The mu-sic got louder the closer she got to the table. Lyfe was talking in his sleep and blurted out his brother's name. Carmen smirked as she tapped the screen on his phone, silencing the girl group that was singing. At that very mo-ment a text message attached to the name Carey dropped down from the top of the phone.

Let me find out Unc got broads, Carmen thought.

When Carmen was in the middle of reading Carey's long-winded speech filled with complaints about Lyfe ignoring her, a new message, this one from a Nicki, popped up. Carmen finished reading Carey's overly emotional text. As she was searching Lyfe's collection of messages for a second dose of drama, she spotted

Renee's text box in Lyfe's top three. Carmen's eyes darted over to her uncle, who hadn't moved a muscle since she first began snooping. She opened the message called "Renee Niece #1" and read the last texts Lyfe had sent to Renee in the past hour.

That shit you pulled was unacceptable, but I shouldn't have put my hands on you. Sent at 2:20 a.m.

Your father wanted better for you too. Sent at 2:25 a.m.

I'll be there in the morning. Sent at 2:50 a.m.

There was no response from Renee. Carmen pushed her shoulder back and straightened out her spine, and a surprisingly sharp pain raced up and down her back. Squeezing the phone, Carmen squirmed and mouthed, "*Fuck!*" She breathed through her mouth, and as the pain subsided, her breathing fell back into its natural rhythm. Carmen now placed her attention where it belonged. She sat down, and her thumbs spoke for her.

Your sister's the least of your problems. At 4:18 a.m. she sent this text.

Jared's unstable. He's snorting your shit. At 4:19 a.m. she sent this second text.

Carmen saw the line of text messages from various women on the screen and was reminded of someone just as vital as Jared. Her thumbs got to work again.

Let go of Julian. He fucked someone in Jamaica.

Carmen pressed the SEND button, laid the phone down, and turned the music back on.

Chapter 36

Lincoln didn't want to admit it, but he missed Sheila. When he first decided to cut off all ties with her, he felt like a weight had been lifted off his shoulders. He was tired of being paranoid and wondering whether or not Page had found out that he knew her secret. But these past couple of days, Lincoln had been missing Sheila terribly. After being around her for so long, he had developed feelings for her. The relationship was supposed to be no more than sex, but that was no longer the case.

When he had first called it quits, she wouldn't leave him alone. She constantly called him and popped up at his house, fighting for them to continue their affair. But as of late, Sheila seemed to have given up and let the relationship go. That was when Lincoln had started to miss her.

He sat on the edge of his bed, holding the spare keys to Sheila's home. He knew he shouldn't be thinking about going to see her, knew he shouldn't want to, but he did. Being separated from Sheila had caused a void to form in his heart, which he desperately wanted to fill but knew he couldn't.

Throughout the relationship, Sheila had done nothing to make Lincoln want to walk away. The only thing wrong with their pretty picture was that she was married, but that wasn't the issue at hand. Page had something up her sleeve, something that Lincoln didn't want to witness, and although Sheila was innocent, she was Page's mother, and in his mind, that was too close to evil.

All the items Lincoln had left at Sheila's flashed before his eyes, and he couldn't fight the desire to retrieve them, which he knew was just an excuse to pay her a visit.

Just one last time, so we can end this the right way.

Sheila's home was so quiet, you could hear a pin drop. Lincoln prayed she was home. Normally, she'd sit in silence and read. Lincoln hoped this was the case now. He wanted to see her, needed to see her, so he made his way straight to her bedroom. He was disappointed to see her room was empty. He checked the entire house and found no one.

Fuck. He paced the floor, stopped, and slammed both hands on top of his head. *Shit. I guess this is the end.*

Although he knew the end result, he searched the house once more. Then, in hopes that she'd return, he lingered in her home, all to no avail.

Fuck it.

Lincoln walked back into Sheila's bedroom and dropped the duffel bag that was on his shoulder onto the bed. He began emptying the drawers Sheila had given him. In twenty minutes' time, he had packed everything in the duffel and was ready to go. After walking over to the vanity table, Lincoln stared at the picture of him and Sheila that hung from the mirror. They were at a barbecue and looked happier than ever. He kissed two of his fingers, then placed them on Sheila. Then he headed over to her dresser, removed her keys from his pocket and placed them on the dresser top.

One foot outside the bedroom, the duffel back on his shoulder, Lincoln remembered the most important thing he had come to get. He dropped the duffel bag on the floor, walked over to the closet, stepped in, and went straight to the left side, which was filled with Curtis's clothes. This was the reason Lincoln had only drawers. Sheila touched none of Curtis's belongings while he was away.

He pushed Curtis's clothes out of the way and got a good view of the countless sneakers and shoeboxes at the bottom of the closet. Instantly, his eyes landed on the black and red shoebox, and he removed the lid. Nothing was there. Lincoln figured he was looking in the wrong shoebox, even though he was sure he had the right one, so he started looking in other shoeboxes, only to find nothing. Lincoln went through the whole closet and came up empty. He stood back and looked at the closet.

Maybe she got rid of it, he thought.

When Lincoln had first started spending the night over at Sheila's, all he'd heard was how manly Curtis was and how safe Sheila felt around him. To prove the same could be said about him, Lincoln had gone out and purchased a gun. Lincoln was a lover, not a fighter, so when he'd purchased the bullets, he'd loaded the clip with only one. That one bullet was enough for Lincoln to feel like a man and keep his conscience at ease. Finding no gun, Lincoln figured Sheila had got rid of it. She allowed a gun in the house only when a man was under her roof. Since that was no longer the case, he understood her actions. Lincoln gave the bedroom one last look, threw the duffel bag over his shoulder, and left.

Chapter 37

Locked in a large room with no light, Renee franticly felt around for a light switch. Nothing of use decorated the walls of the room or gave a clue as to where she was. All she felt was rough paint as she listened to the squeaky wooden floorboards beneath her feet, which were uneven and had many cracks. Air seemed to seep out of the room when pain rushed through Renee's chest and her fingers began to tingle. The unknown pushed Renee to search faster and more aggressively. Finally, she found the doorknob, but she almost lost her mind when she pulled and twisted it and discovered the door was locked. With both hands wrapped around the iron knob, she yanked until the door rattled. Failing to secure her freedom, she backed away from the door and ran to the opposite side of the room. She banged her fist against the raggedy wall and felt the skin on one of her fingers tear from what she imagined was a rusty nail.

She grabbed her wound, stepped back, and dug deep down inside for strength before she yelled, "Get me out of here!" Her piercing tone bounced off the walls and reverberated in her ears. All she wanted was to escape this hellhole. All she wanted was to get out of the dark and see the light.

"Get yourself out of here," a deep voice answered. The words echoed throughout the room and brought it to life.

Renee spun around, a fleet of nerves and instant panic spilling over her once more. Even though she saw nothing but black, it didn't stop her from looking around the room. Then her survival instincts kicked in, and the need to fight and defend herself took over. Renee began swinging her fist around with all her power, aiming to keep whoever was in the room with her at bay.

"You always were a fighter," the voice said. Laughter followed his comment.

Renee dropped her fist. She wrestled to catch her breath and stabilize her breathing. She wondered continuously how this person could see her but she couldn't see him. Suddenly, light flooded the room, and everything was visible. The room was huge but in poor condition. The walls, like the floor, had cracks in them, along with faded paint and blotches of mold. This place appeared to have been abandoned many years ago. After examining her surroundings, Renee looked up and saw him.

"Daddy?"

"Yes, baby girl, it's me." He had the very same smile Renee always remembered. That smile used to light up a room, and it tucked her into bed every night. It was the smile she had inherited from him.

"This can't be," Renee whispered.

One by one, tears cascaded down her cheeks. The light-headedness she felt blurred her vision. The constant rhythm of her heart had her believing someone was beatboxing on her chest. She thought she was losing her mind. This wasn't real, couldn't be real. Renee dropped to her knees, her legs no longer strong enough to hold her up after turning into liquid.

"You can't live this way anymore, baby girl." Daniel walked over to his daughter and helped her up. "Do you see this room? See the horrible condition that it's in?"

Renee nodded her head, unable to take her eyes off him. She feared he would disappear if she did. She rewound her memory and tried to compare the father who stood in front of her to the father she remembered. He was exactly the same. His looks hadn't withered, and his presence remained strong. The only difference between his being in life and death was his aura. It was purer, calmer, and at peace now.

Daniel went on. "This is your life. You're trapped in a room, alone and full of misery. Every day that passes, a piece of you cracks, like these very walls. You can't live like this anymore, Renee. It's okay to be happy. It's okay to let go."

Renee backed away from her father, anger taking her over and boiling over like an unwatched pot. "This is all your fault! You left me! You left me to fend for myself, and look what happened! You're damn right I'm miserable! There's nothing but snakes surrounding me, and now that bastard child of yours pops up. Is that why you were always disappearing? How dare you!"

Renee was shaking. She had never been so infuriated. The anger she felt was so strong that it had seemingly replaced her blood and pulsed through her veins. She couldn't control the countless tears covering her face or the dire need to continue shouting.

"I needed you!"

Daniel grabbed his daughter and hugged her. He gave her the hug he always wanted to give her while watching her endure all her hardships. He gave her the hug she always wanted after his passing.

"I'm sorry for what happened," he told her. "There's so much I never got the chance to discuss with you, and I'm sorry I'm behind pieces of your agony. Know that I never left your side, never left you alone. I was always there, down to the point where I wished I could come back and save you from yourself." His face softened more than it already had. "These feelings, Renee, these feelings of yours are too strong. You will self-destruct if you don't get rid of the darkness. You're killing yourself."

Renee looked up at her father's face, her watery eyes pleading with him. "Let me come with you, Daddy. I don't wanna be here anymore. I can't do this." She shook her head so viciously, her neck hurt.

"Don't you talk like that! You have to stay here, Renee. You have to live and right your wrongs."

Daniel squeezed his daughter in his arms, hoping that he could give her the strength she needed to battle her demons, welcome joy into her life, and live the life she was meant to have. He pulled away from her and grabbed her by the shoulders. "I came to tell you that it's okay to be happy and let go of what hurts. But, Renee, the snakes aren't done coming yet. Not everyone is who they appear to be."

Renee's shoulders dropped, the tension leaving her body. "Who? Tell me who?" Renee grabbed her father by his wrist. He still wore the bracelet Sheila had brought him for Father's Day as a gift from Renee.

"Keep your eyes open," he warned.

Daniel hugged his daughter one last time and turned to walk away, but before he took another step, he looked back at her, his smile brighter than the room's light.

"And don't worry. The baby is with me."

Renee stopped breathing, and for the first time, she could see her baby's face. It was a boy.

Chapter 38

Renee's eyes shot open. Her jaw felt tight, her heart raced, and her face was drenched with tears and sweat. Her dream had been so real, so vivid. A twister made of feelings swirled inside of her. A soft smile touched her lips. The sight of her father had lifted her spirits. During a time when her life was out of order, confusion was in the forefront, and her sanity was out of whack, she needed the comfort and support of a parent, and she had got it. Renee rubbed her eyes, covered her face with her hands, then deeply inhaled and exhaled. Her phone chimed, indicating she had received a text. She exhaled one last time, grabbed her phone, and pulled up several text messages. Before she could read it, she heard heavy breathing in the dark room. Looking up and straight ahead, she detected movement out of the corner of her eye. She turned to look, and there in a corner of the room sat a figure who was staring back at her. It was too dark to make out who it was. Renee inched her arm closer to her nightstand, where her gun sat.

"It's me," the figure told her, then walked out of the darkness and sat on the end of her bed.

"What the fuck are you doing in here, Jared?"

"Watching you sleep. You're so pretty when you sleep."

Renee took a better look at Jared. He was a mess. His hair needed a cut, his beard had grown out, and heavy dark bags hung underneath his eyes. And if Renee was correct, he had worn those same clothes three days in a row.

This motherfucker done lost his mind.

"Jared, you're pulling some stalker-type shit."

"We gotta talk, Renee. We . . . we . . . we really need to talk," Jared stuttered. He inched closer to the middle of the bed and took Renee's phone out of her hand. "I need your full attention." He got up, dropped her phone on the TV stand, and then sat back down on the bed. "You have to let go of Julian. You have to be with me. No more games. It's time we be together." Although Renee had already seen his left hand begin to shake, he used his right to try to conceal the movement.

Jared had officially lost his mind. The strong, confident, fearless man Renee once knew wasn't standing before her now. He was withering away and had mentally checked out. Renee's eyes shifted back to the nightstand.

"Renee! I'm not going to hurt you! I just came up here to talk!" Renee had trained this man so well, too well, because he knew her every thought. He plopped back down on the bed and took her hands in his. "I need you Renee. I love you," he confessed.

Renee could see the pain in his eyes, and it hurt her. She cared for Jared, but not in the way he cared for her. That night was just sex, nothing more, nothing less. She had no intentions of being with him. She knew that ignoring him and sleeping with him were the wrong things to do, but she didn't know what else to do. She had slept with one of her workers, the biggest mistake of her life. Renee slipped her hands out of his carefully and with ease.

"Jared, what happened that night was a mistake. I was hurt and needed an outlet."

"That's not true. If you didn't love me, you would have slept with someone else, but you chose me. Why are you making things so difficult? Why can't you see we're meant to be!" His eyes became enlarged and revealed the red veins on his eyeballs.

"I'm sorry, Jared, but I don't want to be with you. That was a one-time thing, a mistake."

Renee could literally see Jared falling apart right in front of her. For the first time in her life, she honestly regretted hurting another human being. Her father's words replayed in her head. *You have to live and right your wrongs*. Renee knew she had to be honest about how she felt.

Jared's face scrunched up. "It's Julian, isn't it? You can't let him go. I feel you . . . I understand, but if you don't let him go, he's gonna be resting right beside Slice and Waves." A drop of saliva sat on the corner of his mouth.

Renee felt her blood pressure rise. Trying to let him down easy had just gone out the window.

"Don't threaten me, Jared. You'll be a memory before sunrise."

"He doesn't love you like I do."

"You're right. He loves me better."

They sat in silence. Their locked eyes at battle, Renee could hear Jared's hard, labored breathing. He wanted to choke the life out of her. This wasn't how it was supposed to go. This was nowhere close to his fantasy. They were supposed to be making love right now as a couple. But instead, he was seeing red.

"You're such a bitch," he spit.

"Well, thank you." Renee smiled. He had to come at her a lot harder if he wanted to hurt her. "Now get the fuck out of my face." Renee wiped the smile off her face so fast, she seemed bipolar.

Jared rose from her bed, then walked over to the door. Before he left, he told her, "I'ma have fun destroying your world."

With that said, he was gone, and they were now enemies.

Chapter 39

Jared stormed out of Renee's room like a bat out of hell. His rage was at an all-time high. He knew that if he didn't get away from Renee, he'd kill her. Hearing her actually say she didn't want him caused him the worst pain he'd ever felt. Tears threatened to fall from his eyes, but he wouldn't allow them. Tears wouldn't make the situation any better, but revenge would. Jared now wanted to destroy her life. He now wanted her to hurt until she came to her senses and ran into his arms. He'd stop at nothing to have her.

Jared skipped steps while racing down the stairs. He flung the front door open and was surprised to see a beautiful young woman with short hair standing in front of him. It was almost five in the morning. What was she doing there?

"What the fuck do you want?" Jared spit. Her presence was forcing him to stay longer at Renee's than he wanted.

"For you to get the fuck out of my way."

The woman grabbed Jared by his shirt and charged into him. The moment their bodies collided, she shot him. Jared hadn't noticed she was holding a gun. When he opened the door, he'd focused only on her face. Jared's eyes shot wide open, and his mouth dropped. Clutching his stomach, he watched his blood seep through his clothes and stain his fingers. Unable to get a word out, he fell to the floor.

"Y'all make this too easy," she muttered.

Page stepped over Jared's body and made her way toward the stairs, in search of Renee. She was done waiting for the perfect time to strike. She wanted Renee's head now.

As she stood on her bedroom terrace, for the first time, Renee was reevaluating her life. Having her father come to her in a dream and witnessing how broken Jared was had made her want to rethink it all.

I can't keep living like this.

Renee's misery had been eating away at her and causing her to miss out on life's greatest pleasures. For a long time, she'd been content with drowning in a sea of misery. It was all she'd ever known. Looking back, she realized that it had done nothing but weaken her and hinder her from living life.

The thought that the baby was a boy constantly ran through her mind. Knowing her baby's sex alone caused her to see things in a new light, a light she didn't mind basking in. As she gazed out at the city's lights, she allowed herself to get lost in its beauty. Blown away by the possibility of finally being happy, Renee never heard Page sneak up behind her. She never felt her breath on the nape of her neck.

"Take it all in, because you'll never see this city again," Page whispered in her ear.

Renee didn't get a chance to turn all the way around before she was struck in the temple with the butt of Page's gun. Grabbing her head, Renee stumbled to the other side of the terrace. Page followed her and smacked her across the face with the firearm. Renee's lip busted open, and blood leaked out, painting her face and a square foot of the terrace red. Renee held her face and collapsed. She had no idea who was attacking her. Jared came to her mind, but she quickly rejected that thought, because her attacker's voice was not a man's.

Renee looked up and forced her eyes to adjust and focus on the figure standing over her. Her eyes got big. Her attacker was pointing a gun directly at her head.

"Say hi to Sheila for me."

The second the words left Page's mouth, it registered with Renee who the attacker was. Renee felt her heart stop, and the aching in her face temporarily disappeared.

"Page?"

"Yeah, it's me. Don't you love reunions?"

Renee tried to sit up and rest her back against the railing. But the second she moved, Page stomped down on her leg, and she didn't stop until she heard something snap. Renee screamed at the top of her lungs.

"I wouldn't move if I were you. I'd think you would want to die on your back, like the ho that you are," Page snarled as the moonlight hit her face.

Renee didn't know what was going on, but having her younger sister disrespect her and attack her didn't sit well with her. "You don't know what you're doing. Whoever put you up to this won't live to see tomorrow. Neither will you, if you don't put the gun down." It pained her to threaten the sister she hadn't seen in years. However, her pride conquered all. Renee had always told herself, if anyone ever pulled a gun out on her, they had better use it. If not, she'd use hers, and she wouldn't care who stood at the other end of it.

Page smiled. "You really think you bad, really think you run shit. But I'll tell you this. You run nothing but your damn mouth. If it wasn't for you, my father would still be alive right now." A lone tear danced down Page's cheek.

"That's what this is about? You blame me for your father being dead?"

"That's exactly what this is about. First, you fuck him, and then you get him locked up. If it wasn't for you, he would still be alive! You're such a dirty bitch!" Page kicked Renee in her face, and blood flew from her mouth into the air.

Renee fought not to succumb to the pain.

You have to live and to right your wrongs, Renee thought again.

"Page, I know this is hard to hear, because he's your father, and I'm not sure how much our mother told you or what you remember, but Curtis was a horrible person who did a lot of unforgettable things," she pushed out.

"And what are you? A saint? I know all about you."

"Far from it. I'm many things, but a rapist has never been one of them."

Page's lips dissolved into a tight, thin line. The gun she pointed at Renee was no longer steady but swayed a little from side to side.

Renee continued. "He raped me, and our mother allowed it." The truth stabbed Renee so deeply, it over-shadowed the physical torment eating away at her. "And because I left you behind with those two monsters, that makes me a monster." There had always been a need in-side of Renee to admit to her sister where she went wrong during her escape for sanity. "Now look at you. We made you into a scared, blinded little girl."

It felt good, real good—just as good as when you finally drink a glass of ice-cold water on a sweltering summer day—to Renee to speak her faults.

"You're full of shit," Page smirked. She had regained control of the gun, and her hand no longer moved. Her eyes narrowed and lowered, she growled, "You wanted it. I know you did. I bet you craved to have him inside of you whenever he wasn't around."

Renee shot forward, but the pain in her leg made it impossible for her to stand up. "Fuck you!" she screamed. "That bastard deserved what he got. He raped me countless times! You really think I was going to let him get away with that? Fuck outta here! I'm glad that son of a bitch is worm food. My peoples do good work, don't they?"

With a face full of blood, and a swollen eye and mouth, Renee grinned. It felt good to speak ill of the dead. Then, unexpectedly, she screamed, "Checkmate, bitch!" and released a bone-chilling laugh. If she was going to go out, she was going out with a boom!

"Nah, bitch, fuck you! I'm about to send you to hell, right along with our ho-ass mother. Neither of you bitches deserved my father. And for the record, your 'people' didn't kill Sheila. I did. They did all the prep work for me, though, so thanks."

Renee gasped. Her mind was going a mile a minute. What was Page talking about?

"As much as I hate her, I decided to try to save that slut from your goons, until she fucked up," Page continued. "The bitch started talking about how I was no match for you, and how you were so fuckin' special. Well, you bitches can be special together in hell!"

Page aimed the gun at Renee's head. This was the moment she'd waited for, and Page would cherish this like a mother cherished her children. She pulled the trigger and watched as Renee's smile never left her face.

She then pulled the trigger again, only to hear the sound of an empty clip.

What the fuck? Lincoln had only one bullet in this bitch! she thought.

Page thought about Jared laid out downstairs, and she wanted to turn back the hands of time and take back that bullet.

Renee lay there laughing like she had front-row seats to *Def Comedy Jam*. Enraged, Page threw the gun to the side and jumped on top of Renee. She wrapped her hands around Renee's neck and started squeezing the life out of her.

"Die, bitch! Die!" she yelled.

Fighting for air, Renee clawed at Page's face and hands. With her good leg, she started kicking wildly, but it was no use. She was losing consciousness. As her eyes started to close and her body prepared to shut down due to a lack of oxygen, she felt herself going under.

Suddenly, Page's hands released her neck. Air rushed into her lungs, and Renee started to cough violently. She rolled over on her side and struggled to breathe.

Standing behind Page, Carmen had her left hand wrapped around Page's neck. The choke hold forced Page to stand still while Carmen pointed Jared's gun at the side of her head with her right hand.

Carmen whispered in her ear, "You're not fucking up my meal ticket."

She pulled the trigger and watched as Page's body dropped. She died instantly. When Page hit the terrace, Carmen's and Renee's eyes met. No words were exchanged, although their eyes held a full conversation.

Chapter 40

Julian broke into pieces when he walked into Renee's home. When he saw the bodies and the bloodstains in various places, he thought he'd lost the love of his life. The silence in the house was just as disturbing and ripped at his heart. He and Renee had finally become a couple. He couldn't lose her. Not now, not ever.

When he made it upstairs and laid his eyes on her, he felt like he was seeing her for the first time. When they first met, the circumstances were not in the least romantic, but they were life changing. On that day, his heart was born. Now, as he and Renee looked at one another, no words were spoken. Then Julian swooped in, took her in his arms, and held her as tightly as she could handle. Moments later he carried her from the terrace and away from her sisters. Renee stared at Carmen until she was out of sight.

Renee woke up the next day in the hospital. Everything that had taken place the night before was fresh in her mind, and the moment she awoke, the reel of that night began replaying in her mind. Julian placed his hand on top of hers when she didn't turn his way. Last night's events had a hold on her and wouldn't let go right away. Finally, the visuals ended, and Renee took his hand in hers, and their fingers intertwined.

"What happened?" Julian asked.

Renee tried arranging the thoughts swarming around in her mind before she spoke. "Page tried to kill me, and Carmen saved me. The bitch actually saved me." Renee snickered, partially unable to wrap her head around that fact.

Julian tightened his hold on her hand, his silence speaking volumes.

"What are you thinking?" she asked, sitting up all the way and throwing off the blanket. Now Julian had a better view of her broken leg, her swollen face, and her busted lip. The sight alone crushed his insides.

"Lincoln warned me about Page. I just didn't get to her in time," he said in a low voice.

"Why didn't—"

Julian freed her hand and threw his up, interrupting her. "Let me finish." He looked at her in all her perfection and imperfection and explained what he should have before. "Page was . . ." He paused, in search of the right word. "Page was disturbed that Lincoln was seeing your mother. That's how he was able to give me the heads-up that she had plans for you." The look in his eyes told Renee what she already knew, had already experienced. "I was going to take care of her and the rest of your family, but you already know who got to Curtis and Sheila first."

Renee took it all in. She felt the tension inside her chest rise, and she had the feeling that she might lose her mind. Right there in the hospital, she had the urge to scream, kick, throw an adult tantrum, and voice the rage brewing inside of her over these newly discovered, well-kept secrets. Then she thought about it. She had spent too many years being an angry dictator, and honestly, she was tired of the position she played. It had got old, and no growth would come from this lifestyle. She had to let go of the unnecessary anger; it was eating away at her soul.

"Can I speak now?" she said.

"Yeah."

"I'm so sorry."

"For what?"

"For everything." Renee's voice cracked, and her chest pushed in and out. "I brought you this grief. I'm a monster." The words tumbled out of her mouth. Renee's lips quivered, and tears slid down her cheeks. Time was fast-forwarding, and the vulnerable, innocent, "couldn't hurt a fly" Renee had made an appearance in the room. "I just wanted the pain to end. I just wanted it to all go away. But I lost control, I lost my humanity, and then everything spiraled out of control."

Julian abandoned his chair and sat on the bed with Renee. He pulled her swiftly into his arms. Her face got lost in his shoulder, and Julian's shirt absorbed the tears. Her words came out muffled when she spoke, but they still came out.

"I'm so miserable." She let out a few more cries, the release a burden off her soul. "The more things that happened to me, the more I lost myself, and it got to the point where I no longer knew who I was. So instead of finding myself, I fell deeper inside Jordan."

Julian rubbed her back. There were so many things he wanted to tell her; however, he allowed her to speak. She didn't need to listen. She needed to be heard.

"I want to be happy. I *need* to be happy," she confessed.

Julian held her tighter. He tried to squeeze out all her pain and let it seep inside himself. In Julian's arms, Renee felt vulnerable, like prey being constricted by a python, but she ignored this and willed herself to relax.

"I regret the abortion, regret not telling you before I did it. I regret it all." She hugged him as firmly as she could now. She feared he would remember all she had done and would pull away, but he didn't. He continued to listen to her. "Please say that you forgive me," she sobbed.

"I forgive you. Please say that you forgive me for the secrets."

"I forgive you."

"I'll never let you out of my sight again. Whenever I do, something always seems to go wrong." Both of their bodies bounced slightly from their laughter.

"Then move in," Renee proposed. "And put me out of my misery."

Julian removed himself from Renee's embrace long enough to kiss her.

"No more secrets," Renee said. The instant the words left her mouth, her night with Jared flashed through her mind.

"No more secrets," Julian agreed, his mind lingering on the fact that he was holding on to one more secret.

Julian insisted on staying the night at the hospital with Renee, but she talked him into going home and getting some rest. A lot had unfolded, and she needed some time to adjust. However, her mind wouldn't allow her to focus on the present because it was too fixated on the past. On and off throughout the night, Renee harped on the disdain she had for hospitals. Since her father's death, she viewed the place of care in a dark, soul-crunching light. Inside a hospital was where she imagined he had taken his last breath alone, without a loved one near. She never had the chance to say goodbye, never had the opportunity to live a normal life and be the better version of herself had her father had a hand in her upbringing. Now she sat in a hospital, banged up and bruised, with nothing to do other than sit and pinpoint exactly where her life went wrong.

"You look pretty," Renee told her mother. The accurate, clean way Sheila applied her makeup had always mesmerized Renee, and she adored her mother's taste.

Sheila turned to her daughter, her bob bouncing with every movement of her head, a smile so heavy on her face, she blushed. "Thank you, cupcake. I'm going out with Curtis tonight." She blinked her eyes, placed the liquid eyeliner back in her makeup box, and moved on to her lipstick application.

Cupcake? Wow. She hasn't called me that in forever, Renee thought.

"I thought he went back to New York."

"Not until tomorrow. He stayed a day longer after his business meetings to spend more time with me," Sheila said.

"You really must like him. You've been going out a lot with him." Renee forced a smile. She hadn't met the guy, but she already didn't like him. He had become the potential new man in her mother's life far too soon after her father's death.

"I do." Sheila looked in the mirror and removed the excess lipstick on the corners of her mouth. "It looks like you may have a new daddy."

"I don't want a new daddy," Renee spit.

She looked at her daughter's reflection. "That isn't up to you, now is it?"

Renee's eyes became enlarged, and her teeth smashed together in her attempt not to cry.

"I deserve love too," Sheila snapped. *"All that mattered to your father was you. I think I deserve someone to love me."* She used the palm of her hand to slap the top to her cranberry-red lipstick back on. *"I thought you would be happy for me, Renee."*

"I am," Renee lied. *"But I think your dating too soon. Daddy hasn't been gone for a year."* Renee's palms were outward, and a deep frown was on her face.

Sheila's hands were flat down on her vanity table. "You always were too grown for your age, little girl. Always just too damn grown."

"I just feel—"

"Renee, enough! This is not up for discussion!"

Maybe I should shut up, *Renee thought.* She's been a lot nicer since she started dating him. Maybe he is good for her. Maybe it's me.

"I'm sorry. Where are you going tonight?"

Sheila was packing away some of her cosmetics and putting inside her purse the makeup she was bringing along. "We're going to dinner, then out dancing."

Soft and low, Renee responded, "You always were a good dancer."

Sheila zipped up her purse and stood in front of her only child. For an eleven-year-old, Renee was tall, so Sheila didn't have to look down at her much. For the first time in a long time, she got a good look at her daughter. A little of the baby fat in her face had disappeared, and her eyes held not 100 percent ignorance but . . . knowledge.

"I miss him too." She tucked in the tag sticking up on the back of Renee's shirt. *"I would like it for you to do something for me."* She gave Renee a small smile.

"Yes?"

"Trust me. Trust that I can find not only love but also a father figure for you. I have a good feeling about this one." Her hands were on each of her daughter's shoulders, and her eyes were pleading with the child to give her a chance. *"Trust me to find us happiness."* She smiled and waited for her daughter to smile back.

Renee let her guard down and this time gave a genuine smile. "Okay, I'll trust you."

Sheila pulled Renee in for a hug.

I can't remember the last time she hugged me, *Renee thought.*

"We're going to be okay, and when the time comes for you to meet him and if you don't like him, I'll call it quits. Deal?" Sheila held out her pinkie finger for her daughter to wrap hers around.

"Deal," Renee told her. Her smile as wide as the ocean, she held a make-pretend glass in the air. *"To happiness!"*

"To happiness!" Sheila clinked her pretend glass against her daughter's and chuckled.

"Happiness, my ass," Renee mumbled now. She slammed her eyes shut, trying to kick the memory away and avoid the one that followed, but it was too late. It had already taken her over.

"Mommy, what are you doing?" Renee looked around her room and out the window. It was still dark outside, and her closet doors were wide open. Her mother was hand deep inside her dresser drawers, pulling out everything they contained. Quickly, she refolded whatever she pulled out and dumped it in a suitcase.

"We're moving, Renee."

"Moving? What time is it?"

"Two o'clock."

"In the morning?"

"Yes, Renee. It's two in the morning." She moved faster to pack Renee's things. "Curtis asked me to move in with him, and we're going."

She never turned around to face her child. Renee rushed out of her bed, stepped on her slippers, and immediately kicked them out of her way.

"I don't want to move!" The bow that had once held Renee's hair together clung to the tips of her hair.

"Not now, Renee." Sheila moved from the second drawer down to the third. "Why are these drawers so messy!"

Renee stood beside her mother. "Ma, I don't want to move!"

Denying her eye contact, Sheila continued folding. Renee pushed her head in front of the drawer so Sheila was forced to see her. Sheila tossed a striped shirt in the suitcase, cocked her hip out, and threw her hand on it.

"What did we discuss, Renee? What did you tell me you'd do?"

"I don't—"

"I'm not asking what you want, Renee. I'm asking what you told me you'd do for me." Sheila pointed her pointer finger at Renee, then at herself.

"That I'd trust you," Renee replied. She wondered if the red she felt inside showed on the outside.

"Then why the hell aren't you?"

"Because you want to move! I don't want to move, Ma! I don't want to move in with Curtis!" Renee felt the tears well up and struggled to keep them at bay.

"Why not! He's good for us, Renee! Why the hell don't you see that!"

Talking to Sheila was like talking to a wall. She was missing common sense, and even though she was a child, *that gave Renee a headache. She stomped her way over to her desk and crossed her arms over her chest.*

"Answer me, damn it! You don't get the luxury of not explaining yourself to me." Sheila raced across the room and pulled Renee by the arm so that she would look at her.

Her face full of tears, Renee screamed, "I don't like him, Ma! I don't like the way he looks at me!"

"What the hell are you telling me?" Sheila released her daughter's arm and stepped back a little.

"He's always looking me." Renee didn't understand what she was saying, but she understood the discomfort and uncomfortable emotions she experienced when Curtis was around.

Sheila turned her back on her daughter and stuck the tip of one of her nails in her mouth. Biting down on the acrylic cracked it. She snatched the nail out of her mouth and spun around. The back of her hand met Renee's cheek, pushing her backward. The bottom of Renee's back banged against the desk, and her left arm attempted to restore her balance while her right grabbed her face.

"Take it back." Sheila filled in the space between them. Her breath in Renee's face, she snarled, "Take it back!" She slapped Renee again, harder.

Shaking, Renee tried to back up but was forced to remain face-to-face with her mother by the wooden desk she wrote on daily. "I can't." Renee's voice trembled, and it felt like a boa constrictor had wrapped itself around her heart.

Sheila pushed herself farther into her daughter's personal space, her hand around Renee's neck. "Say it," she hissed. Renee looked in her mother's eyes.

This is a test. It has to be. This can't be happening. She doesn't want me to lie. She can't. She hates liars, *she thought.*

Renee stayed silent. Then her mother's eye color grew darker, and her hand squeezed tighter. The feeling that had taken over Renee's heart moved to her throat, and she fought to decide which felt worse. Renee pulled at her mother's hand, and when that did no good, she balled her small hands into fists and punched at her. Nothing changed, not the look on her mother's face or her grip on Renee's neck.

"I take it back." *Renee forced out the words in a raspy, low tone.*

"Apologize to me."

Additional tears wet Renee's face. "I'm sorry."

Sheila didn't let go right away. Her clasp loosened, but she didn't let go.

What is she thinking? *Renee wondered.*

As soon as the question made its way into Renee's mind, Sheila dropped her hand. Grabbing her hair with both hands, she was halfway out the door when she yelled to Renee, "Finish packing! We're leaving in two days."

Renee sank down on the desk chair, her lips quivering and her hands holding her neck and shaking. Her brain told her to close her door, create a barrier between her and her mother, and hide underneath the covers. After standing to her feet, Renee slowly walked to her bedroom door. She closed it, careful not alert her mother of her actions. She slid the dresser drawers closed and moved to the closet. Inside it, nothing hung from the hangers except two shirts. Her favorite shirts, one her father had surprised her with at Disney World and one that had a picture of her and her dad printed on it. Renee ripped them off the hangers and hugged them. She held them so close, they almost melted on her skin. "I don't want to go." She hugged the shirts once more, then placed them inside the suitcase. Moving or not, she would not leave her father's memory behind.

Next, she bent down, reached under her bed, and pulled out the family photo album she'd rescued from the trash after Sheila tossed it out a week after she began dating Curtis. As she carried it over to her suitcase, a picture sticking out from a corner of the album poked Renee in the hand. She pulled the photo out and saw her and Ms. Pam at the beach, posing for the camera in their matching bathing suits. Renee stuffed the album in between her clothes, grabbed the cordless phone, and sat inside her closet, with the door shut. She dialed a number.

"Hello?" said a drowsy, heavy-toned Ms. Pam after she picked up the phone.

"Ms. Pam?"

"Renee?" Renee could hear Ms. Pam shuffling around on the other end of the line. She pictured her removing a sleep mask from her eyes, her head covered with a silk head scarf. "Is everything okay?"

Renee whispered, "I'm sorry I woke you up, but we're moving to New York."

"Moving to New York? When in the world did this happen?"

"Mommy just came in the room and told me Curtis asked her to move in. We're leaving in two days."

"Oh, hell no!" Renee heard the sound of a lamp turning on.

"I don't want to go, Ms. Pam."

"I know you don't, baby."

"Can I live with you?"

Ms. Pam didn't respond right away. "Let me talk to your mother, Ree. Let's figure out what's going on."

"Okay. Ms. Pam?"

"Yes, Ree?"

"My mother told me to trust her to find us happiness, but this isn't happiness, is it?"

"No, Ree, this isn't happiness." Ms. Pam's tone had changed slightly, and this made Renee question whether she was holding in tears.

"Even if she's happy?"

"Even if she's happy," Ms. Pam said, reassuring her.

Renee was jolted from her thoughts by a voice.

"Child, you haven't been in this place for long, yet every time I see you, you're sitting in that same spot, looking out that window for I don't know how long. You sure you don't want to sit in bed and watch television? The idle mind is the devil's playground, ya know." Nurse Binge examined another one of Renee's barely touched trays of food.

"I'm good, Nurse Binge. For once, my thinking is to benefit me instead of driving me deeper in the ground." Renee moved her wheelchair back a little and glanced down at her broken leg.

"Wise words from such a young woman." Nurse Binge placed the tray of uneaten food on her cart and replaced it with that night's dinner: mashed potatoes, corn, chicken, and gravy that looked too lumpy. She moved on to work on fixing Renee's bed to perfection.

"You're not on bed duty, Binge. Stop spoiling me."

Nurse Binge chuckled. "Let this old lady obtain her happiness by making your bed, since you refuse to let me talk you into doing anything except think. You're too young to have such a heavy mind, child." As best as they could, Nurse Binge's wrinkled dark hands smoothed out the creases in the sheets.

"Nurse Binge, can I ask you a question?"

Renee had found a friend in Nurse Binge. The elderly lady's personality reminded her of Ms. Pam: the two were outspoken, open minded, and extremely caring. Renee wished her mother hadn't ruined that friendship. Ms. Pam had spoken up and out against Sheila uprooting her child and disrupting her life by moving from Miami to New York all for a man. She had predicted that nothing but disaster would come from this change and had shared those thoughts with her best friend. Curtis's true colors had yet to be revealed while they were in Miami, yet Ms. Pam had sensed he was no good. Close-minded, Sheila had accused Ms. Pam of not being supportive of her new relationship and had cut off all forms of communication with her. The night Renee called Ms. Pam from her closet was the last time she'd spoken with her.

"As long as it's not about my sex life. There are some things a lady must keep to herself."

"Nurse Binge! No one's going to ask you about your sex life." Renee preferred not to have such thoughts invade her brain.

"Good. Then ask away."

"What do you think happiness is?"

"Oh, you want to have a deep conversation." Slowly and with her hands planted on her knees, Ms. Binge sat down on the chair by the bed. A strand of gray hair escaped from her bun and fell against her cheek. "Now, this is only my opinion. Don't you go taking things to heart."

Renee nodded. She glanced out the window and then looked back at Nurse Binge.

"Happiness is something designed by the individuals themselves. They know what makes them happy."

"Is it worth obtaining?"

Ms. Binge chuckled as she crossed one small foot over the other. "Damn straight."

"Even if it affects those closest to you, even if you know those around you would disagree with what will make you happy, would you still do it?"

The sound of shoes slapping against the hallway floor echoed inside the room.

"Child, your actions will always affect those around you. The key is to not base your happiness off others. You have to do what's right with you. The only way I believe otherwise is if you're a parent. Then your ass must take the backseat and focus all your energy on ensuring that child's happiness."

Renee's throat tightened a little. Where were you when I needed a mother, Nurse Binge? she thought.

When Renee remained silent, Nurse Binge said, "Where is this coming from? What's going on in that head of yours?"

"Thinking about my life, backtracking to where it all went wrong in order to determine how to right my wrongs."

"Yes, that seems to happen when you find yourself in the hospital. Depending on your situation, a whole lot of things run through the brain. Are you getting anywhere with all that thinking that you're doing? Or are you allowing yourself to do nothing but think?"

"I know what will make me happy. It's just those around me won't like it." Renee tapped her finger on the armrest of her wheelchair. "I'm a bad person, Nurse

Binge, a really bad person." Renee didn't know where the words were coming from, but she didn't stop them.

"I've met my share of bad people, and I've met my share of bad people who turned over a new leaf. So my question to you, Ms. Renee, is, What are you going to do?" Nurse Binge slowly stood up, low moans seeping out of her mouth. "Child, don't get old." She shuffled over to her cart. "I've bullshitted enough. Time to get back to business." Nurse Binge left Renee alone with her thoughts and the food she wouldn't eat.

Chapter 41

Renee tried to avoid hospitals at all costs. Not only was life nurtured inside the four walls of a hospital, but it was also taken away. It was a blessing and a curse, a yin and a yang, and nothing but a mere reminder of what she failed to understand most, life. She hadn't wanted to enjoy her stay there, or admit that it had actually given her a sense of peace and awareness, but she had, and the more she'd sat in front of that window and dissected her life in her thoughts, the more confidence she'd developed in order to follow through with her decision.

"Ms. Renee, I'm going to miss you." Arms open, Nurse Binge bent down to hug Renee, who sat in her wheelchair, a smile on her face.

Renee gave in to the warmth Nurse Binge supplied and accepted the affection. "I bet you tell that to all your patients." She let her go and chuckled.

"Only to the ones who gained a place in my heart. Are you ready?"

"Yes. I didn't come in with much, so I'm all packed."

"I mean, are you ready to go back to your life? For some people, being here can be kind of a vacation, and I think you're one of those people." Nurse Binge clasped her hands together in front of her, displaying her perfectly manicured fingernails. The red nail polish complemented her honey-toned complexion.

Renee admired the old woman's meticulousness and looked down at her own hands. The nails that weren't bit down to the quick were jagged and rough. Her cuticles were raggedy. And when she looked closer, what others would have mistaken for dirt, she was sure was blood jammed underneath her nails. She couldn't recall the last time she had got her nails done, let alone had a physical.

"Yes."

Nurse Binge rested her hand on her shoulder. "Good luck." She had turned to walk away when Renee spoke again.

"Nurse Binge, don't you want to know what landed me in here?"

Nurse Binge's respect for privacy and her control over her curiosity were applaudable. Had Renee told anyone else just a pinch of what she'd told Nurse Binge, a thunderstorm of questions would have followed, but not with Nurse Binge. She had listened to whatever Rene had to say, whenever she had to say it, and she hadn't meddled or requested more details.

"No. All I want to know is whether you'll stay away from what got you in here. By the way you sat by that window your entire stay, you know what you're into is no good. You don't need me to remind you of that."

"How did you become so wise, Nurse B?"

"I made a lot of mistakes," she answered honestly.

Julian stood in the doorway. His face brightened when Nurse Binge stepped aside and no longer blocked his view of Renee.

"Ooh-wee." Nurse Binge slapped her hand against her good hip.

Renee held back her laughter and covered her face with her hands, sure of what was to come.

"Renee," she called out.

"Yes, Nurse Binge?"

"Why didn't I see this hunk of a man before or, better yet, have a picture?"

Renee tittered as quietly as possible, still covering her face with her hands. "You were never around when he visited, Nurse Binge, and as for the picture, I didn't think to show it to you."

"You didn't think to show it, my ass." Nurse Binge circled Julian while looking him up and down.

Unsure of what was going on or what to do, he watched her waltz around him and even tried covering his muscular arms, which his tank top revealed.

"Renee, he your man?"

Peeking between her fingers, Renee answered, "Yes."

"Um," Nurse Binge let out. "Little boy, you're lucky you're taken, or I'd teach you a thing a two."

Julian made the mistake of taking his eyes off Nurse Binge to look over at Renee. As the nurse headed toward the door, she slapped his butt, then made her exit. Mouth open, Julian turned back around, then looked again at Renee. Renee dropped her hands and erupted in laughter, tears clouding her eyes, then trickling down her cheeks.

"I feel so violated," Julian admitted, constantly looking behind him to ensure she was gone.

Renee couldn't walk into her penthouse right away when the front door opened. She just stood there and gazed at the interior from the doorway, preparing for the next step she needed to take to venture back into the life she had finally come to terms, the life she needed to change. Her home now gave off a different aura. It contained the exact same furnishings and wall art, and it provided the same privacy she had enjoyed since moving in, yet it was a completely different place.

Julian watched her look at her home in a new way. "You okay?"

Renee didn't respond right away, but when she finally processed what he had asked, she swiftly answered, "Yeah, I'm good."

Walking over the threshold using crutches, Renee said, "I don't know why I thought things would look different."

"Let's go upstairs. I prepared one of the guest rooms for you."

That was one of the reasons Renee's heart beat for Julian: he was considerate and knew her inside and out.

They took the penthouse's elevator up to the second level. When she got off the elevator, Renee walked behind Julian. She needed extra time to adjust to her surroundings and look over what she was walking past. Julian came to a stop and told her to close her eyes.

"Close my eyes? Julian, can we please not prolong this?" Renee's stomach had turned a bit from all the excitement of being home, and she wanted to rest.

He reached into his back pocket and pulled out a sleep mask. "Put this on."

"No, I'm not putting on a mask. Let's just get this—"

Julian slapped the mask over her head, and once it covered her eyes, he snapped it into place.

"Really? Did you mess up my hair?"

Strands of her hair stuck up. "Nah. You good."

He led her into the guest room he had slept in many nights, when they'd argued. Renee remained silent and concentrated on whatever it was she could hear in order to ascertain what she had walked into. But the room was silent. No voices whispering or television blaring. Julian's hands caressed her shoulders before he eased the mask off her eyes. Slowly, the darkness beneath the mask was consumed by light.

Gold balloons and streamers decorated the ceiling and the walls. Huge black balloons read WELCOME HOME in gold lettering, the balloon strings so long, they touched the bed. Teddy bears, big and small, were scattered around the room. They sat on the king-size bed, the piano bench, the windowsill, and the empty dresser. Black, gold, and white envelopes lay below the bed pillows, each and every one with her name on it. Lyfe was standing on a step stool and taping the last balloon to one of the corners of the closet doors.

"What is this?" Renee asked.

"Us welcoming you back," Julian replied.

There were many things Renee hadn't experienced before, and a miniature surprise party was one of them. There wasn't a day in her life when she'd been given a balloon, not even when it was her birthday.

Lyfe hugged her. He didn't ask for permission or give her a heads-up. He just did it, and his action reminded her of her father. "I'm sorry, Renee. I've failed you so many times. No more."

Affection wasn't something Renee grew up with, but with all the love she had received lately, she could see herself opening up more to it.

"I have to run downstairs for something—" Julian began. But before he could dismiss himself and leave Renee and Lyfe to talk, she pulled him in for a kiss.

"Thank you," Renee whispered in his ear as she arranged the crutches in a more comfortable position.

Once Julian had left the room, Lyfe turned to Renee. "Do you like it? One of the girls I'm seeing thought it would be a nice gesture. I think we overdid it with the balloons."

"You did good." Renee made her way over to the envelopes on the bed. "What are these?"

"My friend said words of encouragement"—Lyfe used his fingers to make air quotes—"are helpful during hard times."

Renee snorted, "What, is she a hippie or something?"

"Close. She teaches yoga."

"Makes sense."

Renee sat down on the bed, glad to get off the crutches, as her underarms were a little sore. She sank into the bed as if it were made of butter. She had forgotten how comfortable she had made this room. It was the opposite of her bedroom. This room was welcoming: it was decorated with soothing colors, the bedsheets and the bedspread were bright, and the walls were adorned with modern art that symbolized happiness and love. Her bedroom was nothing like this: it was decorated with dark accents, it was closed off to the world, and it was filled with hiding places, where she stashed away her liquor bottles and weapons. Her bedroom had been decorated for discomfort, as a reflection of what her life was, her reality. Her guest bedroom represented what could have been, had she been the person she should have been. It was supposed to motivate her, but it had done nothing but remind her of failures.

She scooped up the envelopes. "These are from you, Julian, and Jared?" she asked.

"Jared?"

"Yeah, Jared."

"Shit," Lyfe mumbled. He cleared his throat. "He died that night."

Renee dropped the envelopes beside her. "What?"

"That night, your sister got to him. He was found downstairs, in front of the door."

Renee stood up, limped over to the window, and glanced out. A knot formed inside her chest and sat there, taking up space, and then it traveled upward, with the goal of reaching her throat and suffocating her.

"I'm sorry, Renee."

Renee had lived in her New York penthouse for so many years, yet it wasn't until that very second that she noticed how far up she truly was.

He's dead. Jared was a complicated soul, a soul that bore some resemblance to Renee's. He had given her hell and probably would have been her downfall, yet she couldn't ignore her feeling of loss.

"The higher they are, the farther they fall," she whispered. Her voice cracked a bit.

"You good?" Lyfe put his hand on her shoulder.

"Yeah, yeah, I'm good." She shook his hand off her and flopped back down on the mattress. She gestured toward the gold, black, and white envelopes. "Then who are these from?"

He sat next to her. "Me, Julian, and Carmen." He watched her, awaiting her reaction. "I know what she did that night," Lyfe admitted.

Eyeing the envelopes, she identified the one with unfamiliar handwriting on the shiny paper. She tossed it aside, separating it from the rest. Renee grabbed her crutches and made her way to the door.

"You know what to do, Renee. Put it all aside and thank her."

The bass in his tone and the strength in his stance stopped Renee in her tracks. Slower than normal, she turned herself around. He was right. She had a few ideas about what she should do concerning Carmen, but the past didn't make it easy to follow through with them. The past still hurt, and her stubbornness was still intact.

"I haven't been out of the hospital for a full twenty-four hours, and your concern is me telling her thank you. Thanks for the support, Unc." Renee wobbled away quickly. The crutches were not engineered to withstand the speed at which she went, and one collapsed beneath her underarm, and she lost her balance. She grabbed ahold of the closest wall in the hallway just before Julian turned the corner. He hurriedly put down the beer in his hand and helped her get back on her feet, and the crutches back under her arms.

Lyfe joined his niece and her boyfriend out in the hallway. "Welcome home, Renee. When you're ready to read your cards, they're on the dresser," he told her.

He took the stairs down to the main level, the sound of his sneakers beating against the floor echoing throughout the house, every step annoying Renee.

Chapter 42

Carmen had never met anyone she despised more than Renee, who came across as a high-siddity know-it-all with Daddy issues. It took a lot of self-control for Carmen to play the part of an innocent long-lost sister in search of family, a sister who was capable of taking all the bullshit and disrespect thrown at her by Renee and her crew time and time again. These people were cold and unwavering, and Carmen felt so discouraged around them sometimes that she questioned her motives every now and then, but when she pictured the dollar signs, she knew she couldn't give up. If she played this opportunity right, she could end up hitting the jackpot and thus gaining her independence.

Carmen was aware there was major dirt she had to play in, in order to secure the crown, but murder by her own hands, she didn't see happening. Carmen had never killed anyone before, nor did she think she could. The most she could do was order a hit. However, that night Renee was injured, something had come over Carmen when she saw Renee in a vulnerable position, one that threatened everything she wanted. All the money and dreams had flashed before Carmen's eyes and had pushed her beyond her capabilities. She had popped up that fatal night to have a discussion with Renee. There needed to be a breakthrough between the two of them, and there had been, just not how Carmen had expected. Things were looking up after she saved her half sister's life, and she began celebrating this with a shopping spree.

Carmen's heels click-clacked on the floor of the shopping mall. Her hands were filled with shopping bags, and a permanent smile was plastered on her face.

There's no shopping like NY shopping, she thought.

She stopped in front of a store window. A display of handbags hanging on tree branches spoke to Carmen. She dropped her shopping bags at her sides and brushed the glass with her hand to see more clearly, leaving behind her handprints and smudges.

"Aren't you gorgeous! Oh yes, you are. Oh yes, you are," she said to the thousand-dollar purses.

A saleswoman whom Carmen remembered seeing earlier that day came into the window display and replaced a blue leather bag with what looked to be a gold-plated purse with buckles. Carmen's jaw hung low, and saliva eased its way out the side of her mouth. The women saw her eyeing the new addition, and she smiled and pointed it at after mouthing, "She's a beauty, isn't she?" The women looked behind her, then quickly back at Carmen. She put her finger up and mouthed, "Stay there."

Carmen nodded; she had fallen deep into a trance, where she could see herself holding that bag. The pencil skirt–wearing saleswoman came back into sight with the blue leather bag and matching shoes. She held the shoes next to the blue bag and nodded. Carmen read her lips when she said, "Gorgeous." She placed herself in full view and showed Carmen that she, too, owned a pair of the newly released shoes. The shiny shoes matched her green skirt perfectly. Ever since she was a little girl, Carmen had never liked to be outdone. She prided herself on her style and, as sad as it sounded, she used her appearance to define who she was.

Carmen rammed her hand inside her purse, pulled out her wallet, removed something. The credit card stuck to her sweaty palm. She gathered her shopping bags and hustled inside the store. It didn't take long for her to leave the store with both the blue leather bag and the matching shoes in hand. Life was great, and if her uncle spoiling her more than he normally did was any indication of what was in store for her, Carmen couldn't wait for the change of pace. Carmen made it to her car and filled the backseat and the trunk with shopping bags. As she pulled out of the parking garage, a call came in through the car speakers.

"Hey, Unc. What's going on?"

"Calling to check in."

"All's well," she boasted.

"I hope you didn't max out that card I gave you."

Just then she reached a red light, so Carmen picked up her phone and tapped on a bank app. She looked at the balance on the credit card in question and cringed. There was only five hundred dollars left on the twenty-thousand-dollar limit.

"Don't kill my high, Unc. You gave me that card because of my good deed. I'ma lifesaver, remember? Let me live a little." The light turned green, and with a stretch of empty road ahead of her, Carmen slammed down on the accelerator and experienced all the horsepower and freedom the vehicle could provide. People on the sidewalks zoomed by and looked like a blur. New York was this Miami girl's playground.

"There's something I want to tell you." The wind blowing inside the car competed with her uncle's voice, but Renee heard him.

"Hit me!" she yelled.

"Renee wants to meet with you."

Carmen slammed down on the brakes. An elderly lady in the middle of the street would have been hit had Carmen's reflexes not been so swift. The old lady looked at Carmen, hollered words she couldn't make out, then stuck her wrinkly, skinny middle finger up at her.

"She's out of the hospital?" Carmen quizzed.

"Came home three days ago."

"What does she want?"

"I don't know."

Carmen watched the old woman take her time as she walked the rest of the way across the street. With every three steps she took, she spewed what Carmen assumed were more derogatory words. Carmen's head followed the woman until she was safely on the sidewalk on the other side of the street.

"What do you think it is?"

"There's only one thing she can want to talk to you about, Carmen. That night."

Carmen pushed down on the gas pedal, and this time she drove within the speed limit. "Will you be there?"

"I offered to, but she wants to meet with you alone."

Carmen was grateful for the number of turns she had to make. It forced her to focus more on the task at hand, driving. If she had to drive straight, she would get lost in her thoughts. Carmen knew deep in the pit of her stomach that meeting with Renee would be no easy task. Every time they'd been in each other's presence, it hadn't been easy. Each and every time Carmen had been humiliated and insulted. It had taken a lot of drinks for her to work up enough guts to show up unannounced at Renee's house that night, and it would take double that amount to meet with Renee now that she had summoned her.

"When does she want to meet?"

"I don't know. She said she'd let me know."

Carmen remained focused on the road. Lyfe couldn't see her, and her silence denied him the ability to feel her out through her voice. However, he still knew where her mind was.

"Don't worry, Carmen. You'll do fine. Just be yourself."

Little did Lyfe know that this was exactly what Carmen was afraid of.

Chapter 43

New clothes and clothing that was not over a year old were scattered around Carmen's bedroom. There were pants and shorts covering the bed, dresses and blouses on top of the dresser, and skirts and blazers piled in front of the closet. She had already tried on numerous outfits, and nothing had been right. All that she owned was either too tight or too short. She looked herself over in the body-length mirror. "This isn't right."

She unbuttoned the sleeveless top and wiggled out of her jeans. Whatever clothes she paired together didn't seem good enough to meet Renee in. This conversation would determine how close Renee would allow her to get. Had Renee chosen to keep Carmen at a distance after Carmen saved her life, then Carmen would have decided that Renee would never open up to her. But Renee wanted to meet. Today was all or nothing, and if Carmen wanted positive results, she had to have a positive attitude, and that started with having the right attire.

Carmen stepped inside her shoe closet and looked at every pair she owned. She'd allow the shoes to decide on her outfit. Each shoe told its own story, but not one exuded the confidence and control Carmen needed to radiate during her meeting. Her frustration increased and almost spilled over before she remembered the gold-plated beauties resting in the shoebox on her kitchen counter. Her creative juices got the kick start they needed by the mere thought of her new addition. She pulled out her cobalt-blue jumpsuit, which she'd worn only once; dug inside her jewelry box for the right accessories; and put together the vision of a woman ready to take over the world.

"Now we're talking."

The bar Carmen had agreed to meet Renee at gave her déjà vu. The TV screens embedded in the walls, the water beneath the glass dance floor, and the glow in the dark bar stools pulled on her memory. She was sure she'd been here before, yet she couldn't pinpoint when or recall the experience. Carmen was the only customer in attendance; no regular Joes sat around her and the bartender.

"Slow day, huh?" Carmen said to the bartender.

Dressed in a dingy striped shirt, the short Caucasian male turned his back on Carmen without replying and prepared a dirty martini. He placed the glass on top of a napkin in front of Carmen and went to the other side of the bar.

"I didn't ask for this!" she yelled at his back. He was out of sight by the time Carmen finished shouting, and that alone agitated her more. His nonverbal disrespect pulled Carmen out of her seat and compelled her to follow the man. Her gold heels led her to the opposite side of the bar and straight in front of Renee, who was at the door.

"Leaving already?"

Taken aback by Renee's sudden appearance, Carmen stuttered, "Oh, n-no, no." Aware of her weak speech and repetitiveness, she closed her mouth, cleared her throat, and started her response from scratch. "No. I only wanted to have a word with the bartender."

Walking past her, her shoulder slightly brushing against Carmen's, Renee said, "You're here to speak with me, not him. Now, let's have a seat."

Following behind Renee, who strolled farther into the bar, Carmen held her tongue. Her teeth grinding against one another made it possible for her to maintain her composure and remain professional.

Shouldn't she have a cast on? Carmen wondered.

Carmen sat across from Renee at a high table, crossed her legs, and arranged herself so that her shoes and purse were in eyeshot of Renee.

"I love your shoes and purse." Renee gave the items a once-over.

Carmen held back an enormous smile, then narrowed it down to a polite beam. "Thank you."

"Those shoes and that purse are two things from last season that I believe will never go out of style. I admire the designers' work so much, I bought two of each. One set I wear, and one I keep in my shoes and purses hall of fame."

The mute bartender brought Renee over a drink, along with the martini Carmen had left behind at the bar.

Renee took a sip of her drink. "Thank you, Tox."

"You're welcome."

Oh, so he does talk. Carmen damn near inhaled the martini.

"I wanted to meet with you in person to speak with you about that night. Why exactly were you at my house at that time of the morning?" Renee's head was cocked to the side; she'd gone heavy on the black eyeliner, mascara, and foundation. She indulged once more in her drink.

Maybe she's trying to hide her battle wounds, Carmen thought.

"The last time we met, like all the other times, didn't go well. I wanted to talk and try to figure out how we can get along as a family."

Renee turned her head and spit her drink out. Violent coughs followed, and she pounded her chest with her fist. "You want to *get along*?" she asked, her voice raspy. She dabbed at her mouth with the napkin underneath her drink.

"Yes. I know you're not a fan of it, but whether you like it or not, we are sisters. The least we can do is act civil when we're around one another. We both love our uncle, so we're bound to be in the same room together from time to time."

"I don't know him to love him," Renee retorted.

"Okay, but you *do* get along with him."

Renee drank the last of her vodka. With the glass still in her hand, she pointed at Carmen. "Why the fuck would I want to surround myself with the motherfucker who wants my life?" Renee took Carmen's purse off the table and sat it on the floor. "The purse is too fabulous to fuck up with your blood."

Carmen hopped out of her seat, but Renee was already out of hers. Renee leaned halfway across the table. With the collar of Carmen's jumpsuit in her clutches, she said, "No, no, no. Don't go."

Carmen pushed Renee off of her. With her unexpected strength, she knocked Renee back in her seat, and Renee lost her grip on the jumpsuit. This caused Carmen to stumble, and one of the heels on the eye-candy shoes she'd fallen in love with broke, sending her to the floor. She pushed herself up onto her knees, and then she was pulled up on her feet by her hair. She grabbed at the hands wrapped around the high bun on top of her head, and when the hands let go, she looked into the eyes of the person they belonged to. She blinked one time before Tox's fist met the center of her face. Carmen fell backward, her body fully erect. The back of her head banged against the floor, and the impact and shock distorted Carmen's vision. Specks of white flashed in front her eyes, and she temporarily lost the will to fight.

Renee squatted down next to Carmen; she waved her hand in front of Carmen's eyes. Carmen's head moved from side to side, and her eyes rolled upward, but she said nothing. Renee nodded at Tox. He removed his gun from the holster strapped to his belt buckle and handed it to his boss. Carmen's vision was blurry, but she was still able to see a contorted version of Renee standing over her, with a gun pointed down at her. Carmen's head fell to the side, and she was able to make out the tattered, burnt-out sign collecting dust in the corner. It had once hung on the front of the building. She read the words on the sign out loud. "Lyfe's Bar and Lounge. I knew I recognized this place."

"He's my uncle now."

Carmen heard Renee's comment and saw a blast of light before it all went black.

Chapter 44

Failure to breathe was what forced Carmen out of her sleep. She swung her legs over the side of the bed and just sat there, hunched over and holding the exact spot where Tox had punched her. Outside of her dream, she could still feel the impact of Tox's fist on her face and the undeniable throbbing pain in the back of her head. As it was for Renee, dreams were Carmen's worst enemy; whenever she had them, she found herself too connected, so connected she had difficulty distinguishing real life from fake. She remembered that when she was a child, she would say that if she could have a superpower, it would be the ability to never dream. After she closed her eyes at night, a majority of the time she either had nightmares or dreamed about her father. She saw him hurting too much, and this resulted in nothing other than grief as long as the dream continued. Peace didn't exist when she slept.

Ever since Lyfe had told her she'd be meeting with Renee, she'd been on pins and needles. Unsure about what would transpire during her encounter with Renee, combined with not knowing when their interaction would take place, had left Carmen feeling uncomfortable. Her nerves were in a frenzy over the idea that so much good could come out of Renee accepting her inside her circle. It would fundamentally transform her life for the better. Then there was the possibility of absolutely nothing changing and Renee banishing her from her kingdom, thereby kicking Carmen back to square one.

Her eyelids were lowering once again, and her body was slowly swaying. The bed was beckoning Carmen to fall back into a state of slumber, but she knew it was best to ignore this. The worst dreams came about when she fell right back to sleep after waking, as such dreams were merely a continuation of the dream that had shaken her out of her sleep in the first place.

Defeating the dream, she dragged herself out of bed and out of her bedroom, covered by nothing except her spaghetti-strap pink silk lingerie. She slipped into her terry-cloth robe in the hallway bathroom and headed for the front door. She stepped outside and found the lack of night life comforting. There was no activity at this wee hour, no blaring car horns, no partygoers stumbling home, no teenagers sneaking out and racing down the streets in their friends' cars. This summer's night in New York was as soothing as a country day. A short-lived breeze caressed Carmen's skin while she looked up at the crescent moon in a corner of the sky.

Carmen took a seat on the doorstep, and through her robe, she felt every inch of concrete beneath her. The minor discomfort shoved away whatever tiredness re-mained and opened her eyes to the reality that if she really wanted Renee's world, she'd have to take it by physical force. The idea was nauseating: murdering and strong-arming people into doing what she wanted wasn't Carmen's style, and she lacked any relevant experience. Had she dabbled in this lifestyle, watched from a distance as the men she'd dealt with, including her uncle, engaged in violence? Yes, but witnessing those things was hardly comparable to actually doing them.

Battling for comfort, Carmen rocked back and forth, then leaned against the flowerpot tucked in a corner in front of the door.

I have to water this thing.

The flowering plant in the pot was a gift given to her by some random guy she met and slept with from time to time. She barely fed or watered it. She left that up to Mother Nature, and that was what had kept the flowers blossoming and the soil damp. But the weather had been dry lately. She put her nose up to one of the yellow pansies and inhaled the perfume-like scent.

I defiantly gotta stay on top of watering these.

The fragrance made all her stress and anxiety vanish, and she felt like she was in two places at once. First, she felt like she was at a mall, strolling past a perfume counter in a department store; and at the same time, she was in a field of flowers. Her phone chiming inside the pocket of her robe was what stopped her sniffing fest. She retrieved her phone and read the text message.

Renee wants to meet with you tomorrow afternoon at Rockwell's Café.

Carmen took a whiff of the flower once more, the captivating aroma therapeutic. Then she answered the text.

I'll be there, Unc.

She pressed SEND. Placed her clasped hands in back of her head and waited for sunrise.

Renee still had a ways to go, but she was starting to look like her old self again. She had set up the lunch date with Carmen, which she knew she could no longer avoid.

Sitting at an outside table at the restaurant, with a huge pair of shades on, Renee watched as Manhattan's elite walked by in their finest summer threads.

"Hello, Renee."

Renee turned to face Carmen. She looked stunning in a pearl halter dress.

"Hello, Carmen. How are you?"

"I can't complain, but I should be asking you that question. Your face looks good." Carmen wondered how her eyes looked. The sunglasses hid the damage.

"Once this cast comes off, I'll be as good as new. I never stay down for long," Renee said.

Both women quickly glanced down at Renee's broken leg, and then they momentarily flashed back to that horrible night.

"I was surprised when Uncle Lyfe called me and said you wanted to meet up for lunch. I thought you guys would talk more concerning his text." Carmen was fishing for answers. She knew of Jared's death, a big glitch in her plans, but she had to know Renee's plans for Julian now that he was exposed.

"What text?"

"You know, the text about Lyfe warning you about Jared." She searched Renee's eyes for answers.

"What? I never got that text."

"I'm sure Uncle Lyfe mentioned it to me. Maybe you should double check."

Renee's face scrunched up while she dug her hand inside her purse and pulled out her smart phone. After tapping the screen a few times, she paused and read her messages, her lips moving with every word she saw. Renee sucked her teeth and shook her head right before dropping the phone into her bag.

"He tried warning me about Jared, but too little too late. He died that night."

"Is that all he said?" Carmen questioned.

"That and some family stuff."

Renee was calm—too calm for someone who had just learned her boyfriend cheated.

"Are you sure that's all he said?" Carmen continued to pry.

Renee's face tightened as she tilted her head slightly to the side. "That's all," she replied, her voice low and hardened.

Shit. That text didn't go through, Carmen thought. She forced a smile and chuckled a little. "Sorry, just making sure you got it all since you originally missed it. Anyway, what's on your mind? Why have you summoned me?" Carmen asked, her attempt at changing the topic.

"I owe you a thank-you. Never in a million years would I have thought my father's illegitimate child would save my life."

Renee had given thought to a lot of things that led to speaking with Carmen on this day, pushing aside her displeasure for how Lyfe had arranged for her and Carmen to meet. Renee had allowed herself to get to know him, and she had seen a lot of her father in Lyfe, which made it easier for her accept him as family.

Carmen nodded her head. She knew it would take time before Renee could fully accept who she was. "After that incident between us, I came back to try to fix things, but when I saw Jared laid out on the floor, I knew something was up. I know your lifestyle. I may not have lived it like you are, but I've had my dealings with it. So, I grabbed Jared's gun and made my way to you. I couldn't let you die, no matter how bad you treat me."

Carmen's last statement stung a little. Renee's cold heart was officially melting.

"I'm not gonna lie to you, but I need some time to get used to the idea of having a sister I knew nothing about. But we'll touch on that another time. Lyfe has told me everything about you, and after some thought, I have something I want to ask you."

Carmen wished a million times over that Renee wasn't wearing any shades; she wanted to look her in the eyes and get an idea of where this conversation was going.

"Sure? What's up?" Carmen pretended to be calm and chipper, when really her insides felt like they were unraveling.

An Asian waitress with bone-straight black hair came to the table and asked if they were ready to order. Carmen wanted to scream for her to get lost, but when Renee ordered a meal, she knew she had to relax and play things her way. She kindly told the waitress, "I'll have a Caesar salad with grilled chicken." She gave her a fake smile and then turned her full attention to Renee when the waitress walked off.

"I'm getting out of the game," Renee told her. "I've run my course, and now it's time for me to move on. But seeing how you performed when you saved my life, and knowing that you're not totally green to it all, I have decided that instead of letting my empire go under, I'll hand it over to you and make you my protégé, like Metro did me."

Carmen's heart skipped a beat, and her hands started to sweat. She couldn't believe what she was hearing. *She's giving it all to me?* Carmen had to suppress her smile and stop herself from jumping in the air while yelling yippee!

"I don't know what to say, Renee."

"Say yes. You've proved yourself. Therefore, you've earned access to my life. I'll train you, I'll mold you, and I'll make you the queen of New York. All you have to say is yes."

Carmen's dream was coming true faster than she had thought it would, and without much work on her end. She thought of all the money, power, and respect she would accumulate, and she didn't know what to do with herself. She wanted it all, and she was going to get it, Julian included.

"So what do you say?" Renee asked.

"When do I start?"

About the Author

Born and raised in New York City, where she lives with her husband, Brandie Davis-White graduated with a bachelor's degree in English from York College and is the founder of *My Urban Books* blog and My Urban Books Club, a Facebook book club. From home she continues to pen drama-filled novels.

Follow Brandie on Facebook at:
www.facebook.com/brandie.davis.948

Join her Facebook book club, My Urban Books Club, at:
 https://www.facebook.com/groups/232356380133003/

Twitter: @AuthorBrandieD

Instagram: @authorbrandiedavis